By the time she was three years old, Marian Matthews knew that she had been born in the wrong place. A country lover, she hated her childhood home in the London Suburbs. As a teenager she carved out a small stretch of countryside in the middle of Suburbia, on rented Metropolitan Railway land, where she raised pigs, table birds and eggs. She married and moved to the beautiful countryside of the Chiltern Hills.

She took a job as 'Girl Friday' at a national news agency, where her wizardry with the written word was soon discovered and she was promptly promoted to journalist. She went on to write for most of the national papers, TV and radio in a career spanning thirty years. But her passion for the countryside and farming remained. She now lives on Exmoor.

ALONG THAT COUNTRY ROAD

Marian Matthews

ALONG THAT COUNTRY ROAD

Vanguard Press

VANGUARD PAPERBACK

© Copyright 2007
Marian Matthews

A CIP catalogue record for this title is
available from the British Library

ISBN-13: 978 1 84386 303 8

Vanguard Press is an imprint of
Pegasus Elliot MacKenzie Publishers Ltd.
www.pegasuspublishers.com

First Published in 2007

Vanguard Press
Sheraton House Castle Park
Cambridge England

Printed & Bound in Great Britain

I dedicate this book to my dear son, Glen, with whom I share a love of writing, history and the world around us.

Introduction

It was a bright spring morning in 2003 when the idea was spawned to write about the life of Mary Norton.

We had become friends through singing in the village choir, and shared a passion for the countryside and farming. Mary told me that she had been a Land Girl in the Second World War.

'Oh!' I said. 'I have always been interested in the Women's Land Army and I'd love to write a book about it!'

At first we met in Mary's cottage, but later we switched our meetings to my home where she sat beside me whilst I made notes.

Times were stressful for my friend as she was in the throes of moving, but I couldn't help noticing how, during our meetings, her sparkle returned. I listened, entranced. Then I began to write, immersing myself in her life.

As the story unfolded, my familiar surroundings faded, misty pale, and I became a shadow, following Mary across the years.

I was there in a humble two-up, two-down cottage as a tiny blonde-haired scrap of a baby came into the world; and later my feet echoed on bare floorboards in a fine house built by two brothers.

Then suddenly I would be transported to a damp and dreary attic room shared by hungry children, only to be whisked away to a farmhouse deep in wartime Gloucestershire.

I was a ghost at a Garden Party at Buckingham Palace, and,

as a shadowy presence I walked down the stairs behind a young bride in her post war utility wedding dress as she went so eagerly to marry a farmer's son.

What emerged is not just a story of the countryside threaded through with social history and nostalgia. It is a tribute to a long life and Mary's amazing ability to live it to the full!

It wasn't just her willingness to accept whatever life might throw at her, or her ability to adapt and endure, which kept me spellbound. What shined through like a beacon was her amazing passion for making and keeping friends.

It became clear to me that Mary had kept in touch by phone or letter with practically everyone she had met in her long and eventful life!

'Well,' she says today, sizing me up and enjoying her fun: 'They're practically all gone now. But just the other night I was speaking to old so-and so…!'

What follows is the story of the first thirty-three years of Mary's life. I have structured it, filled in details and added dialogue to weave it into the bright tapestry of her memories.

I have also had to fictionalise certain outside events, and some names have been changed to protect identities, but what remains will be, I hope an enduring tribute to a remarkable lady!

I hope that the resulting book will keep you company as you snuggle up by the fireside on many a stormy night.

Marian Matthews, Exmoor 2007

CHAPTER ONE

As Edith Oakley tiptoed into the tiny back bedroom of her home, a shaft of moonlight fell across the floor and illuminated the cradle in the far corner. A soft breeze blew in from the open window, gently lifting the curtains. It was late April in the year of 1921, and although the house was in the centre of Gloucester, the air was sweet with scents from the Malvern Hills beyond.

There had certainly been April showers that day. Edith had seen a rainbow arching across the rooftops whilst she was hanging out her baby's clothes in the courtyard at the rear of the house: precious garments, made by her own hands. The rainbow had seemed like a beacon to her happiness.

Now, as she crossed the room and bent over the cradle, her long honey gold hair, silvered by moonlight fell forward against the sweep of her cheek. She lowered herself onto the nursing chair and sat looking at her sleeping baby.

Edith was feeling better now, slowly recovering from the trauma of the birth. Never very strong, her confinement had been a difficult one. She was forty years old and although in those times it was not uncommon for women to give birth many times until late into their thirties or forties, it had not been like that for Edith.

She had borne only one other child, a boy called James, and she had known the greatest grief this world can deal a woman, for she had lost him. He had died, aged eight years, from peritonitis. The memory of his childhood years, which had once been such joy to her suddenly, made her sick at heart.

Then, two years later she had discovered that she was pregnant once more. This tiny scrap was balm to Edith's suffering.

The cradle was a simple wooden one made by her carpenter

13

husband, Fred. He was a kindly man and, understanding his wife's pain, he had paused whilst climbing into the loft to fetch down their son's cradle, changed his mind, and instead fashioned another for this new child. The baby stirred in it now and Edith reached over and lifted her out and held her in her arms. The little girl awoke momentarily and grasped a lock of the pale gold hair.

At forty Edith was still a beautiful woman, but her fragile looks and slim frame denied the toughness within. The ninth child of a family of twelve, she had been born to mid-Montgomery farmers, Thomas and Mary Bunner. She often joked that the reason she had no middle name was because her parents had run out by the time she was born! As a child, although she looked so delicate she loved the rough life on the rugged Welsh hill farm, and grew up with a passion for fresh air and freedom.

Edith never wanted the hearty farmhouse meals served by her mother, and her father was constantly anxious. He often took her onto his lap and, coaxing her as if she was a young lamb to be nurtured, gently fed her from his own plate.

"Thomas!" his wife said. "You spoil the child!"

"No! Leave us be!" Thomas always countered. "She's delicate, and she needs gentling."

But her father's kindness could not save her from a life of toil. At twelve years old she had to leave the village school and her family, to go into service.

This was virtually the only employment for young country girls, and Edith knew that she must put a brave face on it, in common with all her sisters.

Many years later, sitting in the moonlight nursing her baby, Edith's eyes welled as she remembered the terrible day she had been forced to leave Wales. Her father drove her to Montgomery railway station in the pony and trap. She sat silent and upright, her feet propped against the leather trunk containing her clothes and few possessions as she watched the countryside slip by through a blur of tears. She bit into her lips until she could taste her own salty blood.

At the station her father gave way to his emotions. This was his fair fragile daughter he treasured, and she was going so far

14

from him! And she was so young, no more than a child! They clung together briefly and then she was on the train and the soft lull of the wheels on the rails replaced the cheerful cadence of the pony and trap.

***

Life in the huge Wimbledon house had been bitter at first. Uprooted from all she loved she was lonely and depressed. Her hours below stairs as a kitchen maid were long and gruelling. She missed her freedom; the heather and the cool mountain air, but slowly she adapted to her new life.

It was on her infrequent visits home that the longing and sense of loss always returned. Only her two younger sisters and brother remained at the farm with her parents, and Edith was determined that in their eyes she should be the confident elder sister, living away with a life of her own. But when the time came to return to London, misery overwhelmed her.

"I don't want to go, mum," she would say as she clung to her mother in tears.

Her mother, searching for words of comfort would invariably reply, "It's the way of the world, dear. What else are you to do?"

But she 'kept her ear to the ground', constantly trying to find her daughter a better post, nearer home.

And at last her diligence paid off. She heard of a position at Tewkesbury Park in Gloucestershire.

"This is a great opportunity for you," she said on Edith's next visit. Then she added in a respectful whisper. "It's a position with the Gentry, dear!"

Edith's mother had a regard verging on awe for high society.

"You'd be working for Lady Violet Sergeant!" she added with a flourish.

"I'll be much nearer home," Edith said quietly.

Her application and interview were successful and Edith left London to take up her new post. Lady Violet was a kind and understanding mistress and Edith swiftly rose to the position of Head Parlour Maid and was put in charge of all the china and ornaments in the vast house. Lady Violet had given her some of these treasures and they were now kept as prized possessions in Edith's humble little home. Admittedly they were mostly cracked or chipped, but rare and cherished none the less.

Working in such an illustrious household made a deep impression on Edith and she developed a keen regard for etiquette and good taste.

It was through her employment at Tewkesbury Park that she met her husband, Frederic Oakley.

Edith warmed at the memory. She had joined a staff outing to watch a cricket match in a nearby village. After the game a tea had been laid on in the pavilion, with bread and butter and dainty cakes. Edith was sitting at one of the iron tables in cheery company with her workmates when one of the players came striding in. He was a tall, athletic looking man with slicked-back black hair and a strong, darkly handsome face.

It was a warm summer day with clouds like fluffy galleons gently billowing over the hills beyond the village. As he came through the open doors of the pavilion Edith looked up from her teacup. He was in his cricket whites, tanned and smiling and she noticed that he was that rare thing, a man with true grace. She was attracted to him at once and hoped that he would notice her too. *Strange, she thought, as she was usually so sensible!*

Edith was looking exceptionally pretty, wearing her second-best Sunday frock. She had taken off her sunhat, and her blonde hair, caught back at the neck with a ribbon, spilled forward over her shoulders. Fred saw the mass of golden hair shining like a halo in the sunlight, which poured in through the pavilion doors. He walked over to her table and, ignoring all others seated around it, politely asked her if she had enjoyed the cricket.

"Oh yes," she replied. Her heart was racing and she was searching around for more words to keep the conversation going.

Before anyone could object, Fred had found another chair and pulled it up to the table. He wiggled it between Edith and one of her friends, determined to speak to the beautiful woman who had caught his eye. Such behaviour was out of character as Fred was normally a very shy man!

Later, they strolled around the village together and she learnt that he was a carpenter. He was his own man and she liked that. Living in service, the men she met were mostly servants, footmen, hall porters or the like; but Fred was free, making a living by his own skill. He was not a man who usually talked confidently but he managed to find the words for the lovely woman with the golden hair.

The charabanc arrived all too soon to whisk her back to Tewkesbury Park, but as he helped her aboard he promised that he would call on her.

"Miss Bunner," he shouted, running alongside the vehicle as the horses picked up speed into a lively trot, "when is your next day off?"

Edith's mind was whirling, but she yelled the date through the open window. It was two months away, and she wished it could come sooner!

It was a warm, misty afternoon in autumn when Fred took his beau boating on the river. She felt like a grand lady, reclining on cushions whilst her handsome boatman skilfully feathered the oars, sending their little craft skimming over smooth waters where the tendrils of willows gently touched her face.

It was soon time to row back to the boathouse, but Fred let the punt bump against an island. It came to a stop and he fell on his knees. By the time he had righted himself he had managed to kiss Edith.

"I'm not sure whether it was an accident or whether he did it deliberately," she laughed to her friends back below stairs, "but either way, I didn't mind a bit!"

On their next meeting Fred lost no time in kissing her again. This time it was long and delicious and Edith was whirled away. They continued to meet whenever possible. He was very shy and words never came easily to him, but gradually he told her about his life.

He had been born in a black and white thatched cottage on the north-westerly side of the village green at Bishop's Norton, Gloucestershire, the second son of bricklayer William Oakley and his wife Clara. He had an elder brother, Albert, and younger sister Florence, always known as Flo.

Later the family moved to a red brick semi-detached cottage on the other side of the green. Life must have been hard for his mother because in addition to bringing up her family she took in washing from nearby Norton Court, labouring at her dolly tub, carefully starching the clothes and ironing them with flat irons heated on the kitchen range.

Fred and his brother had both left school at twelve years old and Albert had followed their father into bricklaying. At first Fred worked as a gardener's boy at Norton Court, but in 1900, when he was fifteen, he became apprenticed to the builders Harry Bailey and George Dean in Gloucester. His debentures described him as learning the 'Art of Building', but very soon Fred showed an affinity to working with wood, and he went on to train as a master carpenter.

The indenture cost his father £10, a considerable sum of money in those days. Fred earned three shillings a week in his first year, rising to twelve shillings by his final years, and the hours were hard and long. He worked ten hours each weekday and six and a half on Saturdays. The young, athletic Fred cycled daily from Bishop's Norton to Barton Street, Gloucester, taking with him two cold fried eggs with bread for his lunch.

Edith smiled in the moonlight, musing on her husband's life and the changes for the better that he had wrought for her. They had married after a simple courtship and this had enabled her to leave the drudgery of service.

Her wedding day had been without doubt, the happiest day of her life.

When Lady Violet heard of the engagement she immediately called her young parlour maid up to the drawing room.

"Well my dear," she said kindly, for she was very fond of Edith; "I understand congratulations are in order!"

"Frederic Oakley's a nice young man," Edith replied proudly, thinking it best to refer to him by his full name. "I'm extremely glad we are to be married, madam!"

"Well then," smiled Lady Violet, "I shall be glad to make a contribution to the day! I insist that you borrow my very finest pony and trap. And the reception will be held here, in the servants' hall."

"I would like that very much, thank you Mam," said Edith

***

18

The sun was shining when she stepped from the great house wearing a wedding gown, which she had made herself, and carrying a posy of violets, the namesake flower of her employer.

Her father had travelled from Montgomeryshire and she held very tightly to his arm.

"Oh my!" she breathed when she saw the vehicle in which she was to ride to the church!

That morning the head gardener had set out on a secret mission, gathering flowers from the gardens and hothouse, and her friends had festooned the trap and the pony's harness with them.

Edith lifted the graceful folds of her dress and stepped into the trap to sit on the box seat, proud as a princess beside her father as she rode in a chariot of blossoms to her new life.

After the service there was a grand wedding feast, generously provided by Lady Violet, and the whole happy company danced till late into the night, to the tunes of a fiddle and a penny whistle.

Immediately after the wedding Edith left Tewkesbury Park and the couple moved into a tiny rented cottage at Hardwick, just outside Gloucester, to begin their married life. They were delighted when, in 1908, their son was born. They named him James, but always called him Jim.

Then the Great War came to shatter their lives. At first Fred was refused active service on medical grounds because he had a mild heart murmur, but later in 1916 he was called up.

"So many good men have died," he said to Edith, "that they want me now!"

***

He served six months at the front facing the horrors as a stretcher-bearer, and then was recalled to England where he spent the rest of the war in charge of German prisoners on Chesil Bank, near Weymouth.

But Fred and his brother had ambitions of their own. After the war they decided to set up a partnership.

"I think we should start a building firm of our own," said Bert, who was always the more business-minded of the pair.

"With me as a bricklayer and you as a carpenter we're off to a good start. If we do well we can take on other men. The world's changing and the times are right for it Fred."

The business was a great success and they were able to buy out their employers, Dean and Bailey of Gloucester, and rename the business 'Oakley Brothers!'

Now Edith sat, nursing her baby daughter, in the same little house at 22 Barton Street, which had once been owned by George Dean. It was a strange turn of events! But Edith was a country girl by birth, and Fred had promised that one day soon she would have a much finer home.

As she framed these happy thoughts on her future, a cloud came creeping uneasily upon her. She caught her breath almost in a sob, thinking how her beloved little Jim would never play in the garden of this wonderful new house. She wanted to clutch at his warm body and pull him close to her. She could still remember the soft sweet smell of his hair, and it came upon her with renewed despair that he was gone.

At that moment the tiny baby Dorothy, who was to be known throughout her life as Mary, stirred in Edith's arms. A little hand, silver in the moonlight, twisted and entwined Edith's hair in a firmer grip, causing a little tug of pressure. With this soft reminder of the new life against her breast the vision of little James faded, not sadly or unkindly, but with a gentle slipping away which left Edith in peace.

She raised the baby higher into the enfoldment of her arms and saw that she was waking. Edith knew in that extraordinary moment that this baby was all the more wonderful and precious because of what had come before. As she settled the shawl about her and lowered her breast for succour, she vowed that this new child would have a happy, prosperous and very long life.

CHAPTER TWO

THE MIDDLE CLASS CHILD

From the very first she knew that she was an extraordinarily precious child. She was christened Dorothy in honour of her cousin of the same name, but both families quickly realised this would cause confusion, so thenceforth she was known by her second name, Mary.

She was born on the 2nd of April 1921, the only child of Fred Oakley, a carpenter and his wife Edith, a retired head parlour maid.

Her parents had suffered a great tragedy, losing their son James from peritonitis when he was just eight years old. So when a second child was unexpectedly born to them in Edith's forty-first year they vowed to cosset and protect this new treasure. As a result Mary was fearfully spoiled!

She possessed an almost ethereal beauty, extremely slight of build, with white-blonde hair and luminescent pale blue eyes. Her parents' pampering love could have fallen like a stifling cloak upon her shoulders had it not been for Mary's powerful personality.

Their home was a typical Victorian two-up, two-down mid-terrace with a back kitchen and parlour and a yard at the rear with an outside privvie. It was in the centre of Gloucester, which in those days was just a small market town.

But things were soon to change! Fred and his brother Bert, a bricklayer, had started their own building business and they were so successful that they soon took over the business of their employers.

"We're in the middle classes now!" said Bert. And we'll be needing homes to match!"

"Oo-ah," was Fred's comment. He was a very quiet man and this single word was his main means of communication.

But Bert was different. He saw himself as a social climber and he was keen to join the Grand Order of the Moose and sit for the town council. His wife Annie was a homely person with no interest in such things, but Edith, the ex chief parlour maid to the illustrious Lady Violet, with knick-knacks from the gentry in her china cupboard, was envious.

***

One day the two brothers faced each other across a rough table in the little office that adjoined their workshop. This was a depository for papers and all the paraphernalia which gathers, in a busy work place, and everything upon it seemed permanently covered with wood shavings. Bert swept this debris aside with his arm to reveal a set of plans. He appreciated that under the quiet exterior Fred was a man of keen intelligence and the two men were friends as well as brothers.

"What do you think of the idea that we should build two houses?" Bert asked. "One for each of us! Identical! Both from this set of plans!"

Fred nodded in keen approval.

"They'll not be small," Bert said. "But good houses with nice bay windows, four bedrooms and all the modern conveniences. I'll do the bricklaying Fred, and you'll do the carpentry, and what we can't do ourselves will come out of the business."

At home that evening Fred found sufficient words to communicate the plan to Edith.

She has such good taste, he thought to himself, and a sense of what is right. She'll want a plot of land in the best possible location!

Shortly after, two pieces of land were purchased, at opposite ends of Gloucester.

Bert's plot was at Sandhurst next door to their parents, William and Clara who had left their red-brick cottage at nearby Bishop's Green and moved into town.

"It's all very well," said Edith, "but it's down a muddy track off the main road, and there's no mains water or electricity. It wouldn't do for us!"

"Oo-ah," said Fred, and carried on looking. He found a fine plot in a prime residential area at the very edge of town in a district known as Tuffley.[1]

"We've decided to call our place Bassingham," Bert told his brother. "It's a name with a ring of quality about it!"

Fred and Edith took part of their surname and created 'Oakboro' for their house.

"I like it, Fred," she said. "It's tasteful. And it's a good big plot. You can plant a garden. I know how you've always wanted a bit of land."

The site was in the Stroud Road close to the terminus of the tramline, and the Great Western Railway ran nearby, but it was surrounded by lovely countryside.

***

Fred left most of the business side of their partnership to his brother, preferring to work with his hands. Whilst their house was under construction Mary and her mother sometimes took a tram ride to see its progress. Like all building sites there was plenty of mess and Edith was afraid her daughter might be hurt. Fred had a habit of holding nails at the ready, pinched between his lips as he worked.

"Oh Fred!" grumbled Edith anxiously. "I wish you wouldn't do that! Little Madam's watching!"

But she was a happy woman as she sat on the tram with Mary on her lap, returning temporarily to the cramped little cottage in Barton Street.

"We're marked for better things," she whispered against her daughter's ashy-blonde hair, "just you wait and see!"

***

There was great happiness in Edith's eyes as Fred turned the key in the lock to let his family into the completed house on a fine April day in 1924. Mary wriggled free of her mother's hand

---

[1] *Author's Note: At the time of writing (2006) these houses remain unaltered, but are now swallowed up by the ring road and the city's growth.*

and ran down the hall, her feet clattering on the bare boards.

It was a substantial house built of good red bricks. There were two big reception rooms downstairs with deep bay sash windows. The large kitchen contained a big china sink, a fireplace with an oven set in it, and a back boiler for heating the water. Mary immediately opened the door to the big pantry.

"This Mary's house!" she said petulantly, refusing to come out.

"Now Mary, don't spoil our lovely day!" said poor Edith, fearing a tantrum as she yanked out her daughter and slammed the door.

They went upstairs to see the bedrooms and, most wonderful of all, the fine bathroom.

The family's furniture scarcely filled the large rooms, but Fred lit a fire in the brick fireplace in the lounge and the family sat round it for their tea. Mary perched on her father's lap watching the flames and sucking a slice of her mother's Snow Cake, a home-made Madeira sponge topped with thick white icing. She was fiercely fond of sweet things and always preferred her pudding to a hot dinner.

"Fred," Edith said kindly, "I can't thank you enough for this lovely home. To think that I should ever have such a place! I never thought it possible! Not when I was just a skivvy in that big house in Wimbledon. I thought I was just common then!"

"Oo-ah," replied Fred, who was thinking that his wife was anything but common. She was a farmer's daughter and handsome for a woman in her forties.

"This will be a fitting home for Mary," Edith said. "I want her to grow up middle class!"

But, despite their newly attained status one thing would never change. Mary would always call her parents Mum and Dad, never stiff and formal Mother and Father.

Later they took their cake-sticky daughter up to the bathroom. This was something, which Fred had never owned before, and neither had his family before him. He watched Edith as she knelt by the bath to wash their daughter. Her soft blonde hair was always escaping from its pins and as she turned her head to look at him stray tendrils fell against her face.

"Oh this is wonderful, Fred!" she said. "I shall never have

to fill that old tin bath in the back kitchen again!"

Later, tucked into bed with a nice jelly baby sweet to suck, Mary felt very clean and safe and cosy. She heard an express train rumble by beneath the nearby bridge. It was a cheery drowsy sound and it blended with the rain-rinsed song of a blackbird outside her window, lulling her to sleep.

***

Mary was allowed her own way in virtually everything, especially when it came to food.

"No!" she would snap, as the plate of meat and vegetables was set before her, the tiny foot scraping ominously on the rung of the chair.

"Want pudding!"

Edith usually gave in but sometimes she threw up her hands in anger and Mary would have to eat her dinner. But her cross-faced daughter had another tyranny in store! There must not be the merest trace of a lump in the gravy.

"Oh you are such a difficult child!" her mother wailed, returning again to the stove to remove some tiny speck.

Mary was extremely strong-willed and tough and much given to frowns and stomping of her feet. She also had a preference for boys' games and climbing trees, which was hard on her parents who so desperately wanted to keep her from harm! She insisted on playing outside in all weathers, and this led to further battles.

'Mary! It's raining and you have a cold!"

"Want go out!"

Mary's sharp intake of breath warned Edith that a tantrum was coming on.

"Well, go on then dear, but you must wrap up warm!"

Mary stood, pouting impatiently whilst the brown woollen coat was buttoned and a long knitted scarf wound around her neck. Next came a cloche-type hat made from thick felt, and finally luxurious lambs' wool gloves.

There was a beautiful flowering cherry tree to one side of the house, which in April dripped with pompons of blossom and spilt showers of spent petals onto the grass. One day Mary was cross because her mother had refused her a slice of snow cake.

"No Mary!" Edith yelled in frustration. "Eat your dinner first!"

Mary ran out into the garden, red with rage. Then she saw the blossom lying on the grass and scooped up great handfuls, racing with it and blowing it from her hands like confetti, her grievances forgotten.

Mary knew there had been a brother before she was born and that he had died. She felt no grief because she had not known him. She knew that her parents grieved greatly and this was endorsed by their frequent trips to the graveyard at Norton Church. *Rest in peace, oh much loved son* was emblazoned on his marble headstone. Whilst her parents arranged fresh flowers Mary wandered round the graveyard or sat quietly making daisy chains. It was a pleasant spot with a lovely view across the woods to the Malvern Hills.

Mary had seen photographs of her brother, a fair-haired child like herself, but more robust. How strange that he should now lie beneath the ground. But Mary had no time for thoughts of dying or danger.

***

There was a summer-house beneath the large chestnut tree at the bottom of the garden. She climbed triumphantly onto the roof and high into the tree without a trace of fear. She hated dolls but pushed her pet rabbit round the garden in a pram!

She did not have friends during her early days but that didn't bother her as she made up her own adventures and when he was home, her father was her playmate.

His difficulty with words meant that during her childhood she hardly heard him converse at all. His reply to most comments was simply his very knowing 'oo-ah!' It was amazing how this singular, two syllable sound could impart so much meaning merely by altering the inflexion of his voice. Mary never felt any lack of communication between herself and her father.

Both her parents were strict Wesley Chapel goers and teetotallers, and Sundays were set aside as God's holy day. They went to chapel followed by a good lunch and then took a walk in the countryside.

***

'Oakley Brothers' worked regularly for Bruton Knowles, the large auction house and land agents in Gloucester. Sometimes Fred took Mary and her mother to work with him.

One beautiful spring day they sat in a field of wild daffodils whilst he worked on a dam to provide water for a farmhouse. Edith watched anxiously as her little minx rolled down the hill.

"Be careful," she called. "It's steep!"

Mary took no notice.

"If you stop I'll buy you a sugar mouse!"

Mary sat up straight on the grass.

"Will it be a pink one?"

"Yes, if you like."

"Want two!"

"Oh alright dear, but please come here!"

But her daughter had one more salvo.

"Want daffodils!"

Oh alright! Her mother was growing impatient!

Poor Edith picked armfuls, and in the sweetshop Mary managed to acquire two sugar mice *and* a sherbet dip!

***

Her father's business was extremely successful in those days with forty men on the payroll. In the lounge at 'Oakboro', the family had a three-piece suite covered in the new 'rexine'. Her father was extremely proud of this, and after work he liked to take his boots off, sit in his armchair and put his feet on the mantelpiece. This was perhaps not the attitude of a middle class man, but Fred did as he pleased!

He was an even-tempered man and Mary only remembers him angry on one occasion. Her mother saw an advertisement in the paper for a furniture sale at Knowle's Auction House.

"Oh look Mary!" she said in excitement. "A table is coming up with eight chairs and a sideboard. Just right for when the family comes to lunch!"

She referred of course to Uncle Bert and Aunt Annie who had a string of children.

Edith popped Mary into a neighbour, hitched up her skirt and rode the two miles to the sale on her bicycle.

The saleroom was very crowded and she began to feel out of her depth but she soon located the furniture and checked it over. It wouldn't do for any of it to have woodworm. She knew how fussy Fred was about such things!

A moment of anxiety fluttered in her breast. *I've never taken a liberty like this before, she thought. Not spending money off my own back without so much as a by your leave.*

The auctioneer came in and sat down at a desk on a raised dais. Edith watched, feeling very nervous now.

He went so fast! Hands shot up all round the room as people made their bids. They all seemed to know what they were doing and Edith felt such a newcomer!

Before she knew it the table was up. Two of the auction house porters tried to lift it so all present in the crowded hall could see, but it was far too heavy.

"Very solid table this," shouted the auctioneer. "Now! What am I bid?"

It all happened so fast that Edith nearly missed her chance. She stuck her hand up hesitantly. There was a pause and so she raised it again.

The auctioneer shouted, "Not so fast, lady! You're bidding against yourself!"

A few people sniggered.

"Do I have any more bids?" he shouted. "All done then! Sold to the lady with the blonde hair!"

This auction business is easy! Edith said to herself. And she bought the rest.

"I can't pay for the things now," she told the woman at the cash desk. "My husband takes care of the money!"

The woman was not pleased. "You're meant to pay right away," she snapped.

"I have to go home first," Edith insisted.

"Will you be long? Do you have a car?"

"No," said Edith. "Just a bicycle!"

28

The woman scowled, but seeing it was no use to argue she hissed, "See you come back with the money as soon as you can!"

Edith nodded and fled the hall. As she rode home the enormity of what she had done overwhelmed her. *What if Fred should be angry? It was a lot of money!*

Later that evening, she faced her husband across the kitchen table. This time there was no gentle 'oo-ah'.

"What?" he yelled "You've bought these things without telling me? Without even asking me what I thought?"

Edith hung her head meekly, but the eyes beneath her lowered lashes were rebellious! She was pleased with her bargains!

Later, Fred calmed down and he drove to the auction house with the money and arranged for the things to be brought home by lorry. The oak furniture lasted Edith, and then Mary for more than fifty years. It was then passed to Mary's daughter-in-law Patricia, who has it in her home today.

***

Mary was occasionally taken to visit her grandparents, William and Clara who lived in a house called 'Colerne' next door to Uncle Bert and Aunt Annie. Granny Clara was a smiling old lady who sat stiff and upright and always dressed in black silk.

Mary enjoyed 'trying her out' by doing somersaults on the sofa. Granny was a softie really and very patient with her naughty granddaughter!

Her grandfather was more austere. He looked after his own garden and that of Uncle Bert next door. He was very keen on growing vegetables, and wilful Mary sometimes dared him by deliberately stepping among the plants.

He always shouted 'Get off them there beds, you little minx!'

Mary screwed up her face and reluctantly stepped back onto the path... until the next time! She *was a difficult child!*

CHAPTER THREE

HALCYON DAYS

Mary was a nervous child and sometimes awoke with 'Night Terrors'. Her screams immediately brought Edith to the doorway, blinking with sleep.

"Ah, my little pet," Edith would say as she swept Mary into her arms and carried her off to the safety of the big double bed where Mary would snuggle down with her parents in blissful warmth. These 'terrors' struck so frequently that during the early years of her childhood Mary had no need of a cot.

But Edith had terrors of her own. Forever haunted by the loss of her first child she kept a constant watch for any signs of illness in her adored daughter. One night, when she was about four years old Mary awoke with a great fever.

"Fred! Wake up! You have to fetch the doctor!" screamed Edith, the dreadful phantom of her dead son rising before her.

The doctor diagnosed scarlet fever, and Mary was gravely ill. The livid 'strawberry' rash swiftly crept over her body, as day after day she lay barely conscious. In the 1920s scarlet fever carried off a great number of victims. There was little anyone could do except nurse the patient until the 'crisis' was reached and hopefully passed.

Edith kept a vigil by Mary's bedside, sponging her with tepid water and coaxing her to sip drinks. Dr Alcock, their trusted GP was called in almost every day. All he could do was try to quell Edith's fears.

"Is she any better?" Edith hissed as the doctor bent over his patient.

"No! But she's no worse! You must take heart from that!"

Mercifully Mary recovered but she was left thin and sickly, and soon after she was stricken again, this time by whooping cough.

In her weakened state Mary was again fighting for her life. Fred dreaded the sound of the 'whoop', which echoed through the house, a long gasping strangle of breath.

Despite her frail appearance Mary was tough, and thankfully she recovered. But the illnesses only confirmed her parents' anxieties that their child needed constant cosseting.

"Wrap up warm, darling," they said on chilly days.

"Come on now! Eat your food, pet."

They surrounded her with love and protection but ungrateful little Mary resented it all. She was feeling better and wanted to be out in the garden, and of course it wasn't long before her parents gave in!

When Mary was strong enough Edith felt that some sea air might do her good.

"Fred, let's take the child on a holiday to Burnham-on-Sea," she said.

The residents of the rows of Victorian terraces in seaside towns often rented out apartments. The best rooms in these houses were usually of good size and it was common for the visitors to use the large front lounge and bedroom above, whilst the owners and their children squashed into the smaller rooms at the back.

Edith booked an apartment owned by a Mrs Sealy and the family travelled there by train.

"Oh Fred, this is very nice," said Edith as they unpacked their things.

It was a convenient arrangement. Edith purchased the food for their meals and Mrs Sealy cooked it in her kitchen and brought it on a tray for them to eat at a table in their sitting room.

Mary at the time was extremely fond of pink blancmange, and every day as they sat down to eat Edith asked anxiously, "You do have the blancmange, don't you?"

It better be pink, thought the little tyrant, swinging her legs impatiently beneath the table.

"Oh yes," replied Mrs Sealy with great seriousness. "We have the correct pudding madam."

The 'nervy' side of Mary's nature extended to her social life.

There was a bungalow at the rear of 'Oakboro' occupied by

31

a Mr and Mrs Watts, and they had no doubt seen Mary perched in the chestnut tree.

One day Mrs Watts paid them a visit.

"I've come about my niece," said Mrs Watts, settling down in the kitchen and readily accepting a large piece of Edith's snow cake. "She's getting married."

"Oh how lovely! I expect you're looking forward to it."

"I am indeed. But I rather thought you might be able to help."

"Oh! In what manner, Mrs Watts?"

"Bridesmaids are needed. We have one little girl, a relative of the bride, and we rather thought your daughter might like to be the other. She's about the same size."

"Well," said Edith hesitantly, "I don't know. You see, Mary doesn't take kindly to doing anything in public. She's not four yet, and rather shy."

"Oh but she doesn't have to *do* anything!" exclaimed Mrs Watts. "She just has to wear a pretty dress and walk up the aisle carrying a basket of flowers!"

"Well yes. But…"

Mrs Watts cut her off quickly. "I assure you she will be perfectly alright. She is pretty and blonde and she looks like an angel!"

Edith knew that looks could be deceptive, but Mrs Watts was insistent and an appointment was made for Mary to be taken to the dressmakers.

She stood on a table silent and sour-faced while her measurements were taken.

"There you are, dear," said the seamstress, turning a hem and popping in pins. "You are going to look lovely!"

Mary maintained a frosty silence.

At last she was lifted down.

"There's just the matter of the head-dress, madam."

"Head-dress?" Edith asked nervously.

"A very pretty little arrangement madam."

Mary scowled when she was shown a cap made from pale blue velvet ribbons with daintily dangling daisies, and she looked positively murderous as the concoction was placed upon her head.

"I fear our little princess is not entirely approving," said the dressmaker.

"She may not do this, you know," offered Mary's mother quietly.

"She'll do it," glowered Mrs Watts!

On the day of the wedding Mary stalwartly refused to wear the outfit. It began with a petulantly stamping foot, but the situation soon deteriorated into lusty screams.

Edith was desperate. *What on earth would Mrs Watts say if the blushing bridesmaid failed to turn up?*

"Please darling," she pleaded. "I'll buy you some sugar mice!"

Mary paused, mid-gasp, snuffling and wiping her eyes with the back of her hand as the dress was put on.

"How many?"

"Oh! Lots and lots!"

Eruptions threatened as the cap was lowered onto her head, but the sugar mice carried the day!

They reached the church just in time. Things might have progressed satisfactorily if the bride had chosen posies for her attendants to carry instead of enormous baskets brimming with flowers and ribbons.

Edith was almost sighing with relief when suddenly, just as the groom was slipping the ring onto the bride's finger, Mary's basket tipped over, depositing a mass of ribbons and flowers at the happy couple's feet.

"Don't want this!" Mary yelled, ripping off the head-dress and flinging it at the bride, and then she careered down the aisle screaming with rage! Her mother grabbed her and fled to the porch where they spent the rest of the service, the indignant shrieks all but obliterating the proceedings. In the ensuing photograph Mary is seen at the front of group, wearing the cap but frowning mightily. No doubt more promises of sugar mice were given!

***

Life in Mary's early days revolved around the Ryecroft Chapel in Gloucester where Edith had made several friends. One couple, a Mr and Mrs Grey, shared a strange coincidence, which made a special bond between the two families. They also had lost a son and then later been blessed by the birth of a daughter, Margaret. The Greys were both schoolteachers and Edith, who was still haunted by class distinction, thought they were a cut above her.

There was at the time a fashion for 'sewing bees'. The ladies of the chapel took it in turns to meet in each other's homes for a genteel afternoon of sewing, embroidering and chatting, and Mary liked to go along too.

A fine tea was usually served on these occasions and the ladies always tried to outdo each other, spreading their tables with their best linen and competing fiercely to produce the most elaborate cakes.

Of course they never owned up to this and were very self-demeaning.

"Oh, what splendid scones! How do you make them?"

"They're nothing my dear! I just throw them together!"

Mary wasn't fooled. She knew the competition was keen!

She usually scoffed as many cakes as possible and then went to play in the garden until it was time to return home.

The end product of all this activity was the Annual Bazaar, which was held around Christmas time in the hall adjoining the chapel, with the Minister in attendance.

***

At home Mary ruled the roost! But none of her wilfulness prepared her for her first day at school. For some weeks she held suspicions that her parents were not being truthful with her. They kept chivvying her on, telling her that something exciting was about to happen.

"You're growing up fast now," Edith often remarked with a nervous smile. "You'll soon be going to school, dear. You'll have such fun!"

I won't, thought Mary in disgust!

The day eventually arrived and Mary's mother anxiously gripped her daughter determinedly by the hand and walked her to the school, which was not very far from the house.

To this day Mary has no memory of her mother leaving, but

suddenly she found herself bewildered and motherless, surrounded by the other children. There was no playground, only a small yard with a tall brick wall. The children clustered round Mary and gazed at her with disbelief. Some of them were ragged and dirty, and they jostled together leering at the odd vision. Mary was so thin and small, wearing a short white lacy frock with her spindly knees on show.

Still staring, they advanced until she was forced against the wall. She glared at them and stamped her foot but this only made them laugh. Her mouth twitched nervously and she realised that her bluff was no good. The children knew she was afraid!

One boy, larger than the others, walked up and put his face so close that Mary could see the glints of hazel in his cold grey eyes.

"And who the heck are you?" he sneered.

He took hold of a wisp of her hair and gave it a tug. With the other hand he twisted her left ear.

"Let go of me, you horrid boy!" Mary shouted bravely, but this made the children laugh even louder.

A big, hefty girl came up next and snatched at the hem of the lacy frock. "What's this?" she spat, eyes narrowed in mockery. "Are we going to a party?"

Mary was now flattened against the wall, one thin arm trying to cover her face. Her breath came in little short gasps and she was sure she was going to be sick. *Oh no! She mustn't! That would be too terrible!*

She tried thinking of pleasant things... the cherry blossom, her mother's snow cake, her father carrying her in his arms through the garden. It was no good. She closed her eyes but all she could see was bright flashing sparks, which seemed to keep time with her racing heart. She opened them again. Oh no! The children were closer now, pressing against her. She felt them tugging at her hair and dress.

As she shrank against the wall she glimpsed a kindly faced teacher who had seen what was going on. She was hurrying over, but it seemed like slow motion to Mary.

At last the teacher grabbed the hefty girl and gave her a resounding slap round her face. Next it was the turn of the first bully. She gave him a slap too, which sent him reeling away.

35

Mary felt the teacher take hold of her own arm, none too gently, and she was half led, half pushed inside the school, where she was ordered to sit in the headmistress's study.

It was a dreary grey room smelling of chalk and musty paper. Mary was made to understand that her mother had been sent for and that she must sit and wait. This she did whilst the headmistress made notes with a scratchy pen. Mary kept her eyes downcast. Oh the blessed relief when her mother arrived. Mary ran to her and buried her face in her skirt.

"Come on," Edith said, ignoring the headmistress. "I'm taking you home. You shan't be coming here again!"

From that day on Edith decided that her daughter would have a private school education, as befitted a young girl of the middle classes, and she arranged for Mary to attend a little establishment near their home.

It was run by a Miss Gobie, in the front room of her house, and Mary liked it at once. She joined four other children round a table for lessons and was kindly and patiently treated. Her mother walked there with her most days, or if it was wet they caught the tram. Mary was delighted because during the afternoons she was once again free to climb the trees in her garden and play her private, dreamy games.

***

Christmas Day was invariably spent with Mary's cousins at 'Bassingham', the identical house at the other end of the town, owned by her uncle and aunt. The first school year of Mary's life was no exception.

She and her parents set off on Christmas morning. Mary insisted on holding a hand of both her father and mother, which was difficult as they were struggling to carry all the presents, plus the Christmas cake which had been baked and iced by Edith.

It was a chilly, damp winter day as they walked the three miles to Uncle Bert and Aunt Annie's house. On the way they could peek through windows to see firelight reflected in baubles on Christmas trees.

There was a cold wind blowing with a hint of sleety rain

upon it when Aunt Annie opened the front door, and Mary saw her cousins crowded into the hall to welcome her.

Paper chains decked the house, there was holly on the mantelpiece and trimming the top of the dresser, and in the hearth a cheerful fire was crackling. But there was no Christmas tree. Although the brothers were now comfortably off they did not forget their working class roots. Christmas trees ablaze with candles were for the gentry!

'Bassingham' was situated down a little lane off the main road, and there was at that time no mains electricity. The house was lit by oil lamps and candles, which added to the Christmassy atmosphere.

Mary and her parents planned to stay overnight and Mary was to sleep with her youngest cousin, Joan who had her own double bed.

All the cousins were much older than Mary. Joan was a teenager and very good-hearted and she liked to look after Mary. Nora, the eldest, had a job in the office of the family business in Denmark Road. Her brother Freddie was attending night school classes in architecture and spent many winter evenings at home drawing building plans. Eighteen-year-old Dos (Mary's namesake Dorothy) suffered from asthma attacks which Mary found extremely frightening. That Christmas morning Mary sincerely hoped that the dreaded asthma would not strike to spoil the fun.

Although both families were reasonably prosperous each member had just one Christmas gift, but these were always of good quality and carefully chosen. Mary had already opened her own, a white fluffy toy animal, and she was soon swept away to see her cousins' presents whilst from the kitchen came the delicious smell of roast goose and Christmas pudding.

In addition to the rich pudding there was always a big frothy trifle topped with plump blanched almonds, (nicknamed 'tombstones'.) Mary loved this and always ate it eagerly, but she was not so keen on the rich Christmas dinner. Aunt Annie tutted as Mary pushed away her plate of roast goose. Her mother looked on nervously hoping there would not be a 'scene.'

"The child's too excited," she said. "Don't trouble too much about the dinner on a day such as this! Let her have her sweet stuffs... after all, it's Christmas!"

Mary rubbed her Sunday best patent leather shoes on the rung of her chair and looked on triumphantly as the dinner was removed and the plate of trifle sheepishly slid in its place by her mother. She had won!

In the evening there was more excitement as the cousins' friends arrived. Nora played the piano whilst everyone clustered round to sing all the old favourites. At some point Aunt Annie and Edith crept away and laid out a vast Christmas tea on the table in the dining room. A huge ham was the centrepiece, with every kind of pickle and chutney, thinly cut bread and butter and savoury pastries. Mince pies and Edith's wonderful Christmas cake, together with the remains of the trifle and a fresh jug of cream were all placed on the sideboard for 'afters'. If anyone should still be hungry, there was a bowl of fruit and nuts, and a vast box of chocolates.

"They'll not be starving after this lot," Aunt Annie remarked.

"No indeed! But stand by for indigestion!" retorted Edith.

After tea everyone played games. Mary had been told that something especially exciting had been planned. During the afternoon Uncle Bert produced a large cut-out cardboard head, which he nonchalantly leant against the living room wall. It appeared to be some kind of queen, wearing a crown and with a large, gaping mouth.

"What is it?" asked Mary, excited.

"Ah, you just wait and see," said her uncle mysteriously.

She later learnt that it was the Queen of Sheba!

"You have to worship her," said Uncle Bert.

Everyone was hustled outside the door to await their turn. Mary was quite far back in the queue but she watched, intrigued. Each person in turn had a thick blindfold put round their eyes and was led into the lounge. Mary peeped round the door and saw that it was very dark inside. The oil lamps had been put out and the room was illuminated only by the fire in the hearth and a few guttering candles. Each time a 'victim' was led into the room blindfolded the sound of the most terrible screams issued forth.

Whatever could be happening?

At last it was her turn, the blindfold was on and she was

38

being led forward into the room!

"Pay homage to the Queen of Sheba!" intoned a loud voice. It sounded like her Uncle Bert but she wasn't quite sure! The voice was so strict and masterful! "Kneel down at once!"

Mary was shivering with a mixture of fear and anticipation as she dropped to her knees before the 'Queen'.

"Right," commanded Uncle Bert. "You must put your hand in the Queen's mouth!"

Mary thought nothing much would happen. After all it was only a cardboard cut-out. She felt for the open mouth and thrust her fingers in. At once she was screaming! Inside was all mushy and slimy and messy. She ran from the room yelling and laughing with excitement.

"Whatever was it?" she screamed, but no one would tell her the secret.

Later on she became so agitated that kindly Joan took pity.

"It was a mashed-up banana!" she hissed.

"Come on little maid," said Uncle Albert as he hoisted her onto his shoulder.

The determined look in his eye told Mary that she must not make a fuss and she was hauled away upstairs to a room, which looked so oddly like her own. It was the same size and had a familiar window. But even lying in the luxury of her Cousin Joan's double bed was no compensation as the sounds of the party drifted up from below. Suddenly she heard footsteps on the stairs. It was her father, bearing a crumpled napkin. Inside were three chocolates, all with soft centres, Mary's favourites. He was soon gone but Mary lay quietly enjoying the chocolates. She couldn't remember falling asleep, but very soon it was morning and she awoke to the comfort of finding Cousin Joan beside her.

The menfolk were up and about early, for on Boxing Day they went to a rugby match at Kingsholm; and after breakfast Mary and her parents returned home on the tram.

"Well," said her mother as they stepped into their own cheery hall, "that's another Christmas over and done."

CHAPTER FOUR

EARLY SCHOOL DAYS

In January Mary returned to school with Miss Gobie and soon she was walking the short distance there and back on her own.

One day, when she was about three-quarters of the way home she saw that there had been an accident. A farmer and his wife had been bringing a heifer home from market... in a horse-drawn trap! The weight had caused the cart to collapse and the heifer had been thrown into the road. It scrambled to its feet, snorting and stamping.

"Yer stupid fools," a man was yelling! "What d'yer think yer doin', tryin' ter carry a gurt big heifer in a pony trap?"

"Aw Gawd!" she heard another say. "Now 'ere comes a little girl!"

The heifer squared itself in front of Mary and stood scraping a foot. Mary froze. She knew she had to make her way past it, and decided to skirt round the outside, squashing against the hedge, but the heifer made a lightning turn and cut her off. Mary's terrified screams were joined by the shouts of the farmer and his wife, and the bellows of the heifer.

Then suddenly Mary saw her mother coming towards her. Edith had fretted because her daughter was late and had come to see what the matter could be, and she was glad that she had! Edith ran fearlessly towards the heifer and snatched Mary away.

The farmer grabbed the animal and secured it with a loop of rope.

"Thank God!" Edith breathed, hugging Mary to her. "Let's get home for some tea. It's well earned is all I can say!"

Mary clung tightly to her mother until her heartbeats returned to normal. The farmer was clearly put out and Edith glared at him as they walked swiftly past.

"I would have hated to see the little one hurt," he said

nervously.

"No doubt!" sniffed Edith with a toss of her head. "Next time perhaps you could tie the animal to the back of the cart. It was just a mother's intuition made me come and see what was causing the delay." Arm in arm Mary and her mother stomped away.

Shortly after her sixth birthday, arrangements were made for Mary to attend the Ripston Hall Independent School in Gloucester. She had to catch the tram, jump off at the park and then walk the rest of the way. Her mother went with her to begin with but soon Mary was making the journey alone.

Mary was thrilled with her smart bottle green and gold uniform but she did not take kindly to the navy blue knickers!

She had two pairs of school shoes; a pair of tough black leather lace-ups for outside, and another of fine, soft leather for inside. There were little pigeon holes in the cloakroom for the lace-ups to be stored till home time.

One day after lunch there was a buzz of excitement in the playground. The girls knew something was afoot because they had been told to gather in the hall for an important announcement!

As the headmistress came in, a hush fell upon the youngsters. She told them that there was to be a big party! But it wasn't a normal sort of party. It was to be in the style of a grown-up dinner dance. Preparation for social etiquette had begun!

"Each girl will have a little programme with a pencil on a silk cord," the headmistress began. "As boys approach you to ask for a dance you must fill in their names on your programmes."

There was a nervous shuffle from the assembly. The girls were normally taught separately from the boys, so this coming together of the sexes brought an air of confusion and excitement!

"Dancing lessons will begin immediately," announced the headmistress. "It is imperative that everyone learns the 'Lancers'!"

She added that the girls must wear their best party frocks for the dance.

"I will have to make you something special!" Edith exclaimed when Mary imparted all this news.

A trip into Gloucester was arranged and Mary chose a light satin fabric in a pretty shade of blue.

"I'll not have you in a long gown," Edith said; so a knee-length pattern was chosen, with an overdress consisting of two frills. Her mother sewed it all by hand, but she did not tackle the intricate 'pico' edging. For this she sent the garment to a dressmaker to be 'finished'.

The night of the ball arrived. The hall was decorated for the occasion with streamers and bunting, and most of the girls were very excited, but Mary felt dismayed. *What if nobody asked her to dance? Or worse still, what if somebody did and she didn't like him?* The girls were standing around in little groups whilst the boys eyed them suspiciously, but Mary stood apart from the others, frowning. A boy walked up. She had seen him before in the boys' playground but now he looked extremely clean with his hair slicked back with oil. He kept his eyes downcast as he mumbled a request to dance.

"I will if I have to!" Mary snapped, and wrote his name on her programme.

The 'orchestra', a little quartet with piano and strings, struck into a waltz; but no one was dancing yet.

Several more boys approached and were duly noted on Mary's programme. She glanced across at her friends. They seemed surrounded by partners and a lot of giggling was going on!

I don't care if I hardly dance at all! Mary said under her breath.

She was still scowling as she took to the floor with her first partner, a six year old called Tom. He took her hand and tentatively put an arm around her waist. Mary stiffened and held him at arm's length. Together they scraped around the floor, crab-like. It was the same treatment for all her 'partners'!

In the playground the next day the other girls were giggling about their experiences, but Mary was not impressed.

"Oh! I don't like boys that much," she said coolly, "and I hate the 'Lancers'!"

One evening after Mary and her mother had been on a shopping trip, they came home in the dark. As they drew near the house they were surprised to see that the light was on in the hall.

"What on earth can be happening?" said Edith as she opened the front door.

Spot, their pet dog, was lying on the front doormat looking at them uneasily. Edith stepped over him into the house.

"This is not looking good," she said to Mary, "I am afraid we may have had burglars in. You stay here whilst I go and have a look around."

Her eyes glinted with fear in the half darkness and Mary began to be frightened too.

What if the thieves were still in the house? She wished her mother would not go.

Mary listened to Edith creeping about upstairs and heard mysterious exclamations. Presently her mother came back down again.

"It's alright," she said. "There's no sign of them. They've gone now!"

Mary and her mother went inside, stepping over Spot the Useless Guard Dog, and the kettle was put on for a nerve-settling drink. When Fred came home he went from room to room. The burglars had been all through the house looking for money and valuables but nothing appeared to have been taken. The police were informed, but of course nothing could be done. It was discovered that the thieves had gained entry by breaking a side window. After that day it was a long time till Mary felt safe on returning home.

***

In the 1920s it was commonplace for all kinds of tradesmen to come to the house both to take orders and deliver purchases. Mary often saw the baker's boy on a bicycle with a big iron tray full of fresh loaves and cakes. There was also a greengrocer who had a small market garden out at Sandhurst. He had lost a leg in the First World War and his wooden stump made an odd sound as he left his horse and cart and limped up the drive.

But the most fascinating by far was Vera, the daughter of Mrs Cotton, who owned the local grocery store. Vera was a 'flapper' and fancied herself as a model or even a film star. The 'movies' were a new and much talked about innovation. Vera wore her black hair cut in a smooth shining shingle style. On top of this she sometimes wore a cloche hat. She was always very heavily made up and her lipstick was so thickly applied that her mouth looked like a red, moving slash. In addition she put on a sort of Americanised film star drawl. Her skirts were very short and she teetered on startlingly high heels.

But the most exciting thing was that she went round in a little car. Cars were still a rarity and it was most unusual to see a woman driving! She called to take the orders.

Vera was always shown into the front room and Mary sidled along too. She watched, enthralled as Vera sprawled cross-legged on the sofa showing her fashionable silk stockings.

Looking out from beneath lashes stiff with mascara, she went down the list with her crooning drawl saying: "Flour Mrs Oakley? Sugar, Mrs Oakley?"

Visitors were not frequent at 'Oakboro', but occasionally chapel friends would call. One of them, Mrs Day, had a young boy of Mary's age called Norman whom Mary liked. The attraction may have been due to the excellent iced buns, which Mrs Day baked, and Mary was always glad when she and her mother were invited to tea.

On one occasion Mrs Day had baked an exceptionally large batch of buns, and Mary sat down at the table eager to begin. She took the proffered sandwich but had no intention of eating it. She would far rather fill up with buns! She fiddled around with the sandwich, opened it to peer at the fish paste inside and then curled up the edges. Her mother was watching anxiously, and whilst Mrs Day's back was turned, she took the offending sandwich and transferred it quickly to her own plate. Mary's eyes opened wide with triumph as her fist shot out and grabbed a bun. The sticky hand made repeated trips to the plate as Mary chomped contentedly, all the time rolling her eyes from her mother to Mrs Day and Norman as the conversation flowed.

Very soon a strange, unpleasant feeling began to creep upon her. She lost interest in the bun on her plate and began to casually pick it apart, crumbling it into a sticky mess, which spilt onto the tablecloth. This activity, although vaguely enjoyable, did nothing to quell the stirrings in her stomach. Through a haze she saw Norman's mouth open to take a bite from one of the remaining buns and she suddenly felt extremely ill. Edith, seeing her daughter's face turn a nasty grey, grabbed her by the wrist.

She stood up, saying to her hostess, "Thank you so much my dear – such a lovely tea. We *have* enjoyed our afternoon but we must go now. I have just remembered that Fred is coming home early!"

Outside even the fresh air did not revive Mary, and as they climbed aboard the tram, she was feeling worse. She lowered herself into her seat, looked imploringly at her mother and was then most heartily sick. Poor Edith, with what moppings and scrapings and apologies she tried to erase the mess, but it was with great relief that their stop came into view and she half dragged, half carried her daughter to the privacy of 'Oakboro'.

Poor Mary did not eat another iced bun for several years!

CHAPTER FIVE

SUSAN BUNNER (Edith's sister)

It was a beautiful breezy April day in the year 1928. The young woman had just set off to the bottom field to take lunch to her employers. They were two brothers, both in their thirties, who owned a goodly little farm. It was by far the nicest job she had ever had.

Sue Bunner reckoned she had a lot to be thankful for. The farm was in the beautiful rolling countryside of Shropshire, not far from the pleasant market town of Shrewsbury. Her employers, Ben and Will, had been laying a hedge, a little late in the year, but the heavy snows of the previous winter had held them up. It was a long walk down to that end of the farm but it was a pleasure, breathing in the beauty of the spring day. Like her elder sister Edith, who was married to that fine carpenter Fred and lived in Gloucester, Sue had a great love of fresh air. And she knew that no county in England had finer air than Shropshire. And it was such a wonderful day!

Sue had prepared the lunch for the brothers with her own hands. Her morning had been spent making a good pork and onion pie. It was stuffed with their home-produced pork, and the thin pastry crust was golden and savoury. She wrapped the pie, still warm and fragrant, in a clean white cloth, and packed it into her canvas shoulder bag. In also went a thick slice of cheese and some bread, which she had baked the day before, but which was still fresh enough. Two russet apples, now soft from their winter in the attic, and a flask of light ale completed the meal.

As she walked all her thoughts were happy. In this job she did not feel like a servant. She was treated almost as an equal by the brothers... so much so that they did not expect her to eat separately in the kitchen, but insisted she sat at table with them.

The previous night whilst they were enjoying dinner, the brothers had said that they had a surprise for her.

"You just won't guess!" said Will, his brown eyes twinkling at her across the table.

"Master Will," said Sue laughing, "you are such a one for teasin' me, and I'm in no mood for guessin'. It's obviously somethin' very good as you're so worked up about it!"

"Don't tell her Will," said Ben. "She must guess! Now Sue," and he leaned across the table and fixed her with his stare, "what would be the most excitin' thing Will and me could turn up with? Somethin' amazin'!"

"Oh! I don't know! A new stud bull from Limpton Farm; you know, one of their Herefords, but no, that would be too dear!"

She closed her eyes for a moment and then said with glee, "Could it be one of those gramophone things? An' we could play that newfangled dance! The Charleston! An' then you could take it in turns, dancin' me round the drawin' room!"

There was a hush and Sue caught her breath, fearing she had been too bold, stepping beyond her place.

But she saw with relief that both of the men were laughing.

"No! No! No!" said Will, unable to contain his excitement any longer. "IT BE A CAR SUE!"

She was dumbfounded. Almost speechless in fact; which was a pretty strange turn of events for one normally so full of chatter!

"No, no, Masters," she managed at last, "You be poking fun at poor Sue. Why! However would you be affordin' one of they things?"

Sue had a head of thick blonde hair, which, no matter how she tried to restrain it, had a habit of coming undone. In her excitement she had tossed her head around, and the hair was beginning to tumble over her shoulders. Ineffectually she tried to push it back into its loose, floppy bun at the back of her neck, and secure it with a few scattered pins.

"Well, its true," said Will. "It's not a new one mind you, an' it cavorts about an' makes one heck of a noise. But it's a car. And soon you'll have to be believin' us, because tomorrow we be bringin' it home!"

The brothers explained that Will had met with a bit of luck. Back in March he had been talking to a farmer from Clee Hill, who had told them, whilst they were supping a pint at the village inn, that he knew a man, a friend of his cousin, who worked at Cheltenham Race Course. The man had given him a sure-fire tip for a horse running in the Gold Cup. Will had been so taken over (not to mention a little easier for the drink an' all,) that he had come straight home, taken the four gold sovereigns which they always kept in the gun cupboard for a rainy day, and handed them over to the man, who had duly put the money on the horse. And the horse had come in at twenty to one! This meant, explained an excited Ben, that they had been able to purchase the car! Furthermore, enough had remained for them to put back the four gold sovereigns into the gun cupboard!

All this was imparted with great breathlessness by Ben, who then sat back so hard in his chair that he overturned his plate. As Sue mopped and made clean around him, the brothers told her that they were going to collect the car, from a gentleman in the next village as was selling it, and bring it home the following evening.

Now, as Sue strode out to take the brothers their lunch she was as excited as a tomtit on a kettle, and just couldn't stop thinking how she must write a letter to her sister, Edith, to tell her the news. But the biggest excitement of all was that the brothers had said that they might consider teaching *her* to drive the car. Sue's happiness and the beauty of the day combined in her young heart to bring her a joy, which just swept her away!

She found the brothers in the bottom field and handed over their lunch, pausing to sit with them in the sunshine and nibble a bit of pie. Primroses grew on the bank and the bluebells were breaking bud at the edge of the wood. As she took up the empty bag and left the brothers to return to the farmhouse, the whole breathless beautiful day filled her with happiness.

"Oh my God," she breathed to herself. "It's wonderful to be alive!"

It was later in the afternoon, after she had put a ham and the remains of the pie into the pantry, and prepared the vegetables and an apple cake for supper, and popped to the dairy to turn the cheeses, and skimmed a generous helping of cream from yesterday's milk to set by in a jug for their pudding, that she finally found the time to sit down and write to her sister. Although Edith was ten years her elder, the sisters had always been very close and they kept in touch by letter.

Sue sat in the quietness of her room with the window opened wide, and composed her letter telling Edith about her job, the countryside, the brothers, and of course, the CAR! When she had finished, she folded it and put it into an envelope addressed to Mrs E. Oakley, 'Oakboro', Gloucester, and then, pausing only to fling a light wrap over her shoulders, went downstairs and out into the warm sunshine. She would have to walk into the village to the postbox.

Her feet sprang over the turf and when she arrived the village was sleeping in the bright afternoon. Daffodils blazed in tubs outside the inn and a song thrush was telling the world that spring had arrived. She popped her letter into the postbox and then went into the inn to see her friend, Elizabeth, the chief chambermaid.

After the brightness outside it was cool and dark in the inn. Sue found Elizabeth in the washroom sorting through a pile of linen.

"I've just come to post a letter to my sister, Edith," she said cheerfully. "You know, the one that lost her little boy when he was but eight years old, but has another child now, a little girl called Mary. An' a right spoiled thing she is. Gets her own way in everythin', and a bit of a madam too. Still, she's a pretty little thing. Not altogether bonny or rosy, but sort of frail and delicate. Like a little foal."

It is not certain whether this description served to give a very clear picture to Elizabeth, but the two women went together and sat down in the bar to swap their news, and of course, Sue was soon telling all about the brothers and the car.

Two days later Edith received the letter. The postman often came late to their house and Edith had just finished cleaning the sitting room when she saw the envelope on the mat. She recognised Sue's handwriting and was pleased, as she loved to receive news of her dear sister.

She made herself a cup of tea and then sat down at the kitchen table. She smiled as she read all about the farm and how happy Sue was there, but then she came to the passage about the car and a frown began to develop on her forehead.

Edith knew Sue very well. She had always been her favourite, and when they were younger they had enjoyed each other's company in that close, precious manner which sometimes develops between two sisters. Being ten years her senior, Edith also felt very protective towards her. She had been Sue's confidant and closest friend for many years.

Edith knew how flighty and indeed, often foolhardy her sister could be. Even as a young girl she had been inclined to take risks. She remembered her climbing fearlessly right to the top of the tallest trees. Their parents owned a farm in Monmouthshire and once she had caught Sue attempting to ride bare-back on a wild hill pony. Edith recalled how she had run out into the twilight to see Sue fall from the creature's back and then lie motionless among the heather. The pony galloped off and Edith raced across the turf to find her sister unconscious. Sue had soon opened her eyes and suffered nothing more than a mild concussion but Edith still remembered the horror of seeing her sister so still and silent. And now she was going to drive a car!

Edith could not help her anxiety. It was extremely hilly in the area where Sue now lived and the lanes were narrow and steep. What did Sue intend to do? Would she just climb into the car and attempt to drive it? Take it out onto those perilous lanes? What if the car should run away with her? The situation seemed charged with danger! Edith was beside herself with worry.

That evening when Fred came home, she showed him Sue's letter.

"I've never heard of such a thing!" she said: "It's so dangerous! What does a young girl like Sue know about driving a car?"

"Oo-ah! But she's in her thirties," Fred pointed out.

"Well that's as may be, but she's my youngest sister and she'll always be a girl to me. There's such a lot of good in her. She's such a one for a laugh and joke. And she was so kind and wonderful to me when Jim died."

A brief frown flickered across her face at her dead son's name. It still hurt to say it aloud, even though it was now nine years since she had lost him.

Just then Mary came swinging into the kitchen, a large fluffy toy in her arms. Edith's sad thoughts and worries evaporated as she bent to see a daisy chain her daughter had made.

"Come and see the daisies, mummy," said Mary. "There are such a lot of them."

"Of course we'll come," said Edith, keen as ever to gratify her child's every wish. Fred swept Mary up onto his shoulders and the little family went out into the gold of the evening. Mary beamed. Instant, doting attention from her parents was what she had come to expect!

Later that night, when Mary was asleep, Edith penned a long letter to her sister, pointing out her fears and pleading with her not to take any risks. Mary slept undisturbed in her room above, completely unaware that her life was about to change forever!

CHAPTER SIX

ALL OF AN APRIL'S EVENING

In the farm near Shrewsbury, Sue, her pinafore flapping, was running out of the house in great excitement. There was the car, a sleek black but rather elderly-looking Austin, pulling into the yard. It came to a jolting stop stirring up a flurry of dust and sending the hens scattering and cackling in terror. Sue had been very careful to lock up the sow with her litter of piglets, and she was thinking it had been a good idea. The brothers tumbled out, both red with excitement.

"Ain't she just a beauty?" said Will as Sue nodded enthusiastically. "Be a darlin' girl and get some of Ben's best ale to drink a toast with, and a bit of bread and cheese for a quick bite. Then we'll take you for a spin. She's a wizard motor! Best be quick though 'cos we don't want to be out too late. There be just enough daylight."

The quickest of suppers was eaten, and then the brothers ensconced Sue in the back seat whilst Ben took the wheel. Ben let out the choke whilst Will heaved on the starter handle. The car shuddered, refused, and then stuttered uncertainly into life.

"It be a bit of a game fighting with these blessed gears," complained Ben. An ugly grating sound was heard as he searched for second gear. He missed it and the car jolted into third.

Ben nearly steered the car into the hedge but he righted it quick enough and Sue thought it would be better to pretend she had not noticed.

"How many miles an hour be we doin'?" she asked, a little anxiously.

"Over twenty," replied Ben, "faster than a gallopin' horse!"

"Blimey!" said Will. "My turn soon!"

"I'll be wantin' a go too", said Sue, not sure if she meant it.

Seeing how Ben was having such a struggle with the car she was beginning to think that perhaps her sister was right. She had received a long letter from Edith pleading with her not to try to drive the car.

"What an old stick in the mud!" had been her reaction when she had read it. "How like Edith to pour cold water on somethin' which sounded like fun!" She was far too serious, and much too wrapped up in that daughter of hers. That was a fact! She read the letter and then quickly folded it back into its envelope and slammed it into the top drawer of her bedroom chest.

But now she wasn't so sure. Maybe driving the car was too dangerous. It certainly didn't look very easy. But she couldn't let her nervousness show. To the brothers she must be boisterous and brave, cheery, do-anythin' Sue!

At the end of the lane Ben found a wide gateway and struggled to turn the car round. "It be getting dark," he said cheerily, ignoring the gratings and complaints as he struggled to perform a three-point turn.

Later, darkness was just closing in as Sue opened the farmhouse door and went into the kitchen to stir up the range and boil water for a cup of tea.

An hour later she was up in her little room under the eaves. For decency's sake she had taken the attic room, a whole floor above where the brothers slept, but it was also a large room and comfortably furnished. On that sweet April evening she was unaware that so little time remained to her in that sheltering house. Her casement window was flung wide and from the farmyard below came the sound of the animals settling. She heard the sow and her piglets banging about in the shed where Will had bedded them for the night.

They're trouble those piglets, thought Sue. She could hear Ben in the yard below cleaning feed pails at the pump. He was always so busy; the last to bed and the first to rise.

He'll be needin' a good breakfast in the morning. He'll have done an hour or two's graft before it, she thought to herself as she stripped off the cotton blouse and woollen skirt, which *she wore about the farm.* She washed quickly, using the icy cold water from the ewer on her washstand. It was almost completely dark in the room, as she had not lit her candle, so she felt her way carefully to her bed and slipped contentedly between the sheets to think deeply about the car, and how soon she may have to try to drive it. It was a disquieting thought but it could not disturb her healthy young sleep, which came almost immediately.

A few days later the spell of open weather broke. It rained all day and there were little flurries of hail and even a clap or two of thunder. It was still warm though, and the sweet smell of young wet greenery mingled with the odours of the farm. Sue had felt unsure for a few days about attempting to drive the Austin, but she couldn't lose face with the brothers. They had allowed her to sit in the car in the farmyard. Ben had turned the starter handle for her and she had attempted to drive round the yard. She did not understand the gears and the restricted space made steering difficult.

"I'm sure I would find it easier if you allowed me out of the farmyard," she said irritably. "It'll be a great deal simpler goin' in a straight line!"

But the brothers were jumpy. Sue could feel that they regretted promising to allow her to try. Also, she grated the gears so badly that they flinched. Nevertheless, Sue was determined to have another go.

On the second occasion she had managed to drive the car out of the yard and into the lane, but she soon had trouble with the gears again, and Will insisted she return to her seat at the back whilst he drove.

"I'm not too sure if drivin's really woman's work," he said to her next day. They were in the kitchen, and Sue was standing with her shapely elbows buried in flour as she made the dough for their bread. The young farmer was looking down at her kindly. She was so pretty and, she was a plucky one, but it was difficult to hide his anxiety.

"I suppose it might be handy to have you goin' into Shrewsbury sometimes," he said doubtfully. "You know, when we're busy like, as we were with the lambing last month an' all. But I wouldn't want to put a mite of pressure on you Sue. The car's not easy to drive. It be a bit of a varmint."

"You're always busy," was Sue's retort, "an' you need me to

do as much as I can! Anyway, who's to say it would be difficult for me. Sometimes a woman's better than a man."

Will ignored her. He was off to see to the piglets and had no time for arguments. But he still felt apprehensive. He had a job handling the gears himself. Driving was a whole new concept to country people like himself, who had been brought up with the team and the cart. And it wasn't as if the car was new. It had done a fair few miles an' that were a fact. He was a man, and he'd master it quick enough, but he didn't want Sue risking her neck. He felt he should say a firm 'no', but then she was so persuasive and he didn't want to upset her.

Sue knew that Will was the softer brother, and early that evening she sought him out. He was in the field they called Beeches on account of the large beech trees that grew at its upper boundary. She was out of breath when she reached him. He was checking on a few sheep, which had strayed up there.

Sue soon found him. The clouds had cleared and the air was sweet with the scents of the spring twilight.

"I would like a spin in the car, Will," she said.

"Maybe I'll take you out tomorrow," he replied.

"No Will. I meant with me doin' the drivin'!"

"Awe Sue. I ain't so certain it's a good idea."

Sue pushed back her heavy blonde hair.

She's awful pretty, thought Will, relenting. It was hard to refuse this bright and plucky young woman.

They walked back to the yard in silence but Will's thoughts were running. He really wanted to court her. She would make him a good wife. She was good about the house and farm. He knew she'd had a slip or two, before she'd come to his farm but he wasn't goin' to hold anything agin' her. She had a lovely way with her eyes, especially when she smiled. Sometimes he'd caught her looking at him, sideways like! It did funny things to his emotions!

As they came beneath the shelter of the threshing barn his thoughts were busy wondering if she could fancy him too.

Sue was staring at the Austin. Already a thin film of dust from the farmyard had settled on its bodywork. Sue noticed also that there was a dent in its side. One of the brothers must have hit something. She felt a shiver of fear but it was strangely entwined with excitement. She stepped a little closer to Will and looked up at him with all the mastery of a coquette, her head turned slightly to one side.

"Go on, Will," she coaxed. "I be sure I could do it. I was just beginnin' to get the hang of it last time."

"Awe, I don't know," he said doubtfully.

"Please Will! The sun's still shining. It be such a lovely evening. It kind of lifts the spirits. It would be a good time to do it."

Reluctantly he nodded, and together they walked to the car.

He helped her into the driving seat and, after a few turns of the starter handle, they were ready to be on their way.

"I'll just go through it all again," he said. "That peddle beneath your foot is the clutch, and to your left is the handbrake and gear lever."

She watched and listened, vainly trying to hide her trembling. Some of it was nerves, but a little was because of his nearness. She wasn't sure about men! Not after the last one!

"You don't have to do this you know," Will said.

"I'll soon get the hang of it," laughed Sue. Although she was afraid, her excitement was greater. She, a housekeeper, a farm girl, was about to go driving, and with handsome young Will! She nipped her tongue between her teeth and put her hands on the steering wheel.

She was smiling as the car slowly moved forward out into the lane. She had no trouble with the gears! She was doing so well! Even Will exhaled and relaxed. She looked around her. It was a lovely evening. Everywhere the primroses were out and the trees coming into leaf. How she loved this time of year!

Things went very well, a great improvement on her earlier attempts. Once the car was in gear it was quite easy to keep it moving and Sue, an intelligent girl, soon had a feel for steering. Will helped her drop to a lower gear as they began to climb a steep hill and they were both pleased at how well she was doing. At the top of the hill Sue brought the Austin to a shuddering halt. Will wanted a cigarette, but he knew how Sue hated the smell. He climbed out and stood smoking and looking down over the valley.

All was blissful peace, the sheep below cropping the new

grass in the meadows, their lambs beside them, the dusting of blossom in the hedges, the buds bursting everywhere. The countryside and his life seemed all aglow with promise. He saw his future clearly in the purity and light of that April evening. He would ask Sue to go out with him. He felt certain she would agree!

Sue shifted in her seat and leant across to wind down the window on the passenger side. In so doing, her arm knocked the handbrake, which she had failed to engage properly. With a sad little sigh the handbrake gave way, and with a cry of horror Sue realised that the car was moving. It began to roll backwards down the hill. Her mind racing, she tried to think what to do. The brake! The clutch! The gears! ...But it was all so new to her! She didn't have the faintest idea, and the car was gathering speed, out of control.

She could hear Will yelling but in her panic she failed to reach for the handbrake by her side. Such a tiny distance between redemption and disaster! Her mind dimly registered that it had started to rain again, a pattering April shower. Through a blur she saw the bluebells in the hedge, and primroses... hundreds of them!

She suddenly remembered the handbrake and reached for it, but caught hold of the gear lever instead. In her panic she was totally unable to save herself. A thin scream escaped from her lips as the car hurtled backwards down the hill. The road was straight. No bend or turn or rise came to save her. In a smear of tears and terror she realised that she had no hope. The wheel was rigid beneath her fingers.

Reflected in the mirror she saw the huge oak tree looming behind her. Then she felt a tremendous jolt as her hands lost the steering wheel completely and the Austin careered into the tree. In the merest fraction of a second her mind registered that it was just bursting into leaf. Silently, without a struggle and too swiftly for pain, her young life snapped away, and as the noise of the crash ebbed, in the branches of the tree above a blackbird resumed his interrupted song to the April which was Susan's last.

As she lay shattered in the car she had no way of knowing that Will was running so fast down the hill that he was almost falling, or that there were tears of utter dismay streaming down his face.

***

In Gloucester Fred was looking out onto the peaceful street when he saw the Telegram Boy on his bicycle. This was not a common sight and he wondered which house the boy was headed for. He was surprised when the lad stopped, leant his bike against the railings and knocked on the door of 'Oakboro'. Fred took the thin buff envelope and saw that it was addressed to his wife. There was a lump forming in his throat as he took it through to the kitchen and handed it to her.

Edith saw Fred's face and a silent scream welled up inside her. Her hands trembled as she opened and read the message. She knew what it was going to say. She had been anxious for days, ever since she had received Sue's letter. She seemed struck down, cowered, and she was leaning for support with one hand pressed tightly against the kitchen table, whilst the other clutched the crumpled telegram. Suddenly she cast it from her into Fred's hand, as if it were a poisonous thing.

Fred read it and laid it back down on the table. He knew that he could never find the words to comfort his wife. He was puzzled by her silent acceptance. He well remembered her screaming and weeping at the death of little Jim. Her reaction now was different, somehow worse. It was as if her grief had been sealed up inside her, where it could fester and do dreadful damage. He held out his arms limply to her but she did not come to him. Instead she just sat down hard in the elbow chair by the table. She sat so heavily that her arm swept a little dribble of peelings from the vegetables she had been preparing, onto the floor.

At that moment Mary came rushing into the room. She always became excited whenever there was a knock at the door. But now the sight of her mother made her draw back.

"Mummy! Mummy!" she called in alarm and climbed onto Edith's lap. She leant back against her mother and felt at once the

58

strangeness as the much-loved arms came so uncertainly around her. Mary looked up at her father, puzzled, and he quickly swept her off Edith's lap and into his own embrace.

"Mummy's unwell," he said quietly, "just go into the sitting room and play!" The same old trouble; difficulty with words dogged him again, but this time Mary obeyed without question. As she turned away she took just one quick look at her mother, sitting in the chair so curiously quiet.

CHAPTER SEVEN

A FUNERAL AND TERRIBLE SCREAMS

The day before Aunt Sue's funeral, Fred drove Edith and Mary to Gloucester Station. As he helped them onto the train he leaned forward and put a tentative hand on his wife's shoulder. He didn't want to leave her but Edith insisted that it was something she wanted to see through without him.

"Oo-ah," he said, shaking his head in sadness as the train drew away from the platform.

At Shrewsbury they were met by car and driven to the farm. Edith sat strangely stiff and silent, staring ahead. Mary watched the Shropshire lanes in all the glory of spring. There were hundreds of primroses spilling like clusters of pale stars on all the verges and banks. She had never seen so many.

At last the car turned off the lane and into a farmyard. Mary sat up, interested. It looked a pleasant place with hens scratching, and a litter of piglets ran squealing away into a barn. Edith and Mary were ushered to a door at the side of the farmhouse, which opened into a large stone-flagged kitchen, seeming very dark after the brightness outside.

Mary stood waiting for her eyes to adjust to the gloom, and then she saw her mother's family and in-laws seated round an enormous table. She was put to sit next to her cousin John, a child of her own age, the son of her mother's sister, Li.

The table was spread with a very good tea. Mary declined the ham and pickles but was soon munching some buttered buns and a piece of cake. At first everyone was very quiet, but as is so often the way at this kind of gathering, when people who do not see each other frequently suddenly find themselves thrust together, it was not long before the chatter began.

Mary noticed that her mother was still very quiet, although

she did bridle occasionally when someone made a comment about poor Aunt Susan, so recently dead. Mary was only seven years old but she was sharp, and she noticed that some of the assemblage were none too kindly in their comments.

One of them said: "Well, she was a bit flighty if you ask me. She was heading for trouble!"

This upset Edith who put down her slice of bread and butter, and pursed her lips ready to comment. But she changed her mind and kept her thoughts to herself.

After tea John and Mary were put out to play in the farmyard whilst the men sat round in the living room and the women busied themselves in the kitchen, preparing the funeral feast for the following day.

John and Mary made an exploration of the farm and its buildings in the early evening sunshine. They peered at the piglets and tried unsuccessfully to coax them over. Disappointed, the two children climbed into the hayloft where they sat talking until bedtime.

Neither of them had known Aunt Susan so they were not particularly unhappy, but a shadow of sombreness fell upon them when Will came to call them in to bed. Even two innocent children could recognise abject misery when they saw it.

In the big dark kitchen Edith was waiting, and she and Mary climbed the steep backstairs to the room they had been allocated. It was a plain room with whitewashed walls and a thick cotton quilt spread upon the bed.

"There's no bathroom here," Edith said, "so you'll have to wash in that." She indicated a large china bowl filled with warm water.

Mary obeyed and put on her long night-gown and climbed into bed.

"Will you be up soon, mummy?" she asked.

Edith shook her head. "Not yet," she said firmly, leaving no room for argument.

Mary had never known her mother so stern and uncommunicative. For a moment she considered throwing a tantrum but soon dismissed it. She sensed it would not work in this alien place.

For a while her mother sat beside her and stroked her head

but she hardly spoke at all, and Mary knew for certain that there would be no chance of a bedtime story. It was all very strange, coming from a mother who usually gave in to her slightest whim!

"Sleep tight," her mother said abruptly. "I must go back down and help the others."

"Is John far away?" asked Mary, beginning to feel just a little lonely.

"No," said her mother calmly. "He's only a few doors along the corridor. Did you get on well?"

"Yes mummy."

"Well, you can play some more tomorrow then."

"Are you all going to the funeral mummy? And who will look after us?"

"There's a neighbour coming in to watch over you both. Now close your eyes and go to sleep. I'll be up to join you later." And with that, her mother was gone from the room.

Mary stirred in the big bed. The little casement window had been thrown wide and she could hear the birds singing, and the farmyard noises outside. From downstairs came the hum of voices.

Where was poor Aunt Susan, Mary wondered? Was she hidden away somewhere in the large old farmhouse, or was she already lying in the cold, dark church? And why was her mother so unlike her normal self?

Mary felt homesick in the unfamiliar room and wished that the time would pass swiftly so she could be back in her own house. As she drifted off to sleep she could not know that the following night she would be in yet another strange bedroom and that the life which she took for granted would be changed forever.

***

In the morning Mary awoke feeling much more cheerful. The sun was shining and her mother was already up. She had washed and was pinning up her hair. The only thing different was that she was dressed entirely in black. Mary did not particularly like this and said so.

"Black's normal for funerals," was all her mother said, as she quickly flicked a face flannel around her daughter's neck and ears, and then helped her into a clean play dress.

Downstairs the family was once again seated at the table for breakfast and Mary sat down next to her cousin. Everyone was dressed in black and speaking in whispers. Mary momentarily raised a protest when two brown boiled eggs were set before her, but changed her mind when she saw the scowls round the table. She ate both eggs in silence, and drank all her hot sweet tea. She knew for certain that tantrums would not be effective.

Soon afterwards everyone departed in cars. Mary's mother gave her the briefest of hugs with a "Don't forget – mind your manners and behave yourself," and then the two children were left in the care of the neighbour.

It was a lovely day and they were both happy now that the sombre adults had departed. They went out into the farmyard and spent the time playing.

Later the black cars pulled into the farmyard and the grown-ups, mostly looking teary-eyed, trooped back into the house. Mary ran to her mother but was rebuffed. This had never happened before! She wanted to be angry, fly into a rage; but all she felt was a bitter heart-wrenching hurt.

She followed the adults into the sitting room where she cheered up when she saw that a gate leg table had been opened out and laid with a splendid cold lunch. The children were given a napkin in which to slip their choice of savouries and cakes, and then told to go outside once more.

When they had gone Edith settled herself into an elbow chair. Although it was a lovely spring day it was cold in the stone farmhouse, and a small fire had been lit in the ingle-nook. On the mantle piece someone had placed a photograph of Sue with a black velvet ribbon draped over the frame. Edith could not take her eyes from this. She felt as if the only person in that room who truly understood how she felt was smiling back at her from the photograph. Sue's fluffy hair was, as usual coming undone, and those eyes looked out at her with that same laughing smile which Edith had loved when they were girls. She had always cherished her, and now she would never see that smile again. And she had so wanted her to see Mary. The years had passed swiftly, and there had been many conversations and promises and a meeting had always been 'imminent', but it had never actually happened.

Edith noticed that there was at least one other person in the room who looked as miserable as herself. Poor Will, his eyes downcast, sat over by the window with his hands in his lap. She could see that he had been weeping bitterly. His face was red and puffy.

As Edith sat in silence it seemed that the room and her gathered family receded until they were lost in a misty perimeter. Perhaps it was the clotted tears in her eyes, which wrought this illusion; the tears, which would keep coming unbidden and escaping down her cheeks, so embarrassing and silly. Everyone else seemed to be coping much better.

Edith sank deeper and deeper into misery, and dark thoughts began to take over her mind. She knew it was perilous but she could not help herself. Occasionally someone would proffer her some food, but she could not eat. Her mouth felt dry and the sandwiches lay untouched on their plate upon her lap.

Her thoughts had a power she could not resist. Suddenly she was back with little Jim, leaning over his bed and looking with terror at the pain in his eyes. Then he was pale and dead and Fred was clutching him to his breast and weeping, great heaving sobs of despair. Fred was normally such a quiet man that this outburst of anguish seemed all the more terrible. Then, in her tumbled thoughts she saw Mary. Ah Mary, the answer to their prayers, and a second chance at happiness. She was a precious child. Edith knew that they spoiled her but they couldn't help themselves. Then fresh thoughts formed themselves into monsters to torment her. She knew she was poised precariously on the edge of a great abyss!

Could it happen again? Yes, it was happening! Mary was ill, stricken with Scarlet Fever! Mary! Mary! Don't die!

Suddenly the past and present became confused. There had been so much dying! But hadn't Mary recovered? Surely she had, but she couldn't be sure. She was such a delicate child, and so difficult with her eating.

My God! It was going to happen again! Mary would be taken from her too! Edith was certain of it. Was it her fault? She blamed herself! Guilt and fear and terror all combined in her mind and overwhelmed her.

Then Edith heard the voice, all unbidden from across the room. Suddenly she was snapped back to the present, at her sister's funeral.

"Well, Sue always was a one for trouble. No doubt she brought a lot of it down upon herself!"

Edith wasn't sure who it was that had spoken, but the words unleashed a horror inside her. *How could anyone say such a thing? And at the funeral!* She turned in anger towards the people in the room. She wanted to protest but instead, when she opened her mouth, all that came out was a thin shrill scream. It seemed everyone withdrew from her and she was alone again. Helpless, Edith toppled into the abyss!

***

Mary was safe and happy in the farmyard, sitting on the ground with John watching a mother hen and her chicks scratching for food.

Then suddenly there was a commotion. Her mother came rushing out of the house with her hair streaming behind her and her arms waving wildly, but worst of all, her head was thrown back and she was screaming! She ran out of the gate onto the lane with everyone racing after her!

"Quick! Catch her! She's gone mad!" Mary heard someone say as she watched in horror, her head full of the dreadful screaming. Somebody, it may have been the neighbour, scooped her up and took her into the house, followed by John, who had begun to wail.

Somehow poor Edith was caught and persuaded back into the house. She allowed herself to be pushed, none too gently onto the sofa. The screams had stopped but her eyes were glazed and her ashen face appeared blank and lifeless. She was lost in her own destructive thoughts!

Mary, who was watching from the doorway, heard someone say: "She just went mad! *Completely, screaming mad!*"

Suddenly Edith's brother Charlie loomed large. He happened to be Head Charge Nurse at a psychiatric hospital at

65

Bicton, near Shrewsbury.

"My poor dear sister," he said. "But don't worry. I know what to do!"

Everyone immediately stepped back as he took charge.

Mary remembers him looming there, a huge bunch of keys at his waist. She and her cousin were ushered away into another room.

Her father was sent for, post-haste on the train, and he arrived at the farm in the early evening. Everyone agreed that Edith must be taken home as soon as possible and Uncle Charlie would accompany them back to Gloucester. It was the twilight of a beautiful spring day when the taxi arrived.

The rest of the family stood by as the four of them were ushered into the cab. It was one of the newly designed taxis, with seats facing each other in the back. Mary was squashed in between her mother and Uncle Charlie. As they drew away she heard a relative say, "Mad! Completely mad!"

Uncle Charlie had given Edith a sedative and she now sat silent and pale. Poor Fred looked on, too dumbfounded to speak.

Uncle Charlie said frequently: "Don't worry. I'm used to these things."

He occasionally glanced anxiously at his sister.

All the way home Mary suffered from car sickness. Before leaving she had been given a meal of cold beef and potatoes and now her stomach was in turmoil. Waves of nausea kept sweeping over her.

"Mummy," she pleaded. "Please help me! I feel sick!"

Edith, usually so attentive, ignored her and sat stony still.

"Your mother's not well," said Uncle Charlie. "She can't help you now!"

"But I think I'm going to be sick!" Mary insisted.

Her father leaned over and laid a comforting hand on her arm. Mary felt better and the waves of nausea subsided, but they did not go away completely and she was desperately worried that she would bring up her dinner in the presence of Uncle Charlie. She was frightened that if that happened, he might take charge of her too!

Her mother, the mad woman!

Everything was changed, and the primroses, standing out so

sharp and clear in the gathering dusk meant nothing to Mary now.

At last they reached 'Oakboro' and her mother was taken inside, with Uncle Charlie firmly supporting her by the arm. Edith was put onto the sofa and she started to come round from the sedative. Dr Alcock was sent for. He had helped Mary through scarlet fever and whooping cough, and her parents always put great trust in him. *Surely he would not call Edith a 'Mad Woman'!*

Mary was led away upstairs to her room and told to play quietly, but no one seemed able to spare the time to put her to bed, and curious to see what was happening, she crept downstairs.

Her feet in their white socks made no sound as she crossed the hall and stood at the sitting room door, watching. Her mother was lying on the sofa. Dr Alcock was bending over her and trying to administer some white medicine, but her mother kept spitting it out all over the treasured Rexine upholstery. It was a horrible sight, and suddenly Uncle Charlie noticed Mary and swept her away upstairs again.

Later that night, in a state of complete nervous collapse, Mary's poor dear mother was taken to an asylum at Brislington, near Bristol. Fred was not happy that she was in such a place, and very soon after, decided to pay for his wife to go into a private home. Mary was not to see her mother again for two years.

But on that terrible night events overtook her with lightning speed. It was decided that she would move in with Auntie Annie, Uncle Bert and her cousins at 'Bassingham'. Fred felt his world had split apart and he could not cope with running his own large house without his wonderful Edith. He would find some comfort by moving in with his father who lived next door to Annie and Bert, which meant that he could be near Mary without having the burden of her day-to-day care. The firm's building yard was also nearby, so he would never be very far away.

Mary stood in her room, silent and miserable, whilst her father packed her possessions into an old leather suitcase. He wanted to cry as he emptied the drawers, taking out the piles of perfectly washed and ironed clothes so lovingly placed in them

67

by his wife.

"Want Teddy," whined Mary, her world falling apart, "won't go without him!"

In silence her father bundled the teddy bear into the case, also putting in a few puzzles and some crayons for good measure. His daughter was scowling. She looked hot and cross, but at the same time lost and bewildered. A wave of compassion welled in him and he dropped beside her on the floor, taking the little hands into his own.

"I'll just be next door," he said.

"Why can't I be with you?"

"Grandma's too old to look after you."

"Want you look after me."

"Auntie Annie'll do it better."

Poor Fred had run out of words.

"Can I come and see you every night? And will you read me a story?"

Fred nodded and grunted simply: "Yes. I Promise." And Mary knew that he would. Her father always kept his promises.

She felt desperately tired and wanted her bed.

It was very late by the time they arrived at 'Bassingham'. Aunt Annie took the sleepy child by the hand and led her inside. It seemed strange to be in a house so similar and yet so different, and know that it wasn't just for Christmas or some family occasion. Now she was going to live there! *She had to – because her mother was too mad to look after her!*

Her four cousins greeted her warmly. She knew that they were all much older than her: quite grown up in fact.

Later, whilst everyone was clearing away the remains of supper, Mary decided to wander round the house. She already knew it very well but now that it was to be her home she saw it from another perspective. Where would she sleep? Would she have a room of her own? There were already six people living in the house!

She went upstairs to look at the bedrooms. Her uncle and Aunt Annie were down in the hall, talking. Mary stood on the landing and listened.

"Did you say 'mad'?" she heard Aunt Annie say.

"Yes," replied Uncle Albert. "Completely, screaming mad!"

"Whatever will happen?" asked Aunt Annie, her voice heavy with shock.

"She'll probably have to stay in hospital for a long, long time."

The words were kindly spoken, and never meant to be heard by Mary, but they floated into the little girl's head as lightly as a fall of snow, and settled there like cold, hard poison.

Over the next months Mary would overhear these comments numerous times from various friends and relatives, and they were to scar her for life and subtly change forever her feelings for her mother.

But on that terrible night she could only wonder in panic if she would ever see her again.

Surely her mother, the attentive, caring person who had always shown her so much devotion, would not leave her for long!

Mary was only seven years old, and did not know the implications, but she could tell by the tone of their voices that the situation was serious.

"We must think of the child," said her kindly aunt. "She mustn't suffer. We'll make her a good home here."

"Yes," said Albert, "and she has her father next door. It will be a good arrangement."

"Poor little thing," said Annie: "She never does look very strong. We must do the best we can for her, for your brother's sake, and for hers too, the little pet."

Listening, Mary did not want a new home, however good it might be. She wanted to be back with her mother and father. She felt overwhelmingly tired and looked into her Cousin Joan's room. There was a big double bed in it, which Mary knew was very comfortable. *She thought to herself; wouldn't it be nice if I could sleep in there?*

There was no electric light at 'Bassingham', and a candle in a little china holder was flickering on the bedside table.

To her surprise Joan, who was just seventeen and a kind and homely girl, came in and said, "Mum says you're to sleep in here with me."

She gently helped Mary into her night-gown. It was late and she was tired too. Seeing her cousin's sad little face, she thought

69

of a way to help.

"You can tickle my feet if you like," she said, "Go on… Try and make me laugh!"

Mary couldn't help but giggle at such a strange idea! They were both sitting up in the big bed, so she dived under the covers and grabbed Joan's feet, tickling as hard as she could. Soon they were both laughing, and Mary wriggled up from under the bedclothes.

"I'm glad you're laughing," said Joan. "But I can see your eyes are a bit teary, so I think you've been crying too!"

Mary was silent. A big tear rolled down her cheek. Joan quickly wiped it away.

"That's better," she smiled. "From now on, no more crying!"

"Don't worry Mary," she said as they settled down with their heads on their pillows, "your mummy will soon be home again, and we'll look after you till then."

"Daddy's next door," said Mary sleepily.

There was plenty of room in the bed and the pillows were soft and plump. They had slips on them with crochet lace, made by Auntie Annie. Mary thought it was all very nice. It was also very warm to be cuddled up to her cousin, just like she often did with her mummy. Soon both girls were asleep.

CHAPTER EIGHT

When Mary awoke the next morning, for a moment she did not know where she was. Then she felt her cousin's warm body beside her and the memories of the past two days came flooding back. She was seized by a sudden panic! *How long would she be here with her aunt and uncle? Where was her mother? Where was Daddy?*

At that moment Joan stirred and put out a friendly arm to stroke Mary's head.

"Poor little girl," she said kindly. "Come on, I'll get you dressed and we'll go downstairs."

It was a bright sunny morning and Mary felt better sitting at the big table in the kitchen, which was so like her own at 'Oakboro'. Her cousins were mostly in a rush to depart for their jobs.

Nora, the eldest was working at the Oakley Brothers' office in nearby Denmark Road, dealing with the typing and managing the firm's accounts.

Freddie, the only son, was very lively and outgoing, and considered himself to be a man about town. He was kind to Mary, but perhaps resented the presence of such a young child in his well organised home. He was training to be an architect and attending night school, and he often sat at the dining room table with his drawings and plans spread out. His great hobby was tennis and he took pride in whitening his shoes with 'Blanco'.

Dorothy, after whom Mary had been christened, was always known as 'Dos'. She suffered badly from asthma. The low-lying position of 'Bassingham', close to the River Severn did not suit her frail health. Only dear, kind Joan was still at school but she was seventeen and would soon be leaving.

As she sat eating her breakfast on that first morning, Mary realised that the cosseting and spoiling would stop. She would have to take her place in this large and bustling household, and do as she was told.

Mary sat meekly listening as plans were made for her.

"Mum's far too busy to take you to school each day," said Joan. "So you are going to leave Ripston Hall and come to school with me. You'll love it at 'Denmark Road'!"

Mary made no objection. She knew it would be no use.

The arrangements for Mary to change schools were soon made. She needed a new uniform, so Aunt Annie took her into Gloucester. Mary liked the navy tunic and white calico blouse with blue pin-stripes. She also had a valour hat with a green, red and navy band round it, and a blazer with gold badge on the front pocket.

It was explained that she would first go into the 'transition' class.

"It'll be appropriate as so much in her life is changing," said Uncle Bert to Annie one evening, as they were finalising the plans.

On Mary's first morning Aunt Annie solemnly handed her tuppence, wrapped in a scrap of paper.

"You must be sure to have this," she said. "You'll need it every day!"

"What's it for? Is it for my lunch?" asked Mary, puzzled.

"No," laughed Joan. "You'll soon find out!"

Mary was mystified but she set off with her hand firmly clasped into that of her kindly cousin.

The school was a very grand building, set in green playing fields. They went inside, where everything was bright and cheerful, their feet clattering along the tiled corridor. The whistle blew in the playground and the girls came spilling in.

The headmistress suddenly appeared from a room leading off the corridor.

"Ah Joan," she said. "This must be your cousin, our new girl!"

Poor Mary could hardly believe it! Everything was so suddenly changed!

"Yes, Miss Penson," answered Joan. "Shall I take her along to assembly?"

72

"No, I think not. It might be a bit intimidating on her first day! I'll take her myself and introduce her to the other girls."

Then she turned to Mary with a kindly smile. "We want you to be very happy here dear."

With just one glance back over her shoulder at Joan, Mary was led away.

Assembly was held in the large downstairs hall and the pupils were filing in. Mary glanced up at a varnished wooden board with a gilded edge. On it were engraved the names of all the girls who had gone to university.

"Ah, I see you are looking at our roll of honour," said Miss Penson. "Girls do not often attain university places. So we are very proud of our achievements in this respect!"

Miss Penson approached a row of girls who had just seated themselves, cross-legged on the polished floor of the hall.

"This is our new young lady, Miss Mary Oakley," she told them. "She is to be in your class. See that you take good care of her!"

With these kind words she was gone and Mary was left with the girls. She felt like a stranger as she joined in with the hymns and prayers.

Afterwards her form teacher led Mary and her thirty classmates to their classroom.

"Here you are Mary," she said kindly, "you sit down in that desk next to Barbara."

The desk was wooden, like the one at Ripston Hall, and there was an inkwell in the right-hand corner. She was given a penholder with a nib.

"What kind of writing have you learnt, Mary?" asked the teacher.

"Copperplate, Miss," Mary replied.

"Here we do script," said her teacher, "but you will soon pick it up!"

Mary lent over her exercise book, copying the letters from the board. She thought that script was much nicer than copperplate.

At morning break Mary discovered what the tuppence was for!

"Come on," said Barbara. "It's time for our treats!"

"Treats?" said Mary, mystified.

73

Her new friend grabbed Mary's arm and hurried up the huge staircase among a crowd of excited jostling girls.

At the top Mary caught her breath. Before her stretched a wide corridor, and down its centre a large trestle table had been set up, covered with a white cloth, spread with bars of chocolate, doughnuts and Chelsea buns!

"Come on," said Barbara. "Don't just stand there staring!"

"The tuppence," Mary whispered, bemused. "Now I know what it's for!"

"Come on, you silly-head," chided Barbara. "Choose your stuff and then I'll show you the ropes!"

They were soon joined by several other girls from their class and Mary bent herself entirely to the delightful task of purchasing a bar of milk chocolate and a bun!

"Oh bliss!" she said. "I really like this custom!"

The girls could then wander off, chatting and laughing, to eat their purchases. Leading from the corridor were numerous little side rooms, which were used for secretarial courses.

"These are empty most of the day," said Barbara, "so we snuggle down in them with our cronies and have a good chat!"

The large dining hall was situated right at the top of the building and at lunch time it was set for a repast in the grand manner. Tables were covered with crisp white cloths and cutlery of a very high quality. The food was excellent, always consisting of meat or fish and at least two vegetables, and a desert with custard or cream. Talking was permitted, but only in a quiet and 'genteel' manner.

The only problem was that Mary was too full up with chocolate and Chelsea bun to eat much. But this was how she liked it! Plenty of sweet stuff!

Later, she noticed that some of her friends went home at lunchtime, and she decided she might like to do this too.

This would mean extra work but dear Aunt Annie made no complaint, and cooked a lunch especially for her niece each day. Mary soon knew her way and so was allowed to make the journey to and from school on her own. A heady delight for a girl of seven!

Aunt Annie had a different way of dealing with Mary's passion for sweet foods. If Mary refused to finish her lunch she simply whipped the plate away without comment. The pudding would then be presented and Mary would quickly devour it, but that was it... no second portion of desert to fill her up. This left Mary keenly hungry, and she soon learnt to eat all her first course. Occasionally aunt and niece would lock eyes and Mary set her chin for a second helping of pudding, but she never succeeded. Annie was made of stern and sensible stuff.

Mary was soon moved up to Form One, and on her first morning Miss Penson took her into the class and introduced her. The girl at the next desk was called Kathleen James. She had blonde hair like Mary but she was much taller with a plump motherly figure and a pleasant rosy face. As Mary sat down, Kathleen gave her a warm smile. Mary felt better at once. It was a maths lesson, and as the form recited their multiplication tables out loud, Kathleen kept catching Mary's eye with a kindly look. At break-time it seemed the most natural thing in the world to go out together to the playground. On the way the girls collected little bottles containing one third of a pint of milk.

"Do you pierce your lid with the straw, or take it off?" Kathleen asked with a grin.

"Bang it with the straw to make a hole," said Mary.

"So do I!" said Kathleen.

They drank their milk and then raced upstairs, their pennies in their pockets, to buy their treats. Kathleen was a popular pupil and Mary soon found herself surrounded by a crowd of girls, all laughing and making it clear that they wanted to be friends. They munched chocolate bars and began swapping information about themselves.

"I'm living with my aunt and uncle at the moment," Mary volunteered.

When they asked the reason Mary told them her mother was in hospital. She did not say that she was a 'mad woman'!

"I don't mind at all," explained Mary. "My dad's next door with my gran and granddad and everyone's nice to me."

"When is your mother coming home?"

"I don't know."

Kathleen caught Mary's eye with a particularly kind smile.

"Never mind," she said sweetly. "You've got us as friends now!"

Afterwards as the girls walked down the stairs to their classroom Kathleen drew Mary's arm through her own.

"We're in the 'B' stream," she laughed, "not the 'Brilliant 'A's'!"

"It means that we do cookery and needlework instead of extra languages."

"I prefer it," said Mary firmly.

The 'A' girls learnt Latin and German, whereas Mary and Kathleen only learnt French. But initial gradings can be wrong, for Kathleen later turned out to be a brilliant mathematician and gained a place at Cambridge University!

But this was all in the future, and on that first day together, as they went into class still arm in arm, Kathleen turned to Mary and said, "I'm so glad you've come to Denmark Road. I just know we're going to be friends forever!"

From that day on Mary decided to return to school lunches. It was such fun being with Kathleen and their little circle of cronies' that she didn't want to miss a moment!

Mary soon began to feel truly at home at 'Bassingham', and her uncle and aunt were always keen to treat her exactly as their own children. Joan was having violin lessons with a Mr Morrell in Gloucester, and Mary decided she would like to do this too. A small violin was duly purchased. Mary took it up to her room and sat on the bed. She opened the black leather-covered case and looked inside. The shiny violin lay on a bed of purple velvet, with a bow laid in its own slot alongside. Mary took it out of the case and tried a few scrapes.

Eventually Mary earned a place in the school orchestra but she was still far too self-conscious to appear at a performance!

Her shyness was so extreme that she hated posing for photographs. One day their teacher announced that the school photographer would be attending the following day, and that all the girls must come looking their very smartest.

"I can't face it!" she told an incredulous Kathleen at break-time.

The next day when Mary came down for breakfast she said to Annie, "I don't feel well, auntie. I'll have to stay at home!"

Annie laid a hand on her forehead.

"You don't feel hot."

"Oh but I feel sick!" insisted Mary. She refused to eat and went back up to her room. It was the same every time the photographer came. Annie had her doubts, but played along!

***

Mary's geography teacher was a tall thin woman, called Miss Godfrey. She was the archetypal school 'marm' always immaculately dressed in dark coloured clothes and with very straight grey hair pulled back into a tight bun. One day Miss Godfrey was delivering a lesson which Mary thought particularly boring. The sun was pouring through the classroom windows and, as the teacher's voice droned on, Mary slipped into one of her daydreams.

Exasperated, Miss Godfrey demanded in a loud voice: "MARY! ARE YOU DREAMING?"

"Yes, Miss Godfrey," replied Mary matter-of-factly, still in her dream.

The rest of the class held its breath, and then one or two giggles could be heard.

Mary felt a deep beetroot blush creep from her neck to her face as she sat in miserable embarrassment. Miss Godfrey, who was not renowned for her sense of humour, was furious.

"You must be punished girl!" she snapped. "I will give you some 'lines' to be written out during break-time. That will stop your dreaming!"

The girls noticed that Miss Godfrey was prone to hot flushes herself. She often dabbed frantically at her reddening face with a handkerchief as crisp and angular as herself.

***

Sometimes after school, Mary went to visit her father in his workshop. She liked to chatter on, and Fred was content to listen, adding his wise and understanding 'oo-ah' in the appropriate places, but they never spoke of Edith.

Every evening Mary was allowed to go next door to her grandfather's house so that her daddy could read to her. She still preferred boys' books and she loved the exciting adventure stories from 'Boys Own'.

It was lovely to climb onto her father's lap. Oddly, although Fred found such difficulty in talking he was a wonderful reader, making all the scenes and characters come to life.

But one night after she had been tucked up in bed at 'Bassingham', Mary dreamt she was with her father. Still asleep, she climbed out of bed and went downstairs. She was in the middle of unbolting the heavy back kitchen door when Aunt Annie awoke and went swiftly down to see what was happening. Mary, sleep walking, was just about to step out alone into the night. Realising what was afoot Annie grabbed her and took her back to bed.

In the morning the family asked Mary what had happened and she said, "I was going to see Daddy for another story."

After this experience the readings were deemed too exciting, and they were stopped. Mary was sorry about this but she was so keen to return to the stories that she became one of the first children in her class to read fluently.

She developed a very individual posture. With her book spread on the dining room table she stood on one leg, with one elbow leaning on the table, reading for hours. The rest of the family became used to this strange behaviour and would simply walk past without comment. Mary was happy and never thought of herself as a guest or unwanted.

Aunt Annie was an even-tempered person, not given to shouting when annoyed. For misdoings her one punishment was to send the offender 'to Coventry'. This is an old fashioned method of showing displeasure by refusing to speak to the miscreant. Aunt Annie was capable of keeping this up, and in fact enlisting the support of all others in the household, for a considerable number of days, until she felt that the punishment had been sufficient. Mary was to be on the receiving end of this treatment on a number of occasions.

The person she clashed with most in the household was her cousin Freddie. Mary was still a wilful girl, not much given to seeing another person's side of an argument. One evening Freddie had as usual spread his drawings over the dining room table, but Mary came in, determined to use the table herself. She had just been given a large jigsaw puzzle. It was a jolly picture of zoo animals, and Mary could not wait to start on it. The sight of her cousin seated at the table with his plans spread completely over it, annoyed her.

She said crossly: "You can't have ALL the table! You'll have to move!"

"Oh will I?" retorted Fred, bristling. "And who says so?"

"I do!" snapped Mary. To illustrate her point she sat down quickly on one of the chairs, turned the puzzle box upside down and shook the pieces out all over the table. Mary's rudeness and the sight of the puzzle pieces scattered over his precious drawings made Freddie angry.

"I jolly well will not move!" he said sharply.

Seeing that she was losing rattled Mary further, and she did not know what to do, so she decided, most unwisely, to rip up one of Freddie's drawings. She regretted it as soon as she had done it and her heart went racing. It was a long time since she had done something so naughty. Back home at 'Oakboro' she might have gotten away with it, and her mother would have made a sort of 'giving up' sigh and let her have her way. But this was Aunt Annie's house. Things were very different.

But she did not want to back down so she snapped, with her heart not quite in it, "What does it matter? It was a silly old drawing anyway!"

"It was not. It was very important actually!" and poor Freddie looked down at the ruin of his carefully drawn house plan in some consternation.

At that moment Aunt Annie, who had heard the argument, came into the room.

She took hold of Mary and marched her out of the dining room. Seeing Mary so crestfallen touched Freddie. He did not want to see her in trouble, but it was out of his hands now!

Once safe in the back kitchen Aunt Annie chafed Mary for her wrong-doings.

"That was a dreadful thing to do to your cousin," she scolded, "tearing up his drawing! A proper little madam you are sometimes. And now you must learn to treat people better. I'm sending you to 'Coventry', my girl! Neither me nor anyone in this house will speak to you until I deem that you're truly sorry!"

Mary knew all too well what her aunt meant. She had seen

her send others to her famous 'Coventry' for wrong-doings. But this was different. She couldn't just skip off home to normality. She would have to live through it, in this house, for as long as Aunt Annie felt was necessary. One thing was certain. Mary wasn't going to let them see that she minded!

Aunt Annie went into the dining room and quite sharply asked Freddie to put his things away and lay the table for the evening meal. Freddie cleared away immediately!

Over dinner Annie announced that Mary was to be 'in Coventry' and no one was to speak to her. Mary sat with a sullen 'don't care' face throughout the meal, but she began to feel quite horrible when the family was enjoying a lively conversation and having fun, and she was being so deliberately kept out of it.

Once or twice she tried to interrupt or join in, but everyone ignored her as if she wasn't there. It was not a good feeling. She finished her dinner and went upstairs and spread out her jigsaw puzzle on the washstand. She could hear the happy chatter downstairs and began to feel very lonely.

Aunt Annie came up later with a jug of hot water. Mary tried to make her speak but her aunt continued to ignore her. She simply placed the jug on the washstand, in the middle of the puzzle, and went back downstairs.

Mary undressed, washed and climbed into Joan's bed. She wanted to go downstairs and shout at them all. Tell them that she hated them! But that would only make matters worse. Instead she fished Teddy out from under her pillow, cuddled him and lay there trying to sleep. Big lonely tears began to roll down her face. She thought of Daddy in the house next door and wanted to run to him, but that would only put her in more trouble.

Later, Joan came up and lit the candle on the dressing table whilst she washed and changed into her night-gown. After snuffing the candle she climbed into bed. Mary immediately moved over to her, wanting a cuddle. Joan did not shift away.

"Goodnight, Joan," Mary said in a little voice.

Joan remained silent.

Mary tried again. "Goodnight,"

"I'm not supposed to be talking to you," hissed Joan.

Mary laid there for along time, sleep refusing to come.

Joan heard the unhappy snifflings beneath the bedclothes

and relented. "I'm not going to say anything else," she snapped, "so don't you go trying to make me." In a kinder voice she added, "Goodnight."

"Goodnight darling Joan," said Mary, so grateful that she fell asleep almost at once.

In the morning things were just as bad. No one spoke to her over breakfast and Joan walked with her to school in silence. But she was a kind natured girl and still held Mary's hand. Once inside Mary was relieved, joining in all the chatter with her friends. During the day everything was normal so Mary cheered up, but at home-time the gloom descended again. She knew that the silence would continue at 'Bassingham'.

When she came home from school on the first day she tried to bluff it out, going on with her chatter, but Aunt Annie was not to be fooled, and ignored her. Mary tried getting cross, but that certainly didn't work, so she just settled down to see it out until she was allowed back 'from Coventry'.

On the second afternoon she was completely dejected as she walked home with Joan, who had promised Aunt Annie that she would not relent and break the punishment. It was a dark, drizzly afternoon and poor Mary was as downcast as the weather. Joan couldn't help feeling sorry for her. In the kitchen she sat Mary down at the table and whispered to her mother, "I think she's had enough, Mum. She's ever so miserable."

Silently Aunt Annie gave Mary a drink of cold milk and cut her a slice of cake.

When Mary had finished she stood up and put her arms round her Aunt. "Please Aunt," she pleaded, "I'm very sorry. Please speak to me soon."

Aunt Annie relented and kissed her back. "Well my girl," she said, "I think you're truly sorry. You apologise to Freddie when he gets in and we'll forget all about it."

"Thank you," said Mary in relief, skipping out into the garden to play. She had learned her lesson, for a while, at least.

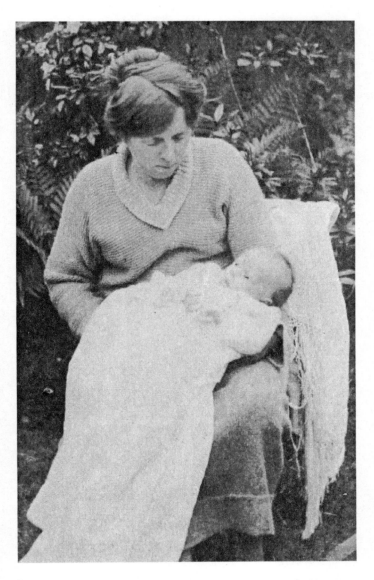

Mary, newborn, in the arms of her mother, Edith Oakley

Mary's father, Fred Oakley, as a young man.

Mary, age two.

'Oakboro' – the house built by Mary's father, and her Uncle Bert.

Mary, the cosseted child, with her mother and father, outside 'Oakboro.'

Mary the bridesmaid, aged four, (front left) in the detested flowery cap.

'I hate this swimsuit!' Mary on holiday at
Burnham-on-Sea, aged five.

Cousin Joan and 'Spot' the dog help Mary (aged seven) adjust to her new life at 'Bassingham.'

**The Second Eleven Hockey Team at Denmark Road School
(Mary, back row, second from right.)**

Gordon – Mary's first love.

Stepping out – Mary (right) and Kay as teenage friends.

Mary, aged eighteen.

The Usk Agricultural College where Mary underwent her
'Land Army' training.

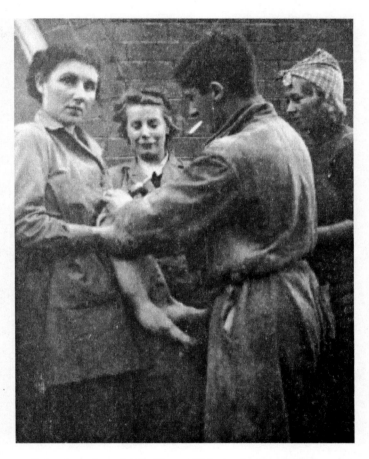

Injecting pigs with iodine at Usk Agricultural College.

Examining a bullock at Usk Agricultural College.

CHAPTER NINE

FRIENDS, FLOODS & DOS LEAVES HOME

Aunt Annie did not think it was healthy for children to stay indoors so she encouraged Mary to make some friends and go out playing and walking in the countryside.

"Come on now! For goodness sake! You need some fresh air, my girl!" she would say if she deemed Mary had been reading for too long. "Book worms don't grow up healthy, and that's a fact!"

Two girls, Toni and Margaret lived just across the road, and two sisters Marion and Ivy lived further up the lane. It wasn't long before they had formed a merry gang; all intent on enjoying themselves.

'Bassingham' was not far from the River Severn, and there were plenty of places for the girls to explore. In the 1920s most farms did not have water piped to their fields, but relied on ponds. These pools were deep and dark and often overhung by trees, and they made irresistible haunts for the girls.

Mary and her friends clambered into the trees to find a good strong overhanging branch on which to sit and tell each other stories. These 'dens' were magical places, secret and hidden away, roofed with leafy branches, and with the water dark and mysterious beneath. The stories were always adventures loosely based on the tales that they read in a magazine of the day called 'The Friend', or 'Boys Own!' These 'boy' magazines were introduced by Mary.

Sometimes the girls fished for newts with an improvised net. The mud was slimy and evil-smelling, but Mary and her friends tucked their skirts in their knickers and waded in. It was enjoyable to feel the cool squishy slime between their toes and no one came to any harm from bacteria or 'germs', and if Aunt

Annie noticed the mucky hems on wash day, she never complained.

Annie was not overly house-proud but she spent a great deal of time cleaning. The house was in the middle of the country and surrounded by farms, so her life was an endless battle against flies.

On summer days the kitchen walls were literally black with them. All the food had to be put away in the pantry, hopefully safe from the revolting hoards that buzzed on the kitchen tiles.

Mary and Joan sometimes played a macabre game. A bowl of water was placed on the floor in readiness. Then they each cupped their hands and moved them swiftly down the wall to trap some flies. Many would escape, but a few each time would be caught, and the girls plunged them to their deaths in the bowl of water. As a method of fly control it was not very effective, and of course, there were no fly sprays.

In winter the rains sometimes swelled the River Severn until it burst its banks and rose up Sandhurst Lane. The first time that Mary heard it had happened, she was very excited. It had rained solidly for days and billowing black clouds hung overhead, threatening more. Her friends came knocking at the door, yelling for her to join them!

"Be quick!" panted Toni. "The Severn's coming in fast!"

They raced down to the river. The water, an evil looking grey-brown tide, was flowing fast and thick as lava over the banks, and the cottages were right in its path. Sandbags had been piled against all the doors but it was obvious they would not hold back the torrent, and all the occupants were fighting to drag their furniture upstairs. The girls joined the little crowd of people gathered on the bank. One woman was hurriedly passing family treasures out of a downstairs window to her husband who stood knee-deep in water.

"My God woman! Look!" he suddenly yelled. "The baby's hanging out of the bedroom window!"

The girls looked up and saw with horror that the baby, a toddler, had climbed onto the windowsill and was precariously leaning over. Frightened by the height he started to scream. His mother reached him just in time and the girls watched as he was grabbed back inside.

"It's this pile of stuff by the window," she yelled to her husband. "He must have scrambled up it!"

"Well at least you've got him," growled the father. "Now get back downstairs and pass the pictures out!"

It began to rain again and almost immediately the swollen waters came surging over the bank. Within moments it had swamped the sandbags and Mary heard the mother yell in despair, "It's no good, John! I'm knee-deep in here!"

"The poor cottagers," said a bystander. "They're swamped out again!"

Mary tried to imagine how it would feel to be driven out of your house like this, and know that even after you cleaned up it was probably going to happen again.

Fortunately the floods never came closer than a quarter of a mile from 'Bassingham'. They invariably stopped at a house called 'Bron Castle', which was a tall villa, not much like a castle.

***

The winters were always difficult for Mary's young cousin Dos, because the damp and cold made her asthma worse. One day Dos suffered a particularly bad attack. Mary heard a gasping, rasping sound coming from her cousin's room and went running in to find poor Dos sitting rigid on the bed, her hands on her chest, and her face blue.

Mary ran down the stairs screaming, "Auntie Auntie! Come quickly! Dos is dying!"

"Don't fret Mary. I'll see to her," said Annie as she raced upstairs.

She tried to take her daughter in her arms but Dos was struggling for air and would not be touched. Poor Annie stood watching and wringing her hands. Sometimes the attacks would abate, but at others they went on for hours or even days, and Dos was unable to work, eat or enjoy her life at all.

Aunt Annie had a sister in Canada called Minnie who often wrote suggesting that Dos might benefit from the wide open spaces and fresh air.

"Oh! It's so far from home," poor Annie wailed.

But at length Dos became so ill that she had to reluctantly agree.

"Alright," she said, her eyes showing a glint of panic. "But only for a few months!"

"It won't be long enough," Bert intervened. "She'll need longer for the change of situation to take effect and be proven."

So it was agreed that Dos should make the trip and stay for six months; but then Annie had another worry.

"The weather!" she exclaimed. "It's so cold over there! Oh Dos! You'll need a whole wardrobe of warm clothes!"

"There's no need for that expense," her daughter insisted. "I'll just buy myself a few new things... a warm coat and some jerseys..."

But Annie was off again. "Mending!" she snapped. "Everything will have to be looked at!"

Dos insisted on using her own wages to buy a thick coat and some fur-lined boots whilst Annie and the other girls worked frantically, washing, ironing and repairing all her other things. The house was in turmoil until the job was done.

Brochures for the big ocean-going liners appeared on the mat and Mary was fascinated by one picture showing a great ship sliced down the middle. There were all the little cabins cut in half, and also the ship's engines, and the dining room.

She walked about the house clutching the brochure and looking at it rapturously and purloining the attention of anyone remotely willing to listen.

"Oh! How I wish I could go to Canada!" Mary wailed.

"You have to do your lessons at school," Aunt Annie tutted.

"Oh Mary, I would miss you so much!" said kind-hearted Joan, which made Mary feel better.

On the day of her departure it was arranged that Uncle Bertie would accompany Dos on the long train journey to Southampton. Mother and daughter said their goodbyes on the doorstep at 'Bassingham'. Poor Aunt Annie gave her a quick hug and a kiss. She tried to be brave and not show how much the parting hurt. She stood on the step watching the taxi drive away, with Dos also in tears, waving from the rear window.

When she had gone Annie came into the kitchen, sat down suddenly on a chair, threw her apron over her face and wept bitterly. Mary stood helplessly watching. She knew that her aunt was a kindly person who loved them all.

Dos kept in touch by letters and told them how much she was enjoying her stay. When at last she returned she looked much better. She had filled out and her cheeks were rosy and healthy. In Canada she had not suffered a single attack!

But back in Gloucester the dreaded asthma returned, and at length it was decided that she should move up to Birmingham to live with some relatives. Whilst there she was asthma-free again, and it was felt that the damp air and living so near the river in Gloucester was no good for her. It was in this way that poor Aunt Annie lost Dos, the first of her children to flee the nest.

CHAPTER TEN

RETURN TO 'OAKBORO'

Mary had been at 'Bassingham' for two years and thought her happy life there would go on forever.

But one day, when she called to see her father at his workshop he told her that they would soon be going to see her mother at the psychiatric nursing home.

His statement, delivered in his usual 'sparing of words' manner created a tight little knot in Mary's stomach. Her mother belonged somewhere in a compartment in her mind marked 'past', and she wasn't sure that she wanted to reopen it. Her mother's disappearance still hurt. Mary had felt deserted, and she could not forget the things, which she had seen and overheard.

She was appalled that she would be forced to see her mother again. *What would she be like? Was she still MAD?*

But there was no escape! A few weeks later her father took her to visit Edith at the nursing home, which was on the outskirts of Bristol. It was a pleasant place, a large country house called The Beeches surrounded by beautiful parkland. Mary clasped her father's hand tightly as they crossed the lawns.

Her mother was sitting in a cane armchair in the shade of a beautiful Tulip Tree. She was dressed attractively in everyday clothes and looked up as she saw her husband and daughter walking towards her.

They all sat in cane chairs looking at each other uneasily whilst a waitress in a spotless white apron brought cold drinks and dainty cakes.

Mary was glad that her mother no longer looked ill; in fact she seemed calm immaculately composed. But Mary was still influenced by the remarks she head heard during the past two years.

Hissed comments such as, 'Mad woman! She's gone mad'!
… had to be put away!

In those days any form of mental illness was thought to be shameful. Mary sensed this and found it frightening.

Edith sat sipping her drink, a plate of cakes balanced on her knee. It had been such a long time, and now here was her much-loved little girl, but altered. Mary was no longer the scowling child she remembered. She was much better behaved but aloof, like a stranger! She wanted so much to return home and look after her daughter again.

And Fred; gentle tireless Fred, always short of words but with such kindness in his eyes. She knew he had paid for her to be in this expensive place, but could she really convince everyone that she was capable of looking after him? Being shut in a home for people with mental disorders, no matter how elegant and expensive, was a shattering experience. But she knew she was ready; but how on earth was she supposed to rebuild her old life?[2]

The following spring Fred heard that Edith would soon be able to come home, and Annie had to tell Mary the news. She chose her moment carefully. They were in the kitchen at 'Bassingham' when Annie laid a hand on Mary's shoulder.

---

[2] *Author's Note*

To this day a look of miscomprehension touches Mary's face, as she remembers the meeting. She became, in her forties, a psychiatric nurse and says wryly that in present times, her mother would probably have been prescribed anti-depressants and counselling, and would certainly not have been locked away from the world for two years!

Mary does not know what treatment her mother received in the nursing home. She assumes it was mostly rest. She believes her mother certainly made a complete recovery, but from that time on, the relationship between them was different. They were never again to be quite so close. The scar of her mother's illness ran deep, and influenced Mary's life.

But she is certain that her mother was also changed in a positive way. Before her hospitalisation Edith often seemed a sad person. But after her return, the warmth of her younger days was restored. Mary believes that the root of her mother's problem was the untimely death of her first child, Jim; and that the doctors in the nursing home helped her finally to grieve and recover.

103

"I've a morsel of news for you," she said gently. "It's a wonderful thing, dear; and I hardly know how to tell you. Your mother will soon be coming home."

Mary was so shocked that all Annie heard was a sharp little intake of breath. Then the blue eyes opened wide to look at her as she said simply, "Where will she live?"

"Why! She'll want to be in her own home, at 'Oakboro'!" Annie replied. "You'll be going there too. It will be lovely for you."

"I like it here," was Mary's flat reply.

She did not cry but she turned away and went silently upstairs to her room. Wise, kindly Annie gave her a few moments, and then followed.

"We'll all miss you," she said softly, "but you won't be far away. We'll be sure to see a lot of you. You can come home to me for your lunches again if you like. You'll hardly notice the difference."

Searching in her mind for comforting words Annie added, "You'll be living with your daddy again dear. You'll like that, won't you?"

Mary nodded but remained silent.

"I'll be down in the kitchen if you need me," Annie continued. "I thought I'd make some of that cherry cake which you like. Do you remember your mummy's snow cake? It'll be good to have some of that again, won't it?"

Mary nodded but her frown remained.

I won't go! I won't! She thought in fury as Annie turned away and went downstairs.

That night she lay restless and tortured by thoughts of leaving 'Bassingham'.

What about her friends? All the fun and glorious freedom they enjoyed? How could she be wrenched away from it all?

When at last her beloved Joan came up Mary could cuddle against her and drift off to fretful sleep.

For two years 'Oakboro' had been let out to Mary's Aunt Flo and her husband Alfred Dipper, a famous cricketer who had once played for England; but they no longer needed it as they were buying a house of their own.

Aunt Annie took the tram to 'Oakboro', rolled up her

104

sleeves and did a thorough spring clean. She aired all the rooms, made up the beds, and she and Joan went shopping to stock the larder.

The doctors had advised Fred to employ someone to help his wife in the house for a few months after her return. They said she was still 'delicate' and that she must not take on too much at first. He found a woman called Mrs Jones, thinking she would be especially suitable as she was Welsh, and Edith had been raised on a Welsh hill farm. One of the spare bedrooms had been made ready for this employee and she had moved into it with her sparse belongs. Fred intended that she should stay for at least six months.

Alone at last, he stood by the big double bed he was to share again with Edith. Then he crept out of the room, locked up the house and went off to pick up his wife from the psychiatric home.

It was later that evening when he arrived at 'Bassingham' to collect Mary. He had left Edith settling in at 'Oakboro' in the care of Mrs Jones.

What a strange, miserable little thing his daughter looked, standing on the doorstep by her suitcase, bedraggled Teddy hanging limply from her hands. At her feet was a large crumpled bag containing her other assorted possessions.

This is not going to be easy! Fred thought.

All Mary's cousins except Dos were there to say goodbye. Freddie in his man about town suit, Nora dabbing at her eyes with a hankie, and wonderful Joan, now so grown up and left school for eighteen months, smudging away tears and saying that she would be right over to 'Oakboro' the very next day.

"Who's going to keep me warm in bed at night?" she said. "Who shall I be telling my troubles to? And who's going to read to me when I have a cold?"

Soon Mary was bundled into the car. It was hardly more than a ten minute ride to 'Oakboro', but when she arrived it felt like she had been whisked away to another world! The house seemed much bigger than the friendly hubbub of 'Bassingham'. Everything was strange.

Edith had been round the rooms, revisiting them like a stranger and opening all the windows. She stood waiting anxiously in the hall, occasionally wringing her hands in anxiety. At last the car drew up and Mary and Fred were inside. They all looked at each other nervously.

Mary was silent and withdrawn. She slipped away into the living room and sat down in one of the 'Rexine' covered chairs. It was the chair where she had once sat on her father's lap to hear stories.

She listened to her parents in the kitchen. There was a wall of tension between them, and it was going to be extremely traumatic for them to get things together again, but Mary was too wrapped up in her own troubles to notice. She sat motionless in the chair till her mother came in and took her by the hand and led her upstairs to the bedroom where she had once been the spoiled and adored child.

Mary gave a sideways glance at her mother, trying to size her up.

Would she do something mad, she wondered? She didn't like having her hand held by this stranger. Things raced in her mind. She remembered the screaming. Would her mother start screaming again?

They stood wordless on the threshold whilst Mary took in the details of her room. She had not been in it for two years. Her pretty coverlet looked the same and so did her bookcase and toy box, and the window with its flowery curtains. It even seemed that the same blackbird was trilling his song of springtime from the newly leafed chestnut tree as the fresh April evening settled over the garden. Daddy had already put her suitcase in, and Edith busied herself fluffing up her daughter's clothes and putting them away in the wardrobe. Mary sat on her bed, clutching Teddy and watching in disapproving silence. Edith was mortified.

When she had finished they went down to the sitting room where Mrs Jones had set a table with their tea. Fred came in and they began their meal; but they all sat round like strangers, snatching looks at each other, not speaking. Mary made it worse by scowling, but she couldn't help it. She was so dreadfully homesick for 'Bassingham'.

Mrs Jones, stern and forceful, came in and out with extra sandwiches and to top up the teapot, but she didn't speak either.

Mary didn't like her one bit!

Fred was at a loss. The past two years had been hard but now he could see that the relationship between Mary and her mother had completely broken down. *It was hardly surprising really, and they were all in for a hard time! He didn't like the presence of the stern Welsh woman either, but the nursing home had told him that Edith must have help in the home.*

Mrs Jones was a tall, strict woman with her grey hair tightly pulled back into a bun. She was much given to folding her bony elbows across her chest and laying down the law. She had a big red blood blister on her upper lip which Mary found fascinating, and which she couldn't help staring at relentlessly.

"We must have routine!" Mrs Jones said as the blood blister bobbed up and down. "I shall do all the cleaning, washing and ironing! And *you,* Mrs Oakley need only cook the meals." Mary dug in her heels for battle!

She soon returned to her tiresome ways, demanding sweet things all the time and wanting her own way in everything. Edith was so desperate to win her daughter's approval that she quickly gave in and baked the beloved snow cake and buns whilst Mrs Jones looked on in disapproval, arms akimbo.

Mary was not to be won over. She still did not trust her mother, who seemed normal enough, but who might suddenly turn into a mad woman. *Surely all the things she had heard people say about her mother's illness must be true!*

Edith would have been amazed if she had seen her daughter at school, behaving like a paragon of virtue, whilst at home she was a tyrant! Mary had become a dual personality!

"Are you alright?" Kathleen asked as they went into assembly. "How are things now your mum's back?"

"Oh fine! Just fine!" Mary lied unhappily.

Edith was so keen to win back her daughter that she would do almost anything to please her, which brought more scowls of disapproval from Mrs Jones.

"Can't you see you're spoiling the child," the Welsh woman rapped, and made her feelings known by tutting and banging about.

On one occasion Edith baked a tray of toffee, which was broken up with a hammer by Mrs Jones, and put away to be stored in a large tin. There was so much it wouldn't all fit in, so a large spare lump was put in a paper bag in the cupboard.

Mary became her very worst!

"Want toffee! Want toffee!" she shrieked till her distracted mother gave in and told her she could have the lump. Mary then proceeded to eat the whole lot, gnawing at it whilst Mrs Jones looked on in disbelief.

"Worms!" exclaimed Mrs Jones, "Worms!" as if this behaviour must be unfailing evidence of the affliction!

"Cleanliness is next to Godliness!" she would shout, throwing up her hands when Mary refused to wash or ran into the house in muddy shoes. Undefeated, Mary scowled back.

"Oh! You sullen little madam!" Mrs Jones shouted.

Fred and Edith fled to the chapel for solace. Fred was a little ashamed, as he had hardly bothered to go at all whilst living in Sandhurst, but almost at once their Methodist friends came rallying round to help. In particular the Greys, who had always felt a strong bond for Mary's family, were quick to offer support. They too had lost a son and later been blessed with their daughter Margaret, who had once been a friend for Mary.

The chapel friends looked at Mary in consternation.

"Playmates! The child must have playmates!" was the battle cry, and Edith knew that playmates must be found!

One day Mrs Grey came round whilst Mary was at school, and sat down at Edith's kitchen table.

"Mary is missing her friends at 'Bassingham'," she said kindly. "She had a right little crowd there and they used to go about together, didn't they?"

Edith nodded and tears began to well in her eyes.

"Mary wants to go back there," she said, her voice shaking with hurt. "She doesn't want to be in her home with me any more. I don't know what to do! Sometimes I think she despises me! Fred says things will improve, but I can't see it myself."

"Well, for a start," said Mrs Grey, "you should get rid of that Mrs Jones! She's just one more thing between you and Mary!"

"I don't like her very much," said Edith cautiously. Her two years locked away had sapped her self-confidence. Sometimes she was haunted by fears that even her dear, wonderful Fred would not want her anymore now that she bore the brand of 'mad woman'.

But Edith knew for sure that she was not mad. She had been nervously ill. Losing James, and then Mary suffering two serious illnesses, all the fear and doubt, and then Sue dying in such a terrible accident had all piled up and caused a nervous collapse. She had never been mad. *People are often ignorant, and sometimes you have to suffer these things to understand them.* Edith had an inkling that solid, dependable Mrs Grey understood!

What shall I do?" she asked humbly.

"Get Margaret round," replied Mrs Grey. "There's only a year between the girls and they always did get on before. Give them a chance and they'll very soon pick up where they left off. You mark my words!"

Edith began to feel better. Here was someone who believed in her. All she had to do was make a few changes.

Dumping Mrs Jones will be a very welcome one, thought Edith, an old spark rekindling in her spirit.

That evening she told Fred about Mrs Grey's visit and the plans to bring Mary and Margaret together again.

"Oh Fred," she said, putting her arms round him, "I so want it to be just the three of us again!"

Fred wasn't sure, because the medical experts had said it was best to have help in the house, but he could see his wife was getting stronger. Besides, he wasn't too keen on the woman either! He agreed, and Mrs Jones was given a month's salary and told kindly that Edith now wished to run her home herself. Her departure was a relief for them all!

When Fred returned from taking her to the station he went out into the garden with a handful of tools and began building a structure from wooden posts. Mary was mystified and followed him.

"What is it?" she asked, her head tilted to one side to look up. Her father was nailing a crossbar onto two strong timbers.

"It's a swing," he said, "big enough to take two girls!"

Mary's eyes opened wide!

Edith had also joined them in the garden. "We thought you might like your old friend Margaret Grey to come and play," she said.

It was arranged that Margaret would come round the following weekend. On the Friday evening Edith sought out her daughter who was sitting alone in the summerhouse. Mary looked miserable. She had been trying to read her book, but thoughts of 'Bassingham' kept coming into her mind. When she saw her mother she looked up, a cross expression on her face.

"Mary darling," said Edith in her customary sweet manner, "we thought you might like to have Margaret Grey round to tea. She is dying to see you again. She's coming tomorrow!"

Mary was neither pleased nor displeased. She quite liked Margaret but in her present mood it didn't matter who came round!

"Alright," she said, and continued peering into her book.

Feeling herself dismissed, Edith turned away and strode back into the house.

But Mary *did* enjoy seeing Margaret and soon the two girls were once again firm friends. They spent hours in each other's company playing games, which they devised. Sometimes they climbed into the chestnut tree from where they could see the tram terminus. In warm weather the Walls ice cream man on his tricycle could be seen catching all the people and selling them ice creams as they came off the trams.

The double swing was a great success. The two girls liked to swing gently, sitting close together talking, lazily moving it to and fro with their feet. When they tired of this they stood up on the long seat and worked themselves higher and higher. The sky was a clear blue and once again the garden rang with their laughter.

But sadly, the tension between Mary and her mother continued. Some days the barrier would slip a little and the two appeared quite happy together, but then some little incident would jog the memories of those unkind words and Mary would think: *Mad woman! I don't like her!*

Then, Edith had an idea! She remembered the happy holidays they had shared at Burnham-on-Sea in the years before her illness. She thought that she and Mary might go away there... and not for just a fortnight... she decided they would stay for the entire summer school holidays, a full six weeks!

"You can come down at weekends and visit us, Fred," she said, her eyes shining at this new idea, "but the rest of the time Mary will have me all to herself. She's bound to remember the happy times! And being with me day after day, we'll surely be friends again!"

Fred took a deep breath. It was an adventurous idea but he would do anything to have his family happy again. As the weeks dragged by even he had begun to think that Mary's behaviour would never improve.

Once, when Edith had refused her something, he had heard Mary call out, "You're just a madwoman!"

He had rushed straight into the room, really angry. But Edith had simply admonished him and chided him away.

"Shush Fred. The poor child's only muddled."

He said nothing, but his admiration and compassion for his wife increased apace. He certainly could not refuse her this holiday!

Mary and Edith caught the train to Burnham-on-Sea. They had booked once again to stay at the apartment in Mrs Sealy's house. The friendly seaside town had changed very little in the intervening two years, and Mary, although reluctant to show it, had found it hard to conceal her excitement at such a long holiday.

The very first afternoon, she insisted on going down to the sea. The air was fresh and the sun shining. There was an atmosphere of merriment between them.

On one corner of the beach they discovered a little seaside show called 'Freddy Fay's Frolics'! A small covered stage had been erected with deckchairs set around for an audience. It was a family affair consisting of Dad on the piano and his wife who sang. Their two young daughters, aged about six and ten, performed tap-dancing and acrobatics. Mary watched enchanted, clapping every new turn. As the final curtain fell, and a bag was handed round for payment, she turned to her mother, eyes aglow and said, "Wasn't it wonderful?"

Edith felt a surge of happiness. She was certain the holiday was going to work!

111

The 'Frolics' performed twice a day and Mary insisted on seeing every show. After a few days Edith had seen enough but Mary's enthusiasm was undiminished.

"Please mummy," she pleaded, "let me go on my own. I'll be perfectly alright!"

To Mary's surprise Edith said yes. This granting of freedom cemented a new bond between them.

My mum's not mad, thought Mary, as she raced down to the sands, a few coppers in her hands. She knows I'll be alright on my own!

Sometimes she asked for extra pennies and went donkey riding. Edith never refused anything and Mary soon began to feel happy again, and each night when her mother tucked her into bed there was a new feeling of warmth between them. Sometimes Edith slipped downstairs to relax in their comfortable private sitting room, but occasionally she simply undressed, pulled on her night-gown and climbed into bed with her daughter. The two fell asleep cuddled up and content. The sea and fresh air, and being together, began to heal them both.

Fred always came down at weekends. Mary looked forward to this and insisted that they must be waiting on the platform to greet him. On one occasion they were late and Edith was puffing as they hurried along. They were almost at the station when they saw a battalion of 'Territorials' marching down the centre of the road.

This would have been excitement enough, but Mary suddenly saw her father on the other side. The army was threatening to cut them off!

"Look," she yelled. "There's Dad!"

The battalion came on in full glory, drums and trumpets blazing, but Edith did not take the slightest notice. She grabbed Mary's hand and charged straight through the middle of them, in her eagerness to see Fred.

The red-faced sergeant was furious and yelled, "What d'yer think yer doing woman?"

But she ignored him and flung herself into Fred's arms. As they embraced Mary stood staring. It was an impressive demonstration of her parents' devotion to each other!

My mum's not mad! My dad loves her! He wouldn't love a

mad woman! These were the thoughts racing through the little girl's mind!

By the end of the holiday Mary and her mother were friends again. Occasionally the memory of those ignorant comments floated into her mind, like a wisp of mist trying to obliterate a treasure, but mostly Mary managed to banish them, and at last the Oakleys became a family once more!

CHAPTER ELEVEN

THE DICKIE SEAT & 'HOLIDAY HAUNTS!'

Sadly, as Mary grew more secure at home, her old ways returned in full and she became quite wild. Edith allowed her to do pretty much as she liked.

Mary now had a whole crowd of friends, and they invariably chose to play at 'Oakboro', which had become 'Freedom Hall'! They took complete advantage and enjoyed the most incredibly rowdy games yelling and rampaging over the furniture!

Poor Edith just turned a blind eye and deaf ears!

Mary was still leading a double life; unruly at home but a model student at Denmark Road School, with her beloved Kathleen and 'cronies'.

When she was ten years old she begged to be allowed to cycle the three miles to school each day, and her parents reluctantly agreed. It was becoming increasingly difficult to coddle their wilful daughter!

There was a craze at school for the girls to slip away into one of the little side-rooms upstairs and do each other's hair. Mary's was thick and straight, but the fashion was for curls.

"Don't worry," said Kathleen, wielding a pack of pipe cleaners, "I can give you sausage curls!"

She wrapped locks of Mary's slippery hair round her finger and then bound them with the pipe cleaners.

"Good heavens!" said one of the girls, "Kate's made Mary look like a hedgehog!"

In school shortened names were not allowed, but sometimes when the girls were carried away by excitement, the name 'Kate' would blurt out.

"There you are," she said with a flourish as she pinned the

114

final curl. "You simply have to do this before you go to bed every night, and in the morning you'll wake up as Dorothy Lamore!"

"More like a *squashed hedgehog*!" intoned poor Mary. Her hair was pinned up so tightly that her eyes were watering!

***

Edith was worried about Mary's continuing love of sweet things. One day the grocer showed her a tin of a nourishing drink called 'Instant Possum'.

"This is good stuff," he said. "It's a cereal drink fortified with vitamins. It will build your daughter up!"

Mary tried the drink, which tasted vaguely of coffee, and decided that she liked it. It became a regular favourite, taken last thing at night, and also in the morning with a good breakfast of scrambled eggs. At last Edith felt she was getting some solid goodness into her daughter.

But she still made the mistake of indulging Mary's every wish.

One day Mary told her that she had been invited to a fancy dress party.

"I shall require a costume," she said haughtily.

Edith lost no time in seeking the advice of Mrs Grey.

"Mary could go as a Hawaiian girl," her friend suggested. "All you need is some raffia sewn onto a belt and a nice circlet of flowers for her hair."

"You don't think the fact of her hair being blonde will matter!" asked Edith doubtfully.

"Heavens no, my dear! It's only a fancy dress!"

Edith was surprised that Mary wanted to dress up. Her daughter was usually so self-conscious. In view of the fact that she might, despite all the effort, refuse to wear it, the simplicity of the costume seemed a good idea. But she need not have worried for Mary was delighted with it and on the day she strode off in her grass skirt, a very blonde and unlikely-looking Hawaiian girl!

One morning Edith came down to make the breakfast and found their elderly dog dead in his basket. He lay curled up, as if

115

peacefully asleep. Mary missed Spot's cheerful welcome when she came home from school, and one night she pushed his basket into the cupboard under the stairs.

"I can't bear to see it anymore," she told her mother.

"Mary is very upset about Spot," Edith informed her husband later that night.

"Oo-ah!"

"I suppose we could get her a puppy."

Fred's further 'Oo-ah' accompanied by a smile and nod of his head was taken as agreement.

They heard of a litter of pups in the nearby village of Matson.

"Please may we go and see?" wailed Mary.

Edith shrugged her shoulders.

"I don't suppose I can stop you!"

Mary and Margaret set out on their bikes. They had to push them up Robin Wood Hill and then freewheel all the way down into the village. They found the cottage and knocked on the door.

"The puppies are half cocker, half Springer spaniel," a man informed them. "They are in the shed out the back. You can take a look but don't you go letting 'em out!"

The girls peered into the shed in the semi-darkness. The puppies were in a cardboard box filled with newspaper and they tumbled out at the sight of the girls, while the bitch sat patiently by.

"They're wonderful!" breathed Margaret, awestruck and envious. "How are you going to choose one?

"You have to choose the puppy which runs towards you!" said Mary.

She crouched on the floor and a little fluffy black pup scampered into her lap. The decision was made!

"I'm going to call him Binky," said Mary as the girls carefully shut the shed door behind them and returned to the cottage.

Only a few pennies were required to pay for Binky. They put him in Mary's bicycle basket and covered him over with a cloth, but he kept peeping out.

"Oh!" said a delighted Margaret. "He's so sweet!"

"I hope he doesn't wee in there," said Mary.

The girls were soon on their bikes, blissfully freewheeling down into the town with the puppy in the bicycle basket.

Binky grew up strong and plucky. He was a very biddable little dog and he enjoyed learning tricks, so the girls decided to teach him to jump. They made a course for him round the garden, and he needed very little encouragement to fly over the obstacles.

***

At Christmas time Margaret and Mary were allowed to decorate the house. No restrictions were placed upon them and they could make as many paper chains and silver stars as they liked. One year they decided to decorate with greenery. They went into the surrounding countryside and gathered an enormous quantity.

The air was crisp and cold and the frost lay on the grass all day. It was exciting rampaging through the woods, shouting to each other.

"Look at this! I've found some holly with loads of berries!"

"Wow! This ivy is so long!"

They even broke off branches of fir to drag back to the house.

The greenery was dumped in a huge pile in the hall and the girls grew even more excited as they set to work.

They festooned it from the picture rails, down the walls and twined it around the banisters. They became so carried away with their efforts that the house appeared quite dark with the light filtering through garlands which even hung over the windows. Edith said it was like living in a forest, but the girls loved it!

In her younger days Mary's parents had insisted that Christmas trees were for the gentry, but inverted snobbery flew out of the window as now Mary insisted on a big tree loaded with glitter and decorations.

Her parents and Aunt Annie and Uncle Bert continued to be very close, and Christmases were always spent together. It was still a tradition for Fred, Edith and Mary to spend Christmas Day at 'Bassingham', but instead of staying overnight as in previous years they returned home to make the preparations for everyone to come to them for a Boxing Day celebration at 'Oakboro'. This was of course a grand opportunity to show off the decorations!

After their traditional Christmas supper, the men sat up late playing a card game called 'Donne', which entailed a wooden scoreboard with little pegs.

Mary loved keeping score. In between rounds she scurried off to the kitchen to filch slices of cake or the occasional bowl of trifle. Everyone said she must have 'hollow legs'!

She stayed up later on Christmas nights now, but raised no objections when her father bore her away with a new furry toy or a book, which one of her cousins had given her.

***

One day when Mary came home from school her mother threw a large book down onto the kitchen table.

"You better have a look at this," she said.

It was thicker than a telephone directory and called 'Holiday Haunts', published by the Great Western Railway. It was packed with photographs of places to visit on the South Western Peninsula, and every page featured pictures showing enchanting bays and beaches.

"There's a job for you," smiled Edith. "You choose where we'll go!"

Edith felt that holidays and happy times together would further cement her family's relationship.

To Mary the book was the Holy Grail. On winter days she sat by the fire, her stockinged feet on the hearth, poring over the book with a cup of 'Instant Possum' on a table by her side.

Fred or Edith looked in at her occasionally and said; "How are the Holiday Haunts today? Have you decided where we're going?"

One day her father came home with a new car.

"Look at this!" he said to Mary as she followed him out to the drive.

The car had a 'dickie seat' ...a clever device which could be raised from the boot of the car to form a lovely high seat, open to

118

the air. Mary always insisted on travelling in the 'dickie' when the weather was fine. But unfortunately the car was very temperamental!

One year Mary chose Ilfracombe in North Devon. The holiday was going to be doubly exciting because the Greys were coming too, and Mary would have Margaret's company.

Both families rented separate apartments in Victorian terraces similar to Mrs Sealy's at Burnham-on-Sea. The families arranged to travel separately and meet up on their arrival.

On their way to Ilfracombe they had to negotiate the infamous Porlock Hill, the steepest hill in England! Fred was anxious!

They drove through pretty Porlock village and the dreaded hill rose before them, with its one in four gradient and sharp twists and turns. The engine revved and struggled. Edith could not help thinking of her sister Sue, and the car rolling back.

"Try not to worry," said Fred as angry steam poured out from beneath the bonnet.

At last they reached the top. On the grassy bank was a large metal tank of water, put there for motorists to cool their radiators after the climb. With the steam hissing, Fred leapt out and took advantage of this facility.

Later, just as it was growing dark, they took the long winding hill down into Ilfracombe, but at the bottom they could see that the road was blocked.

"What is it?" said Fred, peering through the mist. There was a dream-like quality to the scene.

"Fred, I must be mistaken," said Edith shakily. "But there appear to be two elephants on the road!"

As they came nearer, the two dark shapes materialised out of the dusk, made more mysterious by the creeping sea mist.

There was no alternative but to pull up alongside the animals and Edith turned to Mary, fearful that she would be plucked from the 'dickie' seat."

"Get down on the floor!" she hissed. But Mary would have none of it! This was far too exciting to miss!

A man appeared from the mist. "It's alright Guv," he said as he puffed up the slope to the car. "It's just our two elephants, sir. They won't d'yer no 'arm."

Apparently a circus had been pitched nearby and now the animals were being loaded onto their trailers for moving on. Mary could see the enormous crumpled mound of the Big Top, which had been dismantled. What a pity to miss the circus!

But it turned out to be a good holiday. Mary and Margaret had fun playing on the sands and they enjoyed a steamer trip to Lundy Island and a visit to the Clovelly where they rode down the cobbled village street on donkeys.

Whilst on holiday Fred always wore his smart three-piece suit with trousers, jacket and matching waistcoat, set off by his best trilby hat.

Another year Mary decided they would go to the historic little port of Watchet in Somerset. The terraced cottages behind the station also had comfortable apartments. Mary liked the fishing village with its old world harbour, but her favourite place was nearby Hellwell Bay.

"Look at that!" Mary cried on their first visit, pointing to a diving board, which had been set up on the sea wall.

Mary had not outgrown her tomboy ways, and she adored jumping off the board at low tide and landing in the *squelchy mud!*

"Have you seen the state of her?" asked Fred, as his daughter rose from the mud like the phoenix from the ashes, only her eyes visible through her coating of grey-brown slime!

"Oh don't worry, dear," soothed Edith. "Mud's full of iodine, or so I've heard! It can have very beneficial effects!"

For several more years Mary continued to ply 'Holiday Haunts' and choose the destinations for their holidays. She was spoiled and cherished and secure again![3]

---

[3]
Mary describes her childhood as idyllic! She enjoyed her school days, and although she says that she mostly dreamed her way through them, she became a well-educated young woman, with a good understanding of music. One school report describes her sight-reading as 'practically perfect'. In her later years she was to play the piano, violin, handbells, and sing with an accomplished soprano voice.

'Oakboro' was 'home' once more, but she was always delighted to visit 'Bassingham' to see her beloved aunt and uncle who had looked after her so well for those two strange years.

CHAPTER TWELVE

TEENAGE YEARS AND MARY'S FIRST LOVE

As Mary grew into a teenager she counted herself fortunate to attend Denmark Road School. As well as the excellent education offered, Miss Penson, the headmistress, possessed some radical and forward-thinking views.

The school became one of the first in the country to organise school holidays abroad for its pupils. Mary enjoyed two trips in her final years at the school.

She could barely contain her excitement when she learnt that a holiday to Switzerland and Interlaken was being organised. But the cost was twelve guineas, a great deal of money in those days!

"Oh Kay!" she said, as the two friends pored over the pictures in their geography books, "I do hope we can both go!"

Kate had decided that her name should henceforth be Kay, after attending a movie and feeling that this shortened version would be more sophisticated!

Both girls were rapidly growing into attractive adolescents. They liked dressing well, and frequently changed their hair styles, although Mary's remained mostly 'bobbed' or 'shingled'.

Of course Fred and Edith said at once that Mary could go on the holiday.

The girls, with Miss Penson and another teacher, Miss Tatham, travelled to Switzerland by boat and train. They stayed in a 'pension', or small hotel high in the Alps. The weather was wonderful with bright blue skies every day. In between coach outings the girls were allowed to wander freely on their own during the day, but at night they were confined to the pension. In the garden was a paved circle where the adults danced to the music of a small band. Kay and Mary were enchanted by the

121

ladies in their elegant evening dresses. They craned from their bedroom window and watched till Miss Penson came in and chided them. But she was not cross. She told them they needed their sleep... because the days were so full!

For the final five days of the holiday they were taken by coach to Wilderswill, high in the mountains and Mary became intoxicated by the mountain air!

"Whatever's wrong with you?" laughed Kay as the girls climbed Mount Pilatus.

At the top Mary was so exuberated by the beauty and the clearness of the air that she flung caution to the winds and sang her one and only solo ever. With her arms outstretched, head thrown back she sang at the top of her voice "What 'ere befalls, I shall recall that sunny mountainside," from the Maid of the Mountain.

"It's alright," said Kay sheepishly, "she'll be fine once she gets down again!"

But Mary was smitten by the beauty around her, her own youthfulness and the realisation that she was turning into a woman and that the whole glorious world beneath her feet was hers to own!

The next day the girls were taken to see the Rhone Glacier. Mary and Kay stood with their arms around each other, sobered by the height as they took giddy glances down to where the cracked and crinkled glassy green frozen river fell to the floor of the Rhone valley thousands of feet below.

**

Mary still lacked self-confidence and a friend at the Methodist chapel introduced her to 'Pelmanism', a belief that taught that confidence could be gained by priming oneself with special catchphrases, reciting them over and over again.

These included: 'I can! I am! And, I WILL!' Mary could be heard, practising this mantra in a loud voice in her room each night!

"Do you think she's alright?" Edith asked, concerned.

"Oo-ah," was Fred's reply, but his face was perplexed.

"I expect she'll grow out of it!" said Edith.

Before leaving the house each day Mary looked in the mirror and said firmly, "I am an attractive young girl! I am! I AM!"

She need not have worried because she certainly was! As she swept through the streets at break-neck speed on her bicycle, her mane of gorgeous blonde hair flowing behind her; she became known as 'the Lion' by local people.

The tennis club, three miles from her home, was the favourite Mecca for young people. It became the norm for Mary to cycle home from school, devour the lavish tea her mum always put on for her and then cycle all the way down the hill again. But it wasn't really the tennis, which attracted her! Mary had a new interest now! Boys!

It was at the club that young beautiful Mary, aged fifteen, was to fall in love for the first time, and she fell, *very hard!*

She had a merry little group of about seven friends, girls and boys. Most of the boys, a few years later at the outbreak of war, joined the air force, and few returned, but in those carefree pre-war days this future was unknown, and like all youngsters they were out for a good time.

There was a little hut among the trees where the players sat between sets to chat and swap gossip. This became a place for secrets and finding out for the first time that the opposite sex could be fun.

The friends often cycled up into the Cotswolds and walked along pushing their bikes. Sometimes they made the climb to the Beacon, from where they could see the whole Severn Vale spread out beneath them. Then there was the thrill of skimming back downhill, freewheeling all the way!

Some evenings the friends gathered round the piano at 'Oakboro' to sing and flirt, whilst Edith concocted large snacks for them and sighed wistfully for her own youth. One lad, Pat, played the banjo, and another called Henry thumped out the tunes on the piano.

Pat had a friend called Gordon, who was just three months older than Mary. Gordon had a round, jolly face, curly blond hair much the same colour as her own, and warm blue eyes.

One hot summer evening Mary didn't fancy playing tennis, but went to sit in the little hut. To her surprise Gordon was in there alone, reading a book.

He looked up when she came in and said, "Hello Mary."

"I hope I'm not disturbing you," Mary blushed because Gordon was her favourite. "It's very hot and I didn't want to run around."

"Do you fancy a walk?" asked Gordon, innocence in his blue eyes.

Mary wanted to say 'yes', but he was a boy, and she didn't normally go walking alone with boys.

"It'll be nice and cool," Gordon said, and he was so pleasant and friendly that she agreed.

They wandered round the club grounds and then out into the surrounding lanes. It was a lovely summer evening. Mary thought it very romantic, and looked forward to telling her girlfriends about it.

She found that she and Gordon had much in common. On that first evening they walked a fair distance, chatting, and then they retraced their steps to the tennis club. Their friends were in a rush to be on their way home before it became dark, and they hadn't noticed that Mary and Gordon were missing.

"Hello you two," said one of the girls, Gwen, as she was securing her racquet to her bike. "Are you coming Mary?"

The two girls usually cycled home together. It was uphill most of the way and they liked to chat.

Mary nodded and climbed astride her bike. The two girls went home in the sunset, but Mary was surprised that she did not want to tell about her adventure with Gordon. She felt it was, in fact, rather private.

The following evening at the club she was delighted to find that Gordon had decided against playing tennis. Indeed, he was lurking in the little hut again, looking up and down the path, as if he might be waiting for someone. Mary saw him and hoped that he was looking for her. He cheered up immensely when he saw her cycling down the path, but then noticed the racquet and gym shoes in her basket.

"Are you planning to play tonight, then?" he asked, sounding disappointed.

Mary flushed red and couldn't look at him. With lowered eyes she said, "No, not really. How about you?"

"I'd rather go for a walk," he replied lightly. "I say Mary, do you fancy coming too?"

Of course, she did, and so the pair happily set off into the countryside. They found much to talk about once again. The birds sang, the evening sun shone, and in Mary's eyes the world couldn't be more wonderful!

Soon they were spending all their free time together. Their country walks became the pattern for those long summer evenings. Mary deemed that the six mile cycle ride to meet at the club was well worth while. Sometimes they walked nearby, and at other times they cycled out into the Cotswolds, becoming closer in their affections. Mary had never been so happy. In Gordon she felt she had a truly close friend, not just a boyfriend.

On one of their walks they went up Robin Wood Hill, strolling through the woods. It was dark and hushed among the trees and they walked side by side, very close together. At the edge of the wood they came to a stile. The late sun was throwing dappled shadows onto the meadow beyond. Gordon sat down on the stile and pulled Mary to him. Very gently he kissed her, and Mary thought it was the sweetest thing that she had ever known.

That was the start of a wonderful romance! Soon, Mary says, they were kissing and cuddling at every stile, and the grown-ups were saying that they were 'courtin' strong'. Although they were both so young and still at school they were, in fact, very much in love.

In winter they took the familiar paths on Robins Wood Hill, and often dropped down into the village of Matson to lean on the wishing well. Who can say what wishes two young people may have made?

Gordon became a frequent visitor to Mary's home, where with her customary kindness Edith made him very welcome. He often came to tea. On one occasion the remains of the Sunday joint, a rib of beef, which was meant to last most of the week, was put on the table for them. Gordon tucked in hungrily and Mary's mother came bustling in and looked anxiously at the fast-vanishing beef.

"You've had enough of that!" she said sharply, as she bore it back to the kitchen.

Mary made only one visit to Gordon's home, a semi-detached house on the outskirts of Gloucester, where she met his mother. Mary was very nervous. At that time she was growing her hair, as Gordon said he would prefer it longer. She had arranged the famous 'sausage curls' around the nape of her neck, and these were much admired by Gordon's mother. Mary hoped that the meeting had gone well but she couldn't be sure.

Mary became obsessed with her love for Gordon. Everything else in her life seemed to recede and she was only happy when they were together.

In her last year at school another holiday abroad was planned by Miss Penson.

"This time we are going to Denmark," she announced at assembly. "Quite appropriate for us, considering the name of our school!"

Mary wanted to go, but it meant leaving Gordon. The couple promised to write to each other every day!

Just before the departure it was announced that Miss Penson would be unable to accompany the girls. She was very ill. Unknown to the girls she was suffering from Bright's disease and poor, dear Miss Penson later died in her forties, and was dreadfully missed at the school.

The twenty-four-hour North Sea crossing was cold, with a fierce gale blowing. Most of the girls were seasick, but not Mary, who stayed rapturously on deck, enjoying the beautiful fresh air!

"Don't worry about her!" teased Kay. "She's lovesick!"

Several girls were suffering from bad colds, and by the time they reached Copenhagen Mary had one too and she also developed a very painful earache.

The mayor had heard of the school party's arrival, and as the girls assembled in the ship's lounge to disembark, a ripple of excitement ran round the huge room.

"What is it?" Mary whispered. "Why aren't we being allowed off?"

"I don't know," said Kay, "I think there's some kind of deputation!"

"I hope it doesn't mean they're going to send us all back home!" hissed one of the girls.

At last a Danish girl appeared, being hurried along by one of the ship's stewards. She was tall and brown and blonde, and extremely beautiful!

This Danish vision informed them, in the most flawless English, that the mayor had organised a large civic reception.

There was hardly time for the girls to change into their finery.

"Oh drat this earache," snuffled Mary as she struggled into her gown. "It's spoiling everything!"

There was a huge buffet, mostly consisting of seafood.

Kay drew Mary to one side.

"Have you heard?" she whispered. "They're providing us with a guide. It's the blonde beauty!"

She deftly flicked one of Mary's unruly curls back into place.

"I'm so glad we're sharing a room," she said. "I'll be able to keep my customary eye on you! Are you suffering most dreadfully, missing the beloved Gordon?"

Mary nodded.

"Well forget him for a bit and enjoy yourself, for goodness sake!"

They saw the famous 'mermaid' on her rock in the bay, visited churches, and enjoyed a half-day trip to the home of Hans Christian Anderson. Mary pretended that her ills were the cause of her lack of enthusiasm but no one was fooled.

"Lovesick Mary!" they taunted.

One evening she crept away to her room and wrote Gordon a long letter. It was full of declarations of love. But there was still nothing from him!

The next day they made a trip to the world-famous Tivoli Gardens where a huge iron construction dominated the skyline.

"What on earth is it?" asked Mary.

"It's the newfangled thrill maker," confided Kay. "It's called a rollercoaster and we are going to have a ride on it!"

But as each day passed with no letter from Gordon, Mary's tension grew. On her return to the hotel each night she always slipped away from her friends to ask the receptionist if there was any mail for her.

The coach trips continued with frequent drives through the flat countryside. Then one evening she found a letter waiting for her! She went up to her room and trembled as she ripped open the envelope. Her eyes scanned the pages. It was full of endearments and Gordon was missing her. Mary felt better at once!

For the final five days it was planned that the girls would go to a little resort on the east coast. The coast of Sweden was visible in a haze across the water, and the girls crossed on a ferry boat for a day trip there.

Finally, after a rough return crossing, the girls were in England, and soon Mary was back home and into the waiting arms of Gordon. The pair swore never to be apart again!

***

Mary had risen to play first violin in the orchestra, but she still could not perform in public because of her 'terrible nerves.'

During her final years at Denmark Road School several school plays were put on; and the school orchestra was needed.

"Do you think you could oblige us?" asked patient Mr Morrell.

Mary backed away.

"You will only be required to play in the dark corridor alongside the stage, out of sight of the audience," he explained. In the circumstances, do you think you could honour us with your presence?"

Mary nodded that she would play.

"There she is," Kay teased. "Our violist who flowers in the dark!"

By this time Kay was involved in a diversion of her own! She had a 'crush' on Miss Cowan, the Maths Mistress! It was considered very fashionable for girls to have 'crushes' on teachers of either sex, and no shame was attached.

"She's so absolutely gorgeous!" Kay confided in a hissed whisper to Mary, at assembly one morning.

Mary pulled a wry face but said dramatically in true movie style, "Oh my poor dear girl! How dreadful are the pangs of the heart?"

Kay was in a dilemma.

"I want to see her everyday," she told Mary. "And there's only one way to do it. I'll have to start studying maths at

128

advanced level!"

Kay's two-year 'crush' stood her in good stead. Miss Cowan, who knew nothing of her pupil's 'secret passion', was well pleased with her academic progress. Kay attained such high marks for mathematics that, on leaving school she went straight to university in Cambridge... a huge achievement for a young woman in those pre-war days!

On Kay's very first day at the university she met the young man who was to become her future husband, and out of the window flew her 'passion' for Miss Cowan!

Mary did not do badly herself! At age sixteen she attained her School Leaving Certificate, passing in five subjects with several credits.

She often thought back to her early days at Denmark Road, and the young Kathleen's comments that they were in the 'B' Stream... not the brilliant 'A's'!

CHAPTER THIRTEEN

FINLAY ROAD NURSERY & NEW HORIZONS

In her final term, Mary found herself at a bit of a loose end. Her friends, including Kay, were making plans and they would all be going their different ways. She became overtly tearful when she looked back at all the happy times she had known at the school.

Kay said with bravado, "Cheer up, Mary! You have your whole life ahead. This isn't just an end, it's a beginning too!"

"I shall miss it all so much," said Mary, and burst into tears again.

"Oh blow!" said Kay, and started to cry too!

There was a kindergarten attached to the school. Having nothing better to do, Mary asked if she might help out till the end of term.

But there was no turning back the clock and at last her final day at Denmark Road came. During the final assembly she looked affectionately at the sea of familiar faces in the hall. There was the excitement of the prize giving, and then it was over and little bunches of girls gathered everywhere to say goodbye.

Before departing Mary went up to the great hall. She wandered into one of the little side rooms where she had spent so many lunch breaks, chatting and having fun. It had all been so jolly and Mary knew she would never forget those times. Her feet echoed on the floor as she made her way down the magnificent staircase for the last time.

She heard the ghost of Kay's excited shouts ringing round her. "Come on! Let's go and buy our treats!" Mary thrust her hand into her pocket, expecting to find the reassuring presence of the 'treat pennies'. Could it really all be over?

In the downstairs hall there was just one remaining little

throng of girls. Mary joined them for a few moments and then turned her back on that wonderful building where she had known so much happiness.

As she walked into the sunshine she found her mother waiting for her. This was something, which had not happened for years, and Mary was *so* pleased to see her.

***

Her parents wanted her to go to college to train as a teacher but Mary wasn't very keen on this idea. She wanted a more glamorous career! Over the channel in Europe Mr Hitler was screaming his hysterical rhetoric.

"The world might change forever!" she said to her father, although she actually had no such fears. "We might all soon be dead!"

"Nonsense," snapped Edith. "You're a young woman now and you need to make your way in the world!"

Gloucester County Council had just built new infant nursery schools and Mary decided to apply to work in one of them. It would give her thinking time. She was successful and allotted a place at Finlay Road Nursery, which was near her home.

The school was purpose-built and smelt of fresh new paint. There were lovely little cloakrooms for the three and four-year-olds, with tiny handbasins and lavatories.

Mary had a modest salary of about £2.10d per week, half of which she gave to Mum. With the rest she raced down to Woolworths to spend it on sheet music and paperback books.

She had not lost her lifelong habit of leaving everything to the last minute so she always managed to leave home in a great rush. The 'Lion' became a regular sight furiously pedalling her way to work with the famous mane of blonde hair flying out behind. Every night she thought wistfully of Kay as she put this lovely hair in pipe cleaners, rolling it round her finger and anchoring every sausage with a Kirby Grip.

Mary was put in charge of the three and four-year-olds, and in the evenings, when she met up with Gordon she related to him all her doings at the nursery. She felt very grown-up with a job and a wage packet. Gordon told her he had applied for a job in the civil service and was waiting for an interview. He too was keen to begin his career.

Everyday at the nursery Mary had to make the 'Horlicks' for the children's lunches. This was done in a great big urn and she was so short that she had to stand on a chair and reach in with the plunger to mix up the powder.

After lunch the children had a sleep on little folding beds. Each bed had a coverlet in royal blue with an animal embroidered in one corner. It was pleasant to see the rows of peacefully dozing children whilst the nursery windows stood open and pretty curtains billowed in the breeze. Mary knew that some of the children didn't actually drop off, but at least they were resting.

In the afternoons she had the task of making scrapbooks in a room downstairs, next to the headmistress's office. Mary was a little afraid of the headmistress. She had straight hair parted in the middle. It was startlingly black!

Mary hoped that one day she and Gordon would marry; but she was to taste the bitterest heartache.

Gordon obtained the job working for the civil service in Gloucester, and he met a young girl in his office and threw Mary over.

One Sunday afternoon he and Mary met as usual but she could sense there was something different about him. He gave her an empty smile and seemed to be having trouble meeting her eyes. She was worried, thinking he might be ill, but he simply stood there in front of her and told her about the other girl. Mary couldn't take it in at first, it was so unexpected, but he repeated his words and with a searing shock of betrayal she knew that it was all over. He simply turned and walked away.

Mary was sobbing all the way home. It was the most terrible hurt she had ever known. She slammed into the kitchen and dashed up to her room, flinging herself onto her bed in a flood of fresh tears. Her mother came up and Mary told her what had happened, but she was inconsolable. In fact she cried for days, and was so sick at heart that she could not eat.

Then, one morning she awoke with different emotions. In

132

place of the hurt there was anger! She grabbed all Gordon's letters, those blazing endearments, promises, and words of love, and went downstairs to the sitting room. Dressed only in her night-gown she knelt by the empty grate and threw them in. She took a box of matches, lit one and tried to set fire to the letters. She could tolerate them no more! Match after match went into the grate, but some of the paper was very thick and the wretched letters would not burn. They smouldered a little, and then went miserably out. Her teeth chattering with cold and anger, Mary scraped the singed letters out of the grate, spilling a mess of ash and sparks over the carpet. Then she threw some in again, applied a match and blew on them. Specks of burnt paper flew out onto the floor, making a worse mess.

At this point her mother came in and exclaimed, "Mary! What on earth are you doing? What a mess! You terrible girl!"

When she saw Mary's tear-smudged face she softened and said gently, "I think they're burnt enough, Mary. Just put them in the dustbin."

Mary grieved for a long while and then, quite suddenly, recovered.

"There's plenty more fish in the sea!" her mother told her, "and God knows you're a pretty enough girl Mary!"

After that Mary decided to have lots of boyfriends.

"It's going to be boys! Boys! Boys!" she told a friend at the tennis club. "I'll be boy-mad! But no one serious! NOT FOR A LONG TIME!"

Mary sometimes thinks of Gordon today, sixty years later, and wonders if he is still alive. She would love to see him again. He went on to marry the girl from his office and the couple lived in a house in Gloucester. Mary occasionally saw him from a distance but never again spoke to him.

She was glad she had her job at the nursery school to occupy her. She worked as assistant to the two teachers, Margaret and Molly who were both only a little older than Mary. They invited her to go on holiday with them.

"You're not to go weeping again over that hapless Gordon!" said Molly in her cheerful manner. "He must have been mad to throw you over! Jolly good luck to him, I say! He won't find another half as nice as you!"

Mary told them of her decision to have lots of men friends. "There's no denying I like male company!" she added.

"Well then! We know just the thing!" Margaret said. "Have you heard about those newfangled holiday camp places?"

Mary nodded.

"Well, we're fond of going on little holidays and those are the best places to go! They have a good social life going on! Why don't you come with us? You'll get to meet DOZENS of men AND you can dance your socks off!"

"Sounds just the ticket to me," said Mary. "Male company *and* dancing!"

Within days Margaret had booked them into the new Butlins Camp at Seaton in Devon. Poor Molly was ill with a kidney infection.

"I shan't be able to join you," she said in her cheerful way, not knowing then that she had the first symptoms of an illness, which was to cause her death at an early age.

"You poor old thing!" said Mary, genuinely upset that her new friend would miss the fun.

"Oh don't be a silly!" laughed Molly. "Just go and enjoy yourselves! Bring me back some rock! Or better still... a really gorgeous man! I've heard they all hang out round Butlins!"

"If they do we shall keep them for ourselves," joked Margaret!

"Oh! I just can't wait to begin this Adult Social Life!" said Mary.

They travelled to Devon by train and Mary was amazed at the size of the camp. It was small by today's standards, accommodating only a hundred holidaymakers, but to Mary it seemed vast!

The girls each had their own chalet containing a bedroom, bathroom and a tiny kitchenette where a kettle could be boiled for hot drinks. Meals were taken in a huge noisy communal dining room. But what impressed Mary was the fact that the whole camp had been laid out to provide maximum leisure and pleasure. There were tennis courts, a swimming pool, a theatre and a big ballroom.

"Those are the Redcoats," explained Margaret pointing to a group of men clad in smart red blazers and straw boater hats.

"They organise and host all the events and things! You'll soon get the hang of it!"

"What's this?" Mary asked Margaret as they toured each other's chalets. "It looks like a radio speaker but there's no dial. It can't be a radio."

"Oh you'll soon find out!" replied Margaret enigmatically.

The next morning the mystery was solved. It was seven o'clock and Mary was lying in bed wondering about making a cup of coffee and taking it back to bed with her, when there was a blast of static from the speaker in the corner.

"Good Morning Campers! WAKEY! WAKEY!" said a loud voice.

Mary sat up in bed in amazement! The voice invited her to come out into the open air and take part in get fit exercises.

"No thank you! I'm fit enough!" Mary called, not totally sure that the voice could not hear her.

Breakfast in the dining hall was a noisy affair. Margaret gave Mary's arm a nudge.

"Look," she hissed. "Over there on that end table. There's that man who kept asking us to dance at the hop last night! He's with his gang!"

"Positively gorgeous!" said Mary, pausing mid-bite in a slice of toast and marmalade.

"Not just him! *All* of them!"

"That's right, Mary!" laughed her friend. "Play the whole pack of cards dear girl! No more getting stuck into just one! You don't want another Gordon experience!"

"You bet I'll play the pack of cards!" replied Mary. "Just Adult Entertainment! And definitely nothing *serious!*"

Soon the handsome Les came over, followed by his 'gang'!

Margaret, Mary and a crowd of other young girls all palled up and it was the jolliest week that Mary had ever known. They played tennis, swam in the pool and danced every night till the early hours. The Redcoats took them on organised pub walks and cycle rides into the Devon countryside and Mary passed another landmark. She had her first alcoholic drink, outside an inn, with the gang all looking on and cheering.

Another holiday camp break followed, at the new Warners Camp in Prestatyn, North Wales, and indeed, had it not been for

135

the outbreak of war the holidays would no doubt have continued.[4]

As Mary approached her eighteenth birthday, storm clouds were gathering on the horizon. She kept her promise to herself to have plenty of men friends, but not fall in love. She was a beautiful young woman with the world at her feet, but she still had not decided on a career. Soon, fate was to take a hand!

One day she arrived at the nursery school to find Margaret, Molly and the headmistress in the office, involved in frantic activity. Tins of biscuits were piled all round the room and the desk was covered with paper bags.

"What on earth are you doing?" Mary asked in amazement.

"We've been told that any day now we should expect hoards of evacuees! Children from the cities! The government says Hitler will soon be bombing Britain, and the children are to be sent to the countryside for their safety!"

This information was delivered breathlessly by Margaret as she deftly removed biscuits from the tins and stuffed them into paper bags.

"Come on Mary! We need you!" said the headmistress. "We're packing up all these biscuits for the children, so that each can have a bagful when they arrive!"

"To cheer the little darlings up!" added Molly.

It suddenly brought the threat of war closer to Mary, who had not given it much thought.

That evening she told her parents what had happened at the school.

"I think we are in for another nasty show," said Fred, with memories of the dreadful First World War.

4
Author's Note:

Mary formed a strong bond with Margaret and Molly, which was to last into later life. Tragically, Molly died young, but Margaret married a gardener and went to live in Ross-on-Wye. She lived to a ripe old age and Mary recalls seeing her friend at the very end of her life. She called to see her when she was in a residential home, to discover that she was terminally ill. Margaret had a little miniature terrier dog called Quincy, which was staying with her at the home. The dog was so protective that he wouldn't allow Mary near, so she had to stand in the doorway, waving her hand sadly at her friend.

"God help us all," was Edith's reply.

But the expected evacuees never came to Gloucester, and Mary still wonders what happened to the biscuits!

CHAPTER FOURTEEN

FIRST TASTE OF THE LAND ARMY!

In the July of 1939, aged eighteen, Mary finished her job at the nursery school.

In Europe the storm clouds were gathering. Hanging over the radio listening for news bulletins became a national pastime.

"I think it's certain we're in for another war," Edith said to Fred. The couple had been through one world war and didn't want another.

Then in September Hitler invaded Poland and England was at war. Suddenly everything was changed overnight!

Mary and her parents listened, stunned as Mr Chamberlain made the grim announcement of his ultimatum to the German government, and reported that Hitler's forces would not withdraw.

"I have to tell you that no such undertaking has been given, and that consequently..."

"Well... that's it," said Edith. "Here we go again!"

"May God be with us!" said Fred.

Everyone over eighteen had to join up and Mary knew she must decide what her war effort should be.

One day whilst shopping in Gloucester she saw a young girl in ATS uniform. Mary, who was fond of fashionable clothes, looked the young woman up and down and took an immediate dislike to her thick kaki stockings!

I'm not joining that, she thought to herself!

The WAFS or WRENS did not appeal to her either.

For Mary, a country girl, the Land Army was the obvious choice. She had childhood memories of watching the people at work on the farm across the road from 'Oakboro'.

Now men were joining up in their thousands leaving a

scarcity of workforce on the land, and women were being called upon to take their place.

By October she had made up her mind and applied. It seemed only a matter of days before she received orders to attend the Usk Agricultural College, not far from her home.

Her mother helped her pack. There was a feeling of unreality as the two women worked in Mary's bedroom, knowing that she would soon be leaving it. The room meant safety and security but now she must go to go wherever her country might send her. Suddenly everything seemed terribly uncertain. But it was exciting too!

She made the journey by train. Everything was different. There were jostling crowds and young servicemen in uniform everywhere. Mary was suddenly very keen to be part of it!

But when she arrived at the college she was in for a shock. The place was a swirling hubbub. About two hundred girls were crammed into a confused and disorientated throng. The dormitories, classrooms and common rooms were jam-packed. There were girls from all walks of life but Mary soon learnt that the officials were mostly from the upper classes and the landed gentry.

Lady Bathurst was the head of the Gloucestershire division. She was a practical sort of woman and Mary immediately liked her. Despite her brusque manner and plum-in-mouth accent she managed to show a great deal of understanding for the girls, who had been so swiftly uprooted from their homes. They were to spend one month at the college supposedly being trained to work on the land, but Mary soon found that things were chaotic.

She arrived in her smart fashionable clothes and was shown to her dormitory.

"Settle in, and then we'll go downstairs to 'supplies' for your uniform," said the harassed official. "I'll be back for you in ten minutes!"

Mary looked at the diminutive locker into which she would have to cram all her clothes. There were only two hangers!

"Hello," said a girl with bright chestnut curls. "Welcome to the mad house!"

"Is it always this crowded?" asked Mary,

But the girl was pulling on her jersey and boots and brushed Mary aside.

"Sorry!" she said brightly. "I've got to see a man about a cow!"

"It's a constant panic in here!" offered another girl, who was busy unloading textbooks and pushing them under her bunk. "You'll soon find out what you're in for...!"

But she was grabbed by the arm in mid-sentence by a further girl and rushed away.

"Sorry!" she called back over her shoulder as they fled through the door. "We're late for lectures again! My name's Ruth by the way!" But she was gone before Mary had time to reply.

The harassed orderly arrived and chastened Mary for not being ready. Poor Mary let her precious clothes fall to the bottom of the locker and banged the door shut. It wouldn't close because a dropped belt was hanging over the edge. She bent to pick it up but the orderly hurried her away.

"Leave the door," she snapped. "No one in here has time to nick anything!"

Outside in the corridor Mary drew breath, relieved to leave the disorganised atmosphere of the dormitory.

They went down a huge staircase and through a maze of dimly-lit corridors, Mary's fashionable high heels clattering on the bare stone floors. Despite the rush she was beginning to feel cold. She was clad only in her Harris-Tweed travelling suit and a smart cotton blouse.

The supply room was a mess. Dungarees and jerseys littered the chairs, and boxes of boots were stacked against the walls, some open with their tissue paper scrunched up, and odd boots spilling everywhere.

"I really must give this place a tidy-up," said the orderly. "Trouble is so many men have joined up that things are getting serious on the land. It's all we can do to get you girls trained before the cows get mastitis from lack of milking!"

She told Mary to stand by a chair. "You're a bit skinny," she said in a flat-toned voice. "You might find some of the gear a sloppy fit."

Mary stood helplessly as the orderly took out some dungarees and draped them over her arm.

"Here's a jersey," the orderly snapped. "You better try these boots."

Mary sat down on a chair and pulled the boots on over her stockings.

"Are they alright?"

"It's hard to say without socks."

"Sorry. Out of socks at the moment! You'll have to come back on Friday!"

"What do I do in the meantime?"

"IMPROVISE! Don't you know? THERE'S A WAR ON!"

Mary was soon to learn that this comment was the catchphrase at Usk College!

"Oh drat!" hissed the orderly. "We're out of overcoats! I'm waiting for a consignment! The trouble is the suppliers can't make the dratted things fast enough! What sort of coat have you brought with you?"

"Just this tweed suit, and a..." Mary stuttered to a stop, embarrassed to admit that the overcoat she had left in a heap in her locker was a highly fashionable camel hair number with a swing-back and snazzy turned-up sleeves.

"I'll make do with the jersey," she hastily volunteered.

It was late autumn and the air was chilly.

As the days passed Mary was overwhelmed by the sheer numbers of girls, but the schedule was so hectic that it left no time for making friends. She was confused, lonely and homesick.

The work was relentless. On her first morning she arrived at the animal sheds dressed in her dungarees and pullover. The orderly had managed to supply her with some rubber gumboots, but the absence of woollen socks meant the things didn't fit too well, and her feet sweated and made embarrassing noises as she moved!

A white-coated veterinary surgeon was surrounded by a crush of girls as an assistant tried to give out squealing and struggling piglets. Mary pushed her way into the shed, desperately trying to manipulate her feet in a manner which would not cause the rude noises. She didn't always succeed and was mortified to discover some of the girls looking at her in alarm.

141

"Oh pardon! It's just my boots," she stuttered unconvincingly.

"Right girls!" yelled the hard-pressed vet. "I want you each to give your piglet an iodine injection! Just watch me for how it's done!"

Mary found a squirming piglet being pushed into her hands. She held onto it tightly but it squealed and thrashed against her with its sharp little feet as she tried to hold onto it with one hand and inject it with the other. Tightly packed into a shed with girls all around her, it was a hellhole of chaos and noise. She gave a jab with the needle but quite a bit of the yellow fluid skirted out. She was not sure whether her efforts had been a success or not!

More lectures and tasks followed each day but Mary felt she could not absorb much of the information. It all came too fast!

One afternoon she had the opportunity to say as much to Lady Bathurst.

"Oh don't worry your head about it!" said the exuberant woman. "It will all fall into place once you are on the land! There's nothing quite like the University of Life, dear gal!"

In the evenings everyone threw themselves onto their bunks and fell asleep. Social life was nil in this overcrowded, exhausted throng.

There is a war on, she told herself, and I have to do my bit! I must take what comes! I shall have to go wherever I am sent! I'll just have to get on with it!

During her fourth week Mary was interviewed by Lady Bathurst and assigned to a farm. Peering across the table at her senior, who also looked exhausted, Mary felt not one bit like a farmer, ready to take her place in the University of Life!

She was given the address of the farm and only the briefest of particulars. There was very little advice about what to take with her.

Her journey by train had an unreal, dream-like quality. She was headed for a farm on the outskirts of Bristol, not far from the river. It was a grey November day with a thin drizzly rain falling as she climbed down from the train carriage and looked around at the mournful, flat countryside. But worse was to come!

It was late in the afternoon and the murky daylight was fading. The farmer met her at the station. He was a strange, short little man with a peculiar bump on his neck. Mary stared for a few moments at the bump, thinking it ought to be surgically removed. She later discovered that he was more of a dealer than a farmer and he didn't spend much time on the farm, but he had a herd of about twenty milking cows plus some arable land. He wanted a Land Girl to help with the milking.

It was quite late when they arrived at the farm and Mary saw for the first time just how rough her living conditions were to be. The kitchen was grim indeed with bare walls and the rank, unpleasant smell of damp, and another horrible smell which Mary thought must be stale food. She was ravenously hungry and was ordered by the unkempt, weary-looking wife to sit at a large, none too clean kitchen table. She was given some bread and jam with no butter. It was very runny home-made jam, obviously with a minimum of sugar in it. Rationing had not been fully implemented but the poor farmer's wife must have had to make the jam as cheaply as possible. Mary sat munching her meagre supper whilst looking at the bare black square of the kitchen window. It was a huge culture shock for a young lady who had been brought up in a respectable middle class home with every care and comfort.

The farmer and his wife had four small children ranging from two to six years old. They were all grubby and unkempt, sucking at their bread and allowing the sticky jam to run down over their fingers. The toddler was licking it from his filthy hands. He gave occasional mournful wails as if perpetually hungry. All the children were thin, shabbily dressed and had runny noses. Mary could not help comparing them to the little ones at Finlay Road, so well cared for at the nursery school. These little farm mites looked as if they were never sure where their next meal might come from.

After supper Mary and the children were all hurried up to the attic at the top of the house. It was very dark and cold, with just a single candle burning in a saucer. Mary stood shivering, and looked in horror at her surroundings. *This was where she was to sleep! With the children in this horrible place!*

She was shown a bed in one corner, so tight under the eaves

143

that she would have to crawl into it. It was hardly a bed, more a heap of rags on a dirty looking mattress. And it was damp; so damp. Mary had never slept in a damp bed before but she recognised it. Looking around her in consternation she tried to think what to do. Her belongings had been dragged up to the room, and fortunately she had her big posh pink quilted satin dressing gown with her. It looked incongruous in such a sordid place but she wrapped herself in it and lay down.

The children obediently climbed into their beds. They seemed to accept her presence and made no attempt to speak. She lay awake for a while, listening to the sniffs and coughs and stirrings of the poor children and wishing she could be at home in her lovely room and with her kindly mother. She quickly checked these unpatriotic thoughts.

There's war on, she told herself, And I must do my bit! But she couldn't stop herself wishing that she could do it somewhere more pleasant!

It seemed as if she had been asleep for just a few moments when Mary felt the farmer's wife shaking her and telling her roughly that she must get up. It was six o'clock in the morning, bleak November and still dark.

Mary pulled on her dungarees, thick woollen jumper and gumboots, which were lying on the dusty attic floor, and went downstairs to the cheerless kitchen.

A rough reception awaited her. The farmer pointed through the kitchen door into the darkness beyond and said, "Go on! Fetch the cows in! They're through the gate!"

It was pitch-dark but Mary was given a hurricane lamp and she staggered, half asleep, into the yard, following the direction the farmer had vaguely pointed.

Mary was afraid of cows. She remembered the incident in her childhood when she had happened upon one loose in the road on her way home from school. But these were big, full-grown cattle and they were out there, somewhere in the dark. Mary's heart began to pound but this was wartime. She must not complain or think of her fears.

Get on with it, she told herself!

She stumbled across the wet, muddy field, swinging aloft the hurricane lamp, which burnt fitfully with a patchy uncertain

144

light. She saw the cows in the far corner and walked towards them making what she hoped were encouraging noises. As she came up to them she could feel their warmth and see their breath in the cold air. Surprisingly, they followed her across the field to the milking shed. Mary felt they were used to this routine and she was grateful for it. Her fear of them evaporated.

Once inside the dilapidated shed Mary was shown how to tie up the cows. They had the newfangled yokes, and Mary had to put the animals' heads into them and then clip them up so that they were held securely. This took a while but she soon had the hang of it.

With a look of amusement on his face the farmer asked: "Have you ever milked a cow?"

"No" said Mary. Neither the college nor the University of Life had, as yet, provided her with the opportunity!

He gave her a bucket and a milking stool and said: "Have a go!"

She sat down by the nearest cow.

Looking more amused than ever the farmer said: "Careful! She's a heifer!"

Mary hadn't a clue what a heifer might be, and certainly did not know it meant a young cow, and very likely to kick!

She placed her head on the muck-spattered side and took a teat in each hand. She dimly remembered the lectures on milking and gave a few ineffectual pulls, but very little milk came out. Then the heifer kicked and put her back feet into the bucket. An incredible amount of mud and filth mingled with the meagre quantity of milk in the bottom of the bucket.

At this stage it was decided that Mary was not much use at milking so she was given the job of washing the buckets from an outside tap, with a brush and icy water. Her teeth were chattering and the water made her fingers first painful, and then numb. She swilled the buckets out and turned them upside down to dry. The milk, including Mary's soiled and humble efforts, went into the churns, and later to the dairy.

At last the farmer said that they could go inside for breakfast. Mary breathed a sigh of relief. It was growing light and she was starving hungry from the cold and her exertions.

Once back in the kitchen the farmer's wife served a

breakfast of indifferently-cooked bacon and eggs on a filthy plate, but Mary was too ravenous to care, and ate it all.

The farmer ate noisily. He crammed the food into his mouth, and when he had finished, wiped the grease from his plate with a piece of bread, whilst all the time the strange livid-looking bump on his neck bobbed up and down. Mary tried not to look at him.

Finally he grated his chair on the uneven stone-flagged floor, sat back and said, "I'm going off to market. You can hoe some mangolds!"

He had one other worker on the farm. This was a tall shifty-looking character, who Mary immediately knew to be 'subnormal'. He had a very low forehead and slanting eyes, which reminded her of a snake. Mary looked him up and down with uncertainty, and he stared back at her with a lopsided grin. A tight little knot of fear formed in her stomach. She did not like the idea of going out into the fields, alone with him.

But it was obvious she must not protest so she followed him into the chilly, drizzly dawn. She was given a hoe and they walked in silence to the field of mangolds, where she was told to hoe out the weeds between the rows. Mary bent her back to the task and they worked in silence. The surrounding dismal, flat countryside veiled by a greasy November mist did nothing to dispel her depression. Misery and homesickness welled in her throat. *She began to wonder what on earth she was doing in such a horrible place!*

At midday her companion indicated by means of a few grunts that it was time to go in for lunch. Mary trailed behind him across the bleak fields and into the cold, dank kitchen, where a further meal of bread and runny jam awaited. Mary tried to smile at the farmer's wife but her gesture was received with a cross, wordless rebuff. She was almost glad to get back outside and start work again.

Mary toiled alongside the man in the fields until it was time to go in for the milking. She was a young and attractive girl, and unhappy at being alone in the fields with the unpleasant-looking man all day, but he worked silently on, hardly aware of her presence, and she came to no harm.

146

***

As the dismal days passed Mary began to feel very sorry for the farmer's wife. She was quite young and loaded down with four children in that horrible cold, dark house. One morning after breakfast the wife went out into the yard to fetch a pail, and Mary found herself alone in the kitchen. She decided to nose around. She noticed a bowl covered with a plate, and curious, she lifted the plate. The bowl was full of blood-stained rags! Mary stepped back in horror. These were obviously part of the young woman's personal hygiene arrangements. Mary was appalled!

Each evening, feeling hungry and dirty, she had to retire to her wretched damp bed under the eaves. She was so miserable and homesick that only brave, patriotic thoughts prevented her from crying herself to sleep.

Within a few days Mary knew that she could not stand the living conditions. She didn't mind the work. In fact she enjoyed it and the farmer was pleased with her. She was young and inexperienced, but extremely fit because she was used to so much walking and cycling; and she attacked every task with youthful energy.

She had been sent to her first job for a month's approval on either side, so Mary faced the farmer in the cow shed and said: "I've come for a month so I'll stay for a month. But I tell you now that I won't be staying at the end it!"

The farmer looked at his diminutive and mud-spattered helper and said: "Oh well, you had better *go now!*"

He could see it was never going to work, and Mary felt that probably the wife wasn't very keen on her staying. Mary was a pretty, bouncing, eighteen-year-old, and the poor woman didn't like having her around her husband.

The next day Mary packed her few things and took her leave of the dismal farm. No one even bade her 'goodbye'. She simply walked away across the flat fields, carrying her suitcase.

She was glad to settle herself down on the train and watch the countryside slip away beneath the sullen grey sky.

Then all at once she was home, and back in the luxury of her own room. The house seemed so light and bright. Her mother had lit a cosy fire in the sitting room and she brought Mary a plate of hot stew on a tray. It was so good that Mary commented it must have taken a whole week's rations. Edith stood in amazement as Mary downed the meal. She had never seen her daughter so ravenous!

"Goodness me!" she exclaimed. "They must have been starving you!"

Mary nodded, still spooning madly, the gravy spilling down her chin.

That night Mary lay in her dry, comfortable bed, but her head was full of worries.

Her farm clothes were draped untidily over the back of her chair, minus the rubber boots, which her father had taken away to clean. As she fell asleep reality floated into her mind. She was still a member of England's Land Army! Where would they send her next?

CHAPTER FIFTEEN

LITTLE WALLSWORTH FARM

When Mary awoke the next morning she lay in bliss for a few moments, savouring the comfort of her bed and the homely sounds drifting up from the kitchen. She hoped fervently that never again would she have to sleep somewhere dark and damp.

But there was little time for enjoyment. *There's a war on! You can't laze around all day,* was the battle cry ringing in her head!

She washed and dressed and went downstairs to eat breakfast. Her mother insisted that she eat a fresh brown egg... the last of her own week's ration.

"It will do you good, dear," she said. "I think they've been starving you!"

Mary raised her spoon in bliss.

"You might have to take one rap," Edith said sheepishly.

"A rap?"

"Well dear..." Edith was choosing her words carefully. "A lot of people are saying... not that there's any truth in it... but... well you see, they are having a bit of a field day knowing that you have fled your first job on the land!"

Mary looked up in alarm.

"They're saying they knew you wouldn't be able to take the life," Edith said, not wanting to hurt her daughter. "You should have heard them before you left! It was... 'Mary in the Land Army! She won't stick that'!"

"I didn't want you to get upset with their mocking. I'm sure the farm must have been terrible, the way you've described it!"

"But Mum!" Mary said, "I *loved* the work! I really enjoyed it! I'll go and have another interview. I'll tell them I still want to be a Land Girl! But I must have some decent living accommodation!"

Happily the interviewer believed Mary and made arrangements for her to be sent to Sandhurst, on the Tewkesbury side of Gloucester, only seven miles from her home. This meant she would be able to go home every other weekend.

The new assignment was at Little Wallsworth Farm, working for tenant farmer Harry Bishop.

Mary was billeted in a small council house in the village. Her room was tiny, but it was clean and comfortable, and not at all like her damp attic at the previous farm.

"You just make your self at home," said the kindly landlady.

Mary had decided to cycle the mile and half to and from the farm each day.

"You just lean your bike in the hall alongside those of my two grown-up sons," the woman said.

It was a late November afternoon when Mary arrived at the farm and there was a hard hoar-frost. Harry and his helpers were engaged in picking up cider apples in the orchard, from the frozen grass.

"Here's our little helper, just arrived," he said pleasantly. "Come and join us, Miss."

From that moment Mary was always 'Miss' and Harry was always referred to as 'The Boss'!

Mary was immediately put to work. No one wore gloves and her fingers were soon numb with cold. The soft, bruised apples, smelling yeasty and honey-sweet, were gathered into buckets and then tipped into sacks. It was a popular crop because the boss had a cider press and made his own cider.

Mary soon learnt that the farm was owned by a Miss Butt, who occupied the large farmhouse. She had inherited the farm from her father. Previously, she had worked as a housekeeper for Blinkhorns, the big department store in Gloucester. This was in the days when shop girls lived in, and Miss Butt had been in charge of them. Her capable firmness mixed with great kindness had made her a success at the job, but she was now retired, and resided in great contentment at the farm with a companion, Miss Griffiths, who was known as 'Griff'.

'Griff' came from the Rhonda Valley, the big coal mining

area of South Wales, and she was reputed to have a 'South Wales Temper.' It was said that she sometimes had blazing rows with Miss Butt and then sulked for days; but Mary never saw this side of her nature.

Harry and his cheerful wife Rhoda lived in a small farm cottage a quarter of a mile down the track from the farmhouse with Harry's mother, who was known as Mrs Bishop Senior.

Mary was so new to farm toil that the simplest task could lead to trouble.

On the very first morning she met Harry coming across the yard.

"Ah, there you are Miss," he said kindly. "Please could you go down the track and open the gate so we can drive some cattle through."

Mary set off for the gate, which was about 200 yards along the lane. It was a big heavy metal one, and she could not work out how to open it. She pushed, tugged and rattled the blessed thing. She fetched a stone and bashed it, but still without success. She did not realise that all she had to do was lift it slightly so that the catch would open. At length, defeated, she ran back to Harry, flushed and flustered.

"I'm sorry," she admitted, "I can't open it!"

Harry looked at her wide-eyed! It was a look, which clearly said: "By heck! They send me this girl and she can't even open a gate!"

The next day she was given the job of lighting the saddle room stove. This was a little tin shed in the rickyard with a small stove in the middle where the men ate their 'bate'[5], a snack of food such as bread and cheese. They started work early, so were hungry and ready for a break by about eleven o'clock. Mary had never lit a fire in her life.

"You'll find some wood in the rickyard," Harry said as she set off to perform her task.

She looked around and picked up a few twigs she found lying on the ground. They were very small and didn't look enough for a fire. She was still wandering around looking for more when the Boss came and found her. She looked at him

---

[5] Authors note: 'bate' derived from 'abatement' as in 'abatement of hunger'

sheepishly, her sparse collection of twigs clutched in her hand. He eyed her with disbelief.

"No Miss!" he said. "You'll not get very far with that! There's a stack of wood… in the woodshed."

He appeared to be having a problem with his facial muscles!

***

Mary couldn't help feeling nervous as she sat on her stool by a cow at her first morning milking.

"I didn't have much success at my last place," she said to Harry.

"Didn't anyone teach you?" He raised a quizzical eyebrow.

"My last boss tried! But…" Mary struggled to find the words. "He was a bit quick-tempered!"

She soon learnt that Harry was entirely different. He showed her how to hold the teats and get a gentle tension and rhythm going. Mary was delighted when she acquired the knack and sent her first jet of milk hissing into the bucket.

"That's the way, Miss!" Harry praised.

She soon enjoyed milking time, sitting in the cosy little cowshed with her head leant against the side of a shaggy cow and the bucket tucked between her knees.

She was put in charge of the little dairy and shown how to use the milk cooler. This was a metal contraption with corrugated sides and a trough at its top and bottom. A tap supplied constant cold water, which ran down through the corrugations, to cool the milk. The machine's one concession to modernity was a disposable cotton-gauge straining pad at the mouth of the churn. This was changed at every milking. Sometimes, if Mary had suffered the misfortune of a cow putting its foot in the bucket, she would have to change the strainer half way through; and quickly discard the slimy, clogged up pad, hoping no one would notice!

Often Rhoda Bishop called Mary in for a cup of coffee and a chat when the men were eating in the saddle room. Usually Mrs Bishop Senior would be sitting in the corner of the kitchen. She was a dear old lady who always wore black, which reminded Mary of her grandmother. The old lady would be listening to the Morning Service on the radio, with her hymn book open on her lap and, whilst the two younger women talked she lustily joined in with the hymn singing. It made conversation difficult!

After Mary had been at the farm a few months Miss Butt suggested that she might like to move into the farmhouse with herself and Griff.

"It will be more pleasant for you, dear," said Miss Butt, "you're never any trouble, and it will save you the bicycle ride twice a day."

Mary was delighted and immediately moved into a comfortable room at the front of the house, overlooking the farm lane.

Within a few weeks Mary had discovered that she had a true passion for farming.

"I think it must be in my blood," she said to Rhoda.

The farm was producing about thirty gallons of milk a day. The churns had to be dragged down to the end of the drive and hauled onto a concrete stand to await collection by the milk lorry. Whatever the weather, the lorry never failed. In summer it arrived to the sound of early morning birdsong, but in the winter it crawled through the misty darkness. It was a big round and Mary felt sorry for the driver having to lift the heavy, ten gallon churns onto the lorry.

Winter in wartime England meant a lot of time spent feeding the stock. Farmers were ordered to produce as much meat as possible. Imports from the Continent were at a standstill due to the danger to shipping in the channel. Even the calves that in pre-war days had been exported to France for veal were needed for the home market. No concentrates were available, so vast quantities of hay, beet and mangolds had to be carted out to the animals.

One dark winter afternoon Mary was caught in the fields when a squadron of German fighter planes roared overhead. She stopped working and looked up. It was a menacing sight as the swarms of Messhersmits darkened the sky. Later, in the kitchen with Rhoda, she heard on the radio that this was the start of the terrible blitz on the midland cities. London had, she knew, suffered terribly.

Soon a total news blackout was placed on these events but information filtered back, by word of mouth. Mary was appalled when she realised that the planes she had seen had ravaged Coventry and that the beautiful cathedral was destroyed.

One summer night she awoke suddenly, aware of muffled voices outside her bedroom window. She tiptoed barefoot across the floor. There were deep grass verges each side of the lane, and Mary could see dozens of little red specks of light. It was a unit of soldiers on a night training sortie, and the mysterious lights were the tips of their cigarettes. They were seated on the verges, taking a break and talking in low murmurs. Silently Mary crept back to her bed and fell asleep. The soldiers never knew that she had seen them.

***

At Wallsworth Farm there were three working horses; two lovely shires, a grey and a black, called Captain and Dolly; and also a half-heavy horse called Marlow.

Mary soon learnt to drive Marlow in a solid old field trap to carry the tools and barbed wire out to wherever the men were fencing or hedging. On board would always be the big stone cider jar and a tot measure made of horn. When the men were working in the fields they would have a tot about every half hour and it was Mary's job to pour them.

When Harry Bishop called, "Tots out, miss!" Mary had to stop whatever she was doing and climb into the trap to pour the eagerly awaited drinks. It was just a swig, but enough to moisten dusty throats, and brighten spirits.

Harry employed two men as mainstays to help on the farm. Chris, the cowman was in charge of the mucking out and cared for the milking herd.

The second was a man called Phil. Before the war he had been a head groom, and he was also a skilled thatcher and hedger. Mary also noticed that he was extremely good looking. She tried flirting with him but Phil was unresponsive.

"He's married to the horses Mary! You're wasting your time!" Rhoda said kindly.

But Mary couldn't help herself, he was endearingly kind and gentle with the horses and so handsome, that pretty soon she had a crush on him.

"Don't worry," she said to Rhoda. "I'm kept so busy on the farm that I haven't the time for 'mooning'! There's nothing like a bout of hedge overhauling to focus the mind!"

Mary harnessed Marlow to the big trap and drove out to the fields to join the men. She pulled down the brambles with a bill hook and then plunged her arms in among the thorny stems to cut them off. Soon her arms were criss-crossed with scratches. The men took a great pride in their hedging and a section of the total was always laid. The young hazels, ash, sycamore and thorn were cut partly through and then laid over on the ground to take root below and sprout from above, producing a thick stock-proof hedge.

Hedge-laying is an ancient craft, which is still abundantly evident on Exmoor where Mary lives today.

The time out in the fields passed swiftly. After bate they worked until lunchtime, and there was little time afterwards until the three o'clock milking.

It was difficult to work as the short, dark days drew in. There was no electricity in the farm buildings and everything had to be done by the fitful light of hurricane lamps. There was also no mains water, and the supply for the animals had to be drawn up by a pump with a huge iron handle.

Everyone went to bed early to conserve fuel, and they rose long before daybreak to begin the new day's relentless round. The men sometimes mocked Mary's cheerfulness as she walked briskly across the frosted ground on sharp winter mornings, shaking off the last vestiges of sleep as she stepped into the cowshed, bright and ready to begin the milking.

"I could do with some of that energy, Miss!" Harry laughed. And Phil would make some comment about it being good to be young! Mary would look at Phil, trying to draw him in conversation, but he always turned away. Mary was too busy to be hurt.

She showed no fear of any of the animals and was always enthusiastic to try any kind of work, no matter how rough or gruelling. The tough, wiry little 'miss' was often a cause of great surprise to the boss, and it amused him to 'try' her out.

One day he said to his wife with a wicked grin: "That girl beggar's belief. I'm going into Sandhurst for a boxing match next Thursday night. I thought I'd take her with me. See what she makes of *that*!"

His wife sighed. *Men, she thought! As if any young girl would be interested in boxing!*

Mary accepted the offer without hesitation.

It caused quite a stir when Harry walked into the hall with his lovely young companion. It was not usual to see a female at these events and the place was seething with excited, sweating men. Mary was dressed in her Land Army gear but they couldn't miss the bright gold of her hair, or the slim voluptuousness of her figure. Mary looked round the hall with mild interest. She enjoyed the company of good-looking men, and there were plenty at this gathering!

But the match left her disinterested. She secretly relished the sight of the tanned, rippling muscles of the men at work on the farm, but these two appeared to pummel each other senselessly. Harry watched from the corner of his eye to see if she would show any squeamishness or signs of shock. She did not.

Even when one of the boxers was knocked to the ground unconscious, Mary simply yawned.

A short while after, Harry was in the kitchen with his wife when he said: "Let's take Mary to the races at Cheltenham! See what she makes of them!"

The two women had put on their best clothes for the occasion and Mary was glad to be out of her thick itchy land girl uniform. It was such a pleasure to wear a light cotton frock!

"Do you think I'm alright in this hat?" she asked Rhoda as they left the farm in the care of Chris and Phil.

"You look lovely!" said Rhoda, who was very fond of Mary.

Phil was not used to seeing Mary in feminine clothes and he looked long and hard at her, with some surprise.

Mary loved the races. She jostled with the noisy, excited crowds. Everyone seemed bent on enjoying a day out, and keen to temporarily forget the rigours of wartime England. Mary had

156

taken along some of her wages and she eyed the horses and jockeys as they paraded in the paddock.

Harry was fond of a bet now and then and he explained patiently to Mary the principals of form and odds. She listened dutifully but her eye kept returning to the paddock and the horses parading. She fancied one called Home Lover.

Harry poured scorn on the horse.

"It's a rank outsider," he groaned. "It has no form whatever!"

"But I fancy it," said Mary. "It looks a good horse."

"How d'you know it's a good 'orse?" snapped Harry, losing patience with this unreasonable young girl.

"Now you just put your money on this 'ere 'orse I'm recommending. It can't go wrong. He won twice here last year and the odds are six to one. He's not the favourite but he's good!"

Reluctantly Mary obeyed and handed over her money. It would be unseemly for a woman to approach one of the bookies and place a bet in person.

"I suppose I have to do as I'm told," she shrugged, but her eyes were on Home Lover.

At last they were under starter's orders, and then they were away, a long gleaming line of horseflesh galloping flat out.

"Oh this is so exciting!" shrieked Mary as she stood up, one hand holding onto her hat.

Harry's favoured horse was doing well, nicely placed at about fourth and running hard.

Then a roar soared from the crowd as a big bay, with hoofs pounding, came charging up the line or horses. It was Home Lover and he won at thirty-to-one!

Mary quietly seethed at the loss of her winnings and the abashed Harry was silent all the way home!

But the Boss was certain he had one sure-fire way of putting Mary's passion for farming to the test. He ordered her to help with the 'pig-sticking'. Under wartime restrictions just one pig per year was allowed to be killed and kept for home use. The butcher was called in to perform the 'sticking'.

The unfortunate animal was dragged from its sty and heaved onto a strong wooden bench, which was kept for the purpose.

"Those reddy brown stains are blood," Harry said pointedly.

He stood at the head whilst Mary and three other farmhands were instructed to grab a leg each. As the pig struggled, it's sharp trotters beat and bruised Mary's chest, but she hung on manfully. The butcher then stuck a knife in its throat. He knew the exact spot to pierce the jugular vein.

All hell let loose! The blood spurted and the pig thrashed and writhed in panic. Its frantic squeals pierced Mary's ears but she clung on, her eyes closed.

"Mary! Keep a hold on that leg!" Harry bellowed. A stream of blood shot down the front of her shirt and splashed her face. She bent over and wiped it away with her sleeve. It was a scene of complete savagery!

At last the thrashing stopped and the wretched pig was dead, but the procedure was far from over. The butcher chopped off the head, trotters and tail. The gruesome-looking head with its now glazed eyes hit the ground with a squishy thud. It was said that every part of the pig could be used, except the squeal. Even the intestines, called chitterlings, were fried with onions.

The butcher sawed the carcass into two halves, which were wiped clean with a cloth, and then laid, one on top of the other, on a separate bench ready for the salting. This process took three weeks. Every other day Mary or Rhoda had to rub in the salt, which cured the meat and turned it to ham. The salt was rough and damp and stung the sore chaps on Mary's hands. No gloves were worn for such tasks at the farm in those days. Just a little saltpetre, about an ounce, was rubbed around the joints to sweeten the meat, and brown sugar was sprinkled around the hams and hock, about one pound for the whole of the pig.

The joints were then placed in thin dry hessian sacks to hang in the attic of the farmhouse. The sacks kept away the flies but let the air flow through. This process produced the sweetest, most delicious ham, quite unlike anything we could experience today!

Harry decided that Mary had survived her ordeal, and that she was a true farming woman! When he said as much Mary shrugged her shoulders and said: "It's just another job which has to be done!"

Her initiation was complete!

The war brought all manner of new farm regulations. A sharp and determined lady called Miss Colnett from the War Agricultural Committee was dairy instructress at Cannington College, Bridgewater. She oversaw all the new regulations for milk production. Wartime changed the face of British farming and standards were raised considerably. The industry had to be efficient and the milk of high quality because the country's food supply was so important.

Farms were allowed to keep just a small quantity of milk back for butter making. Miss Butts churned some occasionally but this was for house use only. Everyone at the farm had their own rations, and Mary had her few meagre of ounces of butter and margarine in her own little lidded green pottery jar, which she still has today!

The work in the dairy had been streamlined but it was still far from modern-day standards. Miss Colnett demanded that all utensils must be scalded. The water for this was heated in a copper in the back kitchen, a ramshackle lean-to against the main kitchen wall. Mary had to bail the hot water into a bucket and tip it into each milk pail in turn, but the water soon grew cold and it was a somewhat ineffectual attempt at sterilisation. The pails were then simply turned upside down in the dairy and left to dry, along with the cooler and the churns. Perhaps the bugs weren't quite so numerous or tough in those days!

Ready to serve King and Country – Mary in her 'Women's Land Army' uniform.

WOMENS LAND ARMY

AGRICULTURAL COURSE
instituted with the approval of
THE MINISTRY OF AGRICULTURE & FISHERIES
This is to certify that

MISS D. M. OAKLEY
has completed the course in
ELEMENTS OF AGRICULTURE
conducted by the College of Estate Management

17 July 44   Signed   R. C. Hadland

Secretary College of Estate Management

**Mary's 'passing out' certificate from Usk
Veterinary College.**

Wallsworth Farm. Mary's bedroom window is second window from right on the middle floor.

Harry Bishop (The 'Boss') on his tractor.

Handsome Phil with Dolly.

Mary and Captain.

Mary drives the horse hoe.

Miss Butt with her milking goat and flock of hens.

BUCKINGHAM PALACE.

The Master of the Household is commanded by The Queen to invite

MISS OAKLEY

to an Afternoon Party on Saturday, the 3rd July, 1943, at 3 o'clock p.m.

R.S.V.P.

An Invitation from Buckingham Palace.

Gloucestershire 'Land Girls'' Rally at Shire Hall, Gloucester. Mary is first left, second row from back. 'Picture courtesy of The Citizen, Gloucester'

Milking Competition at Stinchcombe Hall, Gloucester which Mary won. Mary is first left, middle row.

Stock Judging Competition at Willington Court, Sandhurst (Gloucs.) Mary 3rd from right, Harold 2nd from right, Frank Dunn, extreme right.

Gloucester Young Farmers' Club 1943 – 44. Mary (Secretary) 2nd left, Harold (Chairman) 2nd right, George Warren far right, Frank Dunn, 4th left.
'Picture courtesy of The Citizen, Gloucester'

**Mary's father in the Anderson shelter which he built at
'Oakboro,' but which was never used as Mary's mother said
they would die of the damp in it!**

Judging stock at Gloucester Market. Mary (seen in her Land Army hat) 3rd to the right of the policeman. Harold, 2nd right of the picture. 'Picture courtesy of The Citizen, Gloucester'

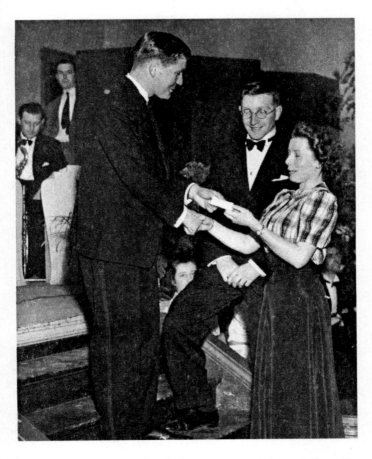

Mary and Harold receive their engagement present from the
Young Farmers' Club – a cheque for twelve guineas, from
Geoff Mann at Shire Hall, Gloucester. Members of the Joe
Loss Band in the background!
'Picture courtesy of The Citizen, Gloucester'

CHAPTER SIXTEEN

MORE LAND ARMY DAYS

During her early days at Wallsworth, heavy horses still reigned supreme, and Mary was taught how to harness and drive them.

"You just walk alongside, Miss," said Harry. "Watch how 'tis done!"

Few today have any idea of the skill which is involved handling a plough and team. The ploughman had to hold on tight to the big wooden handles of the lurching plough, whilst at the same time gripping two sets of reins in his hands and controlling the horses with his voice, using words and phrases handed down through generations.

The big, two-furrow plough was too heavy for Mary but Harry said she could use the hoe, swathe-turner and side-rake. It would save him a great deal of time if he could leave her out in the fields doing the job!

"Our Miss Mary has no fear of the horses at all," he said to Rhoda one morning when they were alone in the kitchen. "I reckon she'll take to driving 'm real quick!"

Soon he was walking alongside Mary checking that she 'were aquirin' the knack'!

One morning he sought Mary out in the dairy and said matter-of-factly, "When you're finished in here Miss, I'd like you to hoe mangolds. Get Marlow harnessed up."

Mary had a smile on her lips as she went into the stable and contemplated the row of collars and harnesses, which hung from the wall. Marlow stood motionless in his stall. He shifted a leg and gave a gentle nickering whinny. Mary laid a reassuring hand on his warm neck. It was as if she had done all this before, in another life!

"Steady, old fellow," she breathed. She had to stand on tiptoe to put on the collar and fasten the haimes. Marlow shifted his weight to the other leg and blew down his large nostrils, a sound of contentment, which Mary loved. The bridle went on last, with the thick leather reins neatly rolled out of the way. She had harnessed the horses many times, but this was special, because today she would be hoeing alone.

She led Marlow out to the field and hitched him to the hoe. Harry was waiting. He ran his expert eye over the harness, as he had done many times before.

"Well done, Miss" he smiled, "all present and correct."

He watched as she put the animal into draught and set off down the rows of mangolds, the hoe pushing a thin strip of freshly turned soil as it went. Mary and the old horse leaned their backs into the chill morning breeze. Harry watched as they carefully turned the headland. This was the tricky bit, and the horse must not be allowed to catch his back feet in the traces. This would lead to broken harness and lost time. Mary turned the field corner with her head turned slightly sideways against her shoulder, her tongue nipped nervously between her teeth. As she came towards Harry down the next row her face was beaming. There was an odd wobble as she lost the tension on the reins but she soon had the horse under control again. Harry knew that she had a natural gift for driving. He had a million tasks to see to. Young Mary was left alone to cope. And she did!

Mary never drove the huge shires, Captain and Dolly as a pair, but she became very adept at working with Marlow. At haymaking time she hitched him to the swathe turner and side-rake. In the fields under the hot blue June skies her skin turned brown and her hair was bleached silver-gold. Mary was a comely young woman, but best of all was the glow about her, her passion for the land and her oneness with the elements and seasons. She knew that farming had to be her life!

She had one more go at turning a furrow with the big heavy plough.

Mrs Bishop was quick to complain. "Harry!" she shouted, "Don't go working Miss Mary too hard! That plough's far too heavy for her!"

Harry was swift to obey. He did not want to start trouble with his Rhoda!

But the war meant modernisation for farming throughout Britain, and soon Harry bought a tractor, a small grey Ford Ferguson, and this little machine meant the end of the era of horses at the farm.

Phil the groom had loved and cared for the horses for as long as he could remember. He gazed at the tractor with his teeth biting into his lower lip. He knew what its arrival portended, but it was wartime and he had to make the best of it. He very swiftly became a mechanic and understood the jaunty little tractor as well as he had understood his beloved horses.

But Mary will never forget the day that Captain and Dolly left. Harry had decided to keep Marlow for a while, but the two shires posed a bitter problem. The Farmers' National Advisory Service, set up to help wartime farmers modernise, would not allow the horses to remain at the farm. Their enormous appetites would be deemed inefficient at the time of national need.

Mary found Phil in the stable. He was tall and handsome in the shadows. The shires were tied up side by side in their stalls and Phil was grooming them. Captain stood supreme, groomed as if for a show with his mane and tail expertly pulled and plaited. The feathering on his fetlocks had been combed out soft as silk, and his coat brushed till little checks of dapples sparkled on his shoulders and loins. He was daintily pulling feathery wisps from his hay net whilst Phil worked on Dolly.

"Why!" Mary gasped, "I didn't know there was a show on!"

"There isn't Miss," said Phil. His voice had a small dark tremble in it, as if he dared not use it. Then, in a flash, Mary knew! The horses were going away!

She saw Phil's last moments with them were a private affair so she quietly withdrew. An hour later she saw Phil and Harry leading them out into the yard. The shires looked magnificent! They were wearing their gleaming polished show bridles with shining brasses, but both men carried head collars. A large lorry stood on the far side of the yard with its ramp down, and the shires were led up to it.

The bridles, which had only been worn for those brief seconds, were removed and plain head collars with ropes attached were put on. Only then did Phil lead his beloved horses, with soft words and caressing hands, into the lorry.

When they had gone he stood beside Harry, stiff and silent, with the bridles dangling from his hands.

Mary wanted to say something, but she was afraid.

"Well Miss," Phil said quietly. "I gave 'em the best – right to the end!"

The shires were gone for slaughter and to be used as meat. Mary put a hand on Phil's arm but he did not want her to see the tears streaming down his face, so he turned gruffly away. Just twenty years old, Mary was learning the bitter facts of farm life in wartime Britain.

Soon the grey tractor was joined by another bigger model, an orange Alice Chalmers, and Mary learnt to drive that too.

Other changes followed. A milking machine was purchased and the days of buckets and hand-milking vanished into history. This meant that the morning milking could begin at six thirty instead of six o'clock. Mary was soon skilled at putting on the teat cups and watching the rubber pipes which led through a clear glass chamber into the heavy stainless steel two gallon bucket. It was all part of her busy day. She was supposed to be working a forty-eight hour week, but the demands of the farm meant much longer hours. Mary never complained. She loved it all!

Haymaking was an annual race against time. The grass had to be cut, turned and built into ricks before rain came to spoil the crop. Damp weather meant bad hay, and as no other foods were available in those pre-concentrate days, the cows would have to eat it, and the milk yield would drop.

In the blazing days of late June, Harry or Phil went out to cut the standing grass, leaving it lying in the fields, the air sweet with the smell of it. After the crop had spent two or three days drying in the sun Mary was sent out with the swathe turner. A single girl with a tractor could do the work, which once would have needed a team of sweating men and horses!

Mary had to turn the hay twice, and then the 'tedder' would be brought out. This machine scattered the hay loosely over the field to aid drying. Skilled timing was required, for if it rained on a field of spread hay the crop would be ruined. The final task was to go over the field with the side rake to push the hay back into neat rows.

Then the wagons came! Pitching loose hay up onto the wagon was heavy work, and left to the men. But Mary had her hours of glory... standing on top of the wagon, tying in the hay. This was important, skilled work as it would be a disaster for the load to slip.

As the hay was pitched up to her, Mary spread it, first around the outside of the cart, overlapping the edges slightly. This layer was then trodden down and the next layer tied neatly into it by Mary's treading and forking. Her arms soon burned in the sun and the hay prickled and itched as it stuck to her perspiring face, but Mary was impervious, her arms and body finding a swift, sweeping rhythm. The hay rose higher and higher, and Mary with it, until she was atop the load. Then it was hauled to the rick yard, rolling and groaning, with Mary usually sitting proudly at its summit. The work would go on till long after dark, and Mary remembers riding the wagon home, her aching body revelling in the coolness, as the soft summer moonlight bathed the scene in silver.

Mary quickly learnt the old skills, which had been used by generations. She was an excellent rick builder, and Harry was relieved to have someone so good at the job.

"Our Miss Mary is so reliable," he often said to Rhoda. "I bless the day she came!"

The quaint-looking ricks were circular with a pointed top, neatly thatched, and there was a great art to building them. The hay was put down in the same manner as loading the wagon. Mary began by building the outside wall, then working round in spirals, like a snail's shell, all the time going higher and higher.

Phil also taught her how to weave the thick thatched cap, which kept the rain out of the rick. Side by side, their bodies close as they lent into the hay, Mary would be aware of his nearness with an exciting thrill. Once, when they found themselves unaccountably on their own, he stopped work and lifted his hand to her face. With his forefinger he tenderly traced a soft line down her cheek, filling Mary with longing. But he quickly stopped and returned to his work without a word. For weeks after, Mary remembered the thrill of it.

In late August and early September, harvest home was the highlight of the farm year, when the wheat, oats and barley were brought in. It was the joyous culmination of all their efforts. Mary never forgot her first harvest home at Wallsworth. The days dawned hot and sultry and a thin silver haze hung over the golden fields. Behind the horses the wheat fell in great rustling swathes as the reaper-binder formed it into sheaves and slid them with a joyous swish onto the stubble. Overhead the hungry rooks circled, their shrill cries joining the cacophony of creaking leather, straining horses and the shouts of the men.

In later years the reaper-binder was pulled by the tractor and Mary's job was to sit on a little iron seat behind it, keeping her eye on the machinery. As the crops fell, the same machine bound it into sheaves with sisal twine, but the men cursed the newly invented contraption, for it frequently went wrong. The blades sometimes hit a stone, or the twine tangled. Everything then came to a halt as Harry or Phil jumped out to rectify the problem, and often Mary had to shut her ears to their curses. Later the men apologised sheepishly.

"By heck, I'm sorry Miss," the Boss mumbled, bowing his head. "The air must 'ave been blue!"

Then it was all hands to the stooking, stacking the sheaves into neat little pointed groups. The method was a ritual, which had been handed down through the centuries, and was probably the origin of square dancing!

Couples stood face to face, both with a sheaf under each arm, and then walked towards each other and banged their sheaves down. The sheaves had to be placed precisely so that they leant together, pointing inwards, to hold each other up. This was then repeated from different sides until eight sheaves had been stooked. It was hard sweaty work and worst of all were the barley spines, which worked their way wickedly up the workers' sleeves.

The cider tot made its rounds, but Mary never drank it, for she feared it would take her off her feet. She brushed back the white blonde hair, which had escaped from her headscarf and swigged from a bottle of clear well water the temperature of blood, to quench her desperate thirst. Sometimes as she worked, she would catch Phil's eye and read the admiration in them, but then he would look quickly away leaving Mary swamped by an uneasy and unaccountable longing.

Perhaps it's true, she thought in disappointment. He's married to the job and a confirmed bachelor!

Whilst the stooks were drying, everyone was in a state of torment, constantly peering skywards for signs of rain. It was imperative for the stooks to remain dry because wet sheaves meant the danger of rick fires.

"Just pray for a warm drying wind," the boss would say, wetting his finger with saliva and holding it aloft, as farmers had done for thousands of years!

Mary remembers one dreadful autumn when it rained incessantly and the grain began to shoot green at the tops of the sheaves; a disastrous situation. But most years the weather allowed the task to be completed with reasonable success.

Once dried, the sheaves had to be loaded onto wagons and taken to the rickyard. These were long, exhilarating days, with Mary once again in her post at the top, spreading and loading the crisp crackling sheaves, which were pitched up to her by the men below.

There was no respite, for the next day the rick-building would begin. The sheaves of grain had to be kept safe and dry until threshing time, which followed in the winter. Usually three ricks were built at the farm... wheat, oats and barley.

Whilst the harvesting was in progress Rhoda, Griff and even Mrs Bishop Senior were kept desperately busy baking pies, tarts and cakes for the feast of harvest home.

Each evening Mary gazed with admiration at the goodies accumulating in the pantry. Rations had been squirreled away all summer to provide this feast.

On the final day Phil and Mary climbed atop the ricks to put the finishing touches to the thatching. In the evening sunset, the gold of stubble fields and sky seemed to combine in one glorious shimmering sheet.

"Come on," Phil said to Mary. "You've done a good job! Let's go in for the supper." They walked across the yard to where the lights of the farmhouse twinkled a welcome. All was neat and tidy, save for stray wisps of straw scurrying lightly in the cooling breeze. Mary was caught in the romantic, languorous mood of the moment and ached to kiss Phil.

In the big farmhouse kitchen the table was laden with food,

whilst the womenfolk grinned at the praise for their efforts.

Mary went up to her room and enjoyed a good wash before descending the stairs to the cheerful gathering below.

"Ah! Here's our Miss," Harry said, raising the cider flagon. "Come and have a drink, Miss! 'Tis well-earned!"

"'Tis indeed," agreed Chris, whilst handsome, broad-shouldered Phil held out her glass and smiled.

During the feasting and general jollity Mary tried to steal a kiss, but even though she might slip an arm around his waist and look up into his eyes with her famous 'come hither look', Phil managed to turn it to a simple gesture of friendship. It broke poor Mary's heart!

Later she retired to her room, replete with food and drink, but full of a strange heavy sadness. One year she looked from her window and saw him walking along the grass verge at the edge of the lane, no doubt going to give a final check on the ricks.

A huge coppery harvest moon hung over the fields and Mary wanted to be out there with him, walking in the sheer romantic wonder of it. She watched as his broad back vanished from sight.

Ah well, she thought wryly, there's plenty more fish in the sea.

And it was true. For Mary was *never* short of admirers!

***

By far the most exciting event at Wallsworth was the annual arrival of the threshing machine! This monster was owned by a contractor who worked his way round all the farms in turn, bringing mechanisation to the task of separating the grain from the chaff and straw.

One cold December night just after her first Christmas at the farm, Mary heard a chug, chug, chug as it lumbered into the rick-yard, sending dogs and cats fleeing in fright.

The source of the noise was the black, oily traction engine, which towed the thresher. The machine itself resembled a large wooden shed with fan belts and chutes on its sides and a cavernous hole at its top where the sheaves were fed in. The contractor parked it alongside one of the ricks and went off to spend the night in the saddle room. This was to be his home for the next three nights, and Rhoda Bishop ministered to him with hunks of bread and cheese, washed down by mugs of cider and tea. Extra men had been engaged to help with the threshing, and they would also be fed by hard-working Rhoda, who had laid-in vast stores of biscuits and cakes.

The next day dawned crisp and clear, and there was great haste at the morning milking. Afterwards everyone gathered to begin work. The contractor had set the engine going and fan belts whirred so fast that the whole contraption vibrated and shook. The noise was appalling. Mary stood back, impressed! The rick alongside it had been uncovered... its roof of thatch taken off to reveal the sheaves of wheat below.

"Alright!" yelled the Boss to Mary. "As you like to be on top of the 'ay wagon, you can have the job of bond-cutter!"

The machine was so high she had to shin up a metal ladder. The whole machine shook in a deafening clatter. The men stood knee-deep at the top of the rick, shouting instructions to her. Towering above the yard on her precarious perch, Mary could see into the huge gaping hole to the thresher's belly where a wicked-looking set of blades rotated.

"Keep yourself steady!" yelled Phil. "We don't want you getting chewed up!"

Mary earnestly agreed.

As the men pitched the sheaves to her she had to catch them with a pitchfork and swiftly cut the binding twine and slide them, sideways into the hole. Mary could hardly bear to look into that dreadful, growling cavern! She did the task quickly, fearing for her fingers each time. But worst by far was the thick cloud of choking dust, which soon came spewing out of the machine as the crops were pummelled below. Poor Mary stepped back, coughing and spluttering. Soon her face and clothes were clotted with dust, her eyes sore and her mouth and throat rasping. At lunchtime she was so weary that she half-fell down the ladder. In the kitchen she downed huge, refreshing glasses of water, but nothing seemed to wash away the clinging dust.

There was very little time for rest and soon Mary was back

at her post, catching more sheaves as they were tossed up by the men.

All day the grain poured out of the machine in a golden shower. It was guided into sacks by sweating, toiling men who then hauled them away to the wagon. From another chute came the straw, which would be used as bedding for the animals. Some of the best was put aside for thatching next year's ricks. From a third chute spilled the dusty chaff, which would be mixed with chopped mangolds and fed to the cattle. Absolutely nothing was wasted.

There was mounting excitement as the bottom of the rick was reached and the rats and mice, which had infested it, were exposed. Dogs lay in wait and men stood round with sticks.

"Come on down!" yelled the Boss.

Mary was given a club-like stick. As the rats and mice scattered, she ran after them, a white dusty savage with a sweat-stained face and streaming hair. Oh how she ran and whacked, but she was disappointed because the rodents ran faster and she did not manage to kill many. But the dogs were quicker. They rushed in, barking and growling with excitement!

As the December darkness fell over the rick yard and the last watery rays of the winter sun faded from the sky, the clattering machine drew to a standstill and the weary workers went gratefully in for their tea.

In the bright kitchen, safe behind the heavy black-out curtains, Mary listened to the rumble of planes overhead as she ravaged her plate of bread, jam and fruitcake. It was companionable and warm in the room, with country folk who shared this routine of seasonal toil. As the excitement of the day ebbed and the chatter fell to a sleepy murmur, Mary crept away to the pantry and fetched the remains of the goat's milk to make herself her favourite treat.

"Ah," said Harry, who knew of this nightly ritual enjoyed by Mary. "Our Young Miss is going to make herself some custard. I hope you've left her some milk, Rhoda! She needs it to wash down all that dust!"

"The poor girl has breathed in so much of the stuff we can only hope it sticks to the custard!" the others joked.

Often dear Griff would say, "Let me do it for you dear.

184

You're worn!"

Mary always enjoyed this bedtime ritual, sitting by the fire's last embers, listening to the homely clattering and chinking as Rhoda and Mrs Bishop Senior washed the dishes. Then Griff would hand her the warm creamy custard and Mary spooned down her small private feast.

Lastly, she filled a jug with boiling water and went upstairs. Her room was unheated, although warmed slightly by the chimney from the kitchen stove. A December wind was getting up outside in the fields, and Mary thought regretfully that she would have to put in a long, hard day on the morrow, whatever the weather.

But at least in the winter she had plenty of hot water for washing herself. In the summer, when the kitchen range was let out, Griff had to boil all their personal washing water on a small oil stove, and each was allowed just one pint. Mary's 'en-suite' consisted of a jug and bowl on the washstand in her room, and she had to mix the hot water with the cold from her ewer and wash as best she may. But she had become skilful at this, and would start at the top, working her way down, till she felt perfectly clean and fresh. It may be wartime, but one's standards must be kept up!

In winter she had plenty of hot water to sponge away the dust of the day, and she was soon in her pyjamas and fast asleep, the sound of the threshing machine still in her ears.

No one really enjoyed threshing time because of the noise and dust. One year, they threshed a barley rick, which had become wet and then dried out. A thin crust of mould had formed on the sheaves, and this caused so much dust that poor Mary was half-choked. The next day her lungs ached and there was a burning pain in her chest.

She stood in the kitchen after breakfast looking pale and ill.

"Goodness Harry! Young Miss Mary cannot work today!" said Rhoda. "Another blast of that dust will kill her!"

Mary was told to go back to bed where she lay, short of breath. The sound of the thresher and the shouts of her comrades came through the window and although Mary was unwell she wished she could be out there with them.

At lunchtime Miss Butt climbed the stairs with a tray

loaded with dainties. There was hot buttered toast and two soft-boiled eggs.

"Oh! This is luxury!" Mary exclaimed as the kindly woman helped prop her into a sitting position with pillows. Poor Mary was so breathless she could hardly speak.

"Oh! It's the least I can do!" said Miss Butt. "You just enjoy your lunch, dear!"

Mary was grateful, and she soon recovered and returned to her tasks!

CHAPTER SEVENTEEN

WORK & PLAY

Although Mary's years at the farm were full of hard labour she had a happy social life and a merry circle of friends.

Shortly after settling at the farm, Rhoda Bishop told her about Young Farmers' Club.

"There's a fair sized branch in Gloucester," she said. "It'll be a good way to make friends. I've heard they do some splendid things."

Mary lost no time in joining, and when she learnt that they needed a secretary she volunteered for the job.

There were about forty members in the Gloucester branch, and she often had to send out notices not just to her own branch but to other clubs as well.

One day Mary told Miss Butt that she had over a hundred envelopes to address. It was a cold November afternoon with a keen wind blowing, and patchy rain lashing the windows, so Mary was quite pleased that she had the afternoon off.

"I know what we'll do," said Miss Butts. "We'll get the fire going and you can sit by that, dear. It'll make the job a sight more pleasant for you!"

Griff was called to stir up the coals in the grate in Miss Butt's office cum sitting room, and then both women fussed around, making sure their young charge was comfortable. Soon Mary was sitting by the fire and a table was drawn up to take the pile of envelopes and a cup of milky coffee.

A little while later Griff came to ask how the young cleric was feeling, and brought a plate of hot buttered toast. Mary had a suspicion that some of the butter had come from their own rations, but of course, neither would own up to it. Listening to the wind whistling in the chimney, and with a tray for writing on

187

perched across her knees Mary knew that she could not possibly be more content or happy!

Young Farmers were given a small ration of petrol with which to attend meetings and, mindful of a good time, the youngsters always tried to follow the meetings with a dance in the village hall. These dances were good affairs and there was nearly always an excellent band. Farming was an important part of the war effort and entertainers were encouraged to make their services available.

One day Harry told Mary that another young land girl was coming to work at the farm. Jean Barbour was a tall, pretty girl with a mass of dark curls. Mary liked her at once. The girls were soon great friends and they went to the meetings and dances together.

The blackout was total and extremely strict. Not a light showed anywhere in Gloucester or the surrounding countryside. The girls had to ride their bikes with their frocks tucked up to avoid them becoming entangled in the wheels, through the winter-black lanes. The only lights permitted were the smallest of headlamps, and even these were shaded, giving only a little spot of light on the road in front.

One evening they were making their way to a nearby village when they heard planes in the distance.

"Gosh!" exclaimed Mary, springing from her bike, "It's the Jerries!"

The girls had heard stories about German fighters picking off people they saw below them in the countryside. In seconds the girls were in the hedge, lights doused and hearts racing. Soon the planes were droning overhead, no doubt on the way to bomb a Midland city. The night sky was filled with the throbbing of their engines, a menacing intrusion into the silence, and a reminder to the girls that their country was engaged in war! When at last they were gone, the girls scrambled out from the hedge, relit their headlamps and went on their way.

This manoeuvre became a regular occurrence. It was safer, even when they saw the feint lights of an approaching car, to leap into the hedge rather than risk being knocked down in the darkness.

Mary and Jean made friends with another land girl, Barbara

Cane, who was working at a market garden just outside Gloucester. Barbara was a great beauty!

Mary enjoyed the company of her numerous men friends and liked flirting, and going out with her favourite of the moment, but she was sticking to her promise not to fall in love. The experience with Gordon had left her wary. Phil might have been a different story!

"You're never going to make any headway with him," chided Jean.

"He can't be married to the horses anymore," Mary wailed. "They've gone!"

"Well he's probably transferred his affections to the tractors!" Barbara teased. "For heavens sake, Mary! When are you going to give up?"

"Oh I have! I have!" Mary said, unconvincingly. "Don't you know? I love 'em and leave 'em!"

"It's the best way," agreed Jean. "It's no good getting in too deep anyway, because they go off to fight and come back dead!"

Whenever Jean cracked this joke Mary felt guilty, for it seemed that the war was passing them by, tucked away in the heart of the Gloucestershire countryside. Although Gloucester was considered a 'safe' zone, she frequently saw the German planes passing overhead, and knew that they meant death and destruction for the poor bombarded people in the Midland cities. And, occasionally, the planes mounted an air raid on Gloucester.

On one of her weekends off, Mary was staying at home with her parents, when there was a very bad raid. As the sirens wailed the family took cover under the stairs. Dad had dug a shelter in the garden but Mum would not go down it. She said the damp would kill them all!

Fred was in the Home Guard and owned a tin helmet and battledress. Edith had extra work too, as she took in evacuees. Most of these were important civil servants from government departments who had been moved from London to safer areas in order to carry out their work. Mary knew her parents were stressed. They had been through one world war and were now having to cope with another.

One evacuee billeted with them was a Major Williams, an ex cavalry officer. He decided to stay with them over Christmas.

Whilst eating his Boxing Day breakfast the major stared long and hard at Mary and said to her parents, "Your daughter is a delightful young woman! Does she ride?" and then, without waiting for the answer he said loudly, "I shall take her out on a horse today!"

The statement was fired with such authority that no on dared raise any objection but Mary did manage to say that she had not been on a horse before, unless one counted the donkeys at Burnham-on-Sea!

"No problem at all!" declared the bombastic major. "I know of an excellent riding establishment. It is not very far, and we can go in my car!"

He whisked the uncomplaining but nervous Mary away to some riding stables in the nearby Cotswolds. Throughout the journey Major Williams tried to discourse about the war, whilst Mary just as determinedly brought the conversation back to farming matters. They must have made a frustrated pair!

They reached Stroud as the sun was breaking through and the frost at the roadside was beginning to melt.

"Here we are!" snapped the major as a man in riding britches strode towards them.

"And a Merry Christmas to you, sir! Or whatever is left of it!" bellowed the major. "I need two mounts. A large one for me and a smaller sort of pony thing for Miss Oakley here. She's a land girl, don't you know!"

Mary blushed, never liking to be the centre of attention.

Very shortly a young man approached, leading their mounts. The major's was a large thin-looking animal, with a ewe neck and a large Roman nose. The stables assured them that this unlikely looking animal was in fact 'a galloper'!

"Ah good!" enthused Mr Williams. "Nothing like a good gallop on a nice crisp day like this! What Ho!"

A small, rather shaggy pony, possibly owing something of its confirmation to the robust and well known Exmoor breed, was to be Mary's mount.

"Now then!" the major shouted to the assistant. "You just hold onto the stirrup leather on the off-side and I'll give this excellent young woman a leg-up!"

He was heartened to see that Mary appeared enthusiastic.

"Mark my words! I have taught hundreds of young cavalry men! Nothing to it, dear gal!" said the major.

Mary put her foot in a stirrup, gathered up the reins and sprang on board.

"Good heavens dear gal! Lightly done! Oh I say! Lightly done! And you seem to have a natural seat. Excellent!"

He then mounted his own horse. "We always start off at the walk, young woman!" he said as they turned out of the yard and onto the open road. "Give the horses a chance to warm up, don't you know!"

They went riding on a flat ridge, which overlooked the town, and did a great deal of trotting, which flung Mary about, until she learnt how to rise or 'post'. Then she really began to enjoy herself!

"Are you ready for the orf now?" bellowed the major, letting out his reins and not waiting for an answer.

Suddenly they were galloping! Mary clung on tightly with her knees and thought the movement a lot smoother than the trot, but very fast! The wind whistled in her ears!

Considering it was the first time she had ever ridden, it is a wonder she did not hit the turf. In fact she did not feel perturbed at all, except for one nervy moment when she lost a stirrup, but she clung on tight and managed to regain it.

Afterwards, back in the stable yard Major Williams leaned down to her and said: "Well done my gal! Jolly well done! You definitely have a natural seat!"

On the way home he was humming contentedly. "A natural seat!" he reiterated as they turned into the drive at 'Oakboro'. It's a pity you don't ride more awften!"

Another character billeted with her parents was Miss Reef, a civil servant and member of staff for the RAF administration corps in Hampshire. She was a meek and mild bird-like little person, and extremely nervous. One day when Mary came home from the farm she found a cosy log fire burning in the sitting room, but Miss Reed was mysteriously huddled in a chair in the far corner. Mary thought it very strange.

Her mother was rolling out pastry in the kitchen.

"Mum" she inquired, "why is Miss Reef sitting in the corner of the living room?"

"It's the fire, dear," said her mother. "Miss Reef can't bear sitting near it! She's afraid, you see!"

"Afraid?"

"Well... it might spit!"

Night after night the German planes roared overhead on their way to the Midlands and occasionally, the war would come close enough for Mary to feel its breath. A battle would ensue overhead as British fighter pilots tried to drive off the German planes, and the angry stutter of anti-aircraft gunfire rent the air.

On one occasion such a battle caused a panic for Mary. There was a fashion for wearing Spirella corsets to give young girls the fashionable hourglass movie-star figure. This fearsome garment was a thick, whaleboned contraption with laces all down the front, which could be drawn in tightly. Each corset was made strictly to the measurements of the 'victim'. With all the healthy farm food and, in particular, her regular indulging of the goats milk custards, Mary had put on weight, and she decided to be fitted for a corset to wear at the next Young Farmers' dance. With this in mind she went into Gloucester on her day off.

The corset rep took out a specimen model and proceeded to lace Mary into it, when suddenly, the air raid siren sounded.

"Oh! What shall I do?" said Mary in dismay, looking at the formidable row of tightened laces down her front. "It will take ages to get me out of this thing, and I can't go into a shelter like this!"

The two women decided to turn a blind eye. The sales woman continued lacing, nipping and pinning as the battle raged overhead. Anti-aircraft guns started up and then the whine of engines as an English pilot engaged the German fighter in the air. The noise grew frightening!

"Ignore it!" said the corset fitter, and Mary nodded breathlessly. This may have been due to nerves, or possibly the tightness of the corset. The guns were wide of their mark but at length the German plane was chased off.

***

When Mary first joined Young Farmers, a handsome chap called George Warren was chairman. His father was well known in the

Gloucester area, the owner of a large farm. George was twenty-seven, two years older than usually permitted for Young Farmers, but was allowed to stay as an advisor because of his knowledge. Another member, Frank Dunn, had been club secretary before Mary joined. Frank introduced Mary to a young man, Harold Norton who took over the chairmanship. This meant that Mary, in her position as secretary, sat next to Harold at every meeting. She soon began to suspect that he was attracted to her.

He was a farmer's son and he had unusual bright red hair. His parents lived at a place called Middletown Farm, which they leased from two lady landlords, but they had no security of tenure, and just before Mary met Harold they had been told they must leave as soon as the war ended.

They had been prosperous farmers in their day but had moved around Gloucestershire, tenanting about nine farms in all. Mary listened sympathetically as Harold told her his family's troubles.

He had bought a tractor and was working as a contractor, clearing land as part of the war effort. Vast areas were going under cultivation to increase the nation's food supply. Imports from the continent were virtually at a standstill, and everyone was being urged to grow as much food as possible. Harold was kept desperately busy on his contract work, but his parents, now growing old and disheartened by their eviction, had decided to put their farming days behind them. They felt they did not have the strength to start again with all the difficulties of a new tenancy.

Harold was working through every daylight hour and struggling to maintain his parents too. He couldn't help liking the attentive young Mary, and she in turn felt herself drawing closer to him. He was such a hard-working and dedicated young man. She admired his initiative in carving out a lucrative occupation for himself. Mary thought him courageous and began to look forward to seeing him at meetings. But apart from little forays of conversation, and the routine discussions because of their positions on the committee, the couple did not make any headway. On several occasions Mary had thought he might be about to ask her out, but then they would be interrupted or

Harold would appear to change his mind and begin another topic.

"This affair is as bad as the Phil crush! It's never going to get off the ground if you don't make a few advances yourself," advised Jean.

"What affair," asked Mary innocently?

Then fate took a hand. One evening after a meeting Mary and Harold found themselves alone, trying to tie up a parcel, a birthday present for a fellow club member. Mary was never very good at such tasks. She wrapped the brown paper round the lumpy gift and tucked in the ends, quite roughly. As she flipped it over and urged Harold to hold onto the string, the ends popped out again. Soon her giggles took over.

"Here! Let me have a go," urged Harold and he deftly rewrapped the present, only to have it collapse again. The ball of string fell onto the floor and rolled across the room, unravelling as it went. Mary collapsed into helpless laughter, and as she looked up into his attractive green-blue eyes a silence fell between them.

"I say," he volunteered breathlessly, "I suppose you wouldn't like to come to the pictures one night?"

"That would be very nice," Mary said.

Soon they were going out a great deal, and they always danced together at the club hops. Mary had a feeling that her life was about to change again.

Meanwhile, Harold's parents continued to live in the huge farmhouse to await the end of the war and their subsequent eviction. They were a very devoted couple, and delighted to see that their son had found such a nice girl and looked like settling down. They were pleased that young Mary was so keen on farm life!

In fact, Mary had set her heart on marrying a farmer and wanted to spend the whole of her life on the land. She was also growing more and more fond of the dependable young Harold.

They sat holding hands at the cinema watching Pathe News, and wondering at the scenes of the war; mighty battleships, squadrons of fighter planes and the scenes of devastation caused by the Blitz. It seemed a long way off from relatively peaceful Gloucestershire. But amazing stories of farm life filtered through. A land army girl in Kent had plunged into a blazing cowshed during an air raid to rescue a herd of pedigree cattle. Another girl had sat milking every evening, grimly ignoring the sound of air raids raging overhead, determined to keep the nation's milk supply flowing. Mary and her friends talked about the war and they knew there was a threat of invasion, but never did they accept anything but that Britain would win and life would one day return to normal!

One evening, during a dance at Sandhurst village hall, Mary found herself, as usual dancing the last waltz with Harold. It was not the Ritz. The wooden floor of the hall was a little rough and there were ugly blackout curtains at the windows. The make-shift bar sold only soft drinks, but the band was good, and playing a slow number, and the mirrored 'glitter ball' was revolving in the centre of the ceiling, throwing glamorous glints of colour onto the young women's dresses. It was romantic enough, and Mary felt herself floating and happy, and extremely aware of Harold's strong arms about her. Away flew thoughts of the unobtainable Phil! Mary knew she was falling in love!

Next morning, at the milking, she was in a pleasant glow. The neat row of cows stood swishing their tails and munching hay from their racks. Completely content, Mary attached the teat cups to the first of the cows. She automatically connected the rubber pipes to the machine and watched as a froth of milk ran into the collection chamber. Her mind was lost in a pleasant reverie, thinking of Harold and that feeling of his arms about her.

Maybe I've had enough of flirting around, she thought to herself. Perhaps I should settle down.

Romance might be in the air but the work on the farm carried on relentlessly. It was early winter and the cattle had to be fed. The new concentrated feeds had just come in, a useful innovation for wartime farming. The cows still munched hay at milking time, but later, as darkness fell, they had learnt to come trailing into their barn where the cattle cake awaited them. Mary bent her back to the task, scooping out the feed and filling racks and troughs.

Mary noticed that her friend Jean appeared to be suddenly very friendly with George Warren. During the war all the big farm shows, including the famous Bath and West, had been cancelled, but stock judging contests were organised by the NFU to provide some contact and interest for the young farmers. Often Jean and George, with Harold and Mary made up a foursome to go to these competitions. Sometimes a team came down from Cheltenham and the contests were jolly occasions, despite all the hanging around in the cold.

They were usually held at Andrew Warren's farm, and Mary watched Jean and George, wondering if romance was in the air for them too. She often saw them laughing as they inevitably manoeuvred themselves near each other.

Mary wished that Harold would let himself go a bit more. He was a serious young man, and often disapproved when she broke into her giggling attacks. He looked on in embarrassment, unable to see the funny side. It was a shame, but he was strong and good-looking, and most importantly, a farming man, and very attractive.

"The Cheltenham team's coming down again for a stock judging contest at the weekend," said Harold. "I'll drive you over to the Warren farm if you like."

When they arrived, the Cheltenham 'gang' was already hanging round drinking hot tea from thermos flasks. It all seemed very chummy and Mary felt the glow again; that warm contented feeling of being part of a way of life which suited her utterly.

They had to judge groups of Friesian cows, listing the animals' points in order of merit, whilst the adjudicators in turn judged the young farmers. It was good fun and all the more enjoyable because Mary's team won. On the way home she leaned against Harold and begged him to stop the car.

"I desperately need a kiss to warm me up," she said playfully. Harold obliged, of course!

A few weeks later the girls heard that a milking contest had been organised by Lady Bathurst, the Secretary of the Land Army, who had interviewed Mary in her early days at Usk College.

It was to be held at Collam End Farm, Leckhampton, using Farmer James Brierley's herd of Jersey cows. Mary decided to enter, and motored over on the day with Harold.

They pored over the schedule, to see what they had to do.

"We'll be judged on our management and grooming of the cow!" said one of the Cheltenham girls, her face breaking into a merry smile. "Well I suppose you could give it some of your famous sausage curls!"

"At which end should I apply the curling tongs?" laughed Mary.

"Look at this!" her friend continued, reading from the sheet of paper. "The milk has to be skilfully hand drawn and free of sediment! Isn't this just so absolutely typical of the ministry! Practically every damn farm in the country now has milking machines, and yet their contest is for *hand milking!*"

"Yes," agreed Mary, "especially when you think it was them that tried so hard, and persuaded us to go in for milking machines!"

Mary felt nervous as she sat down on her stool. She had not milked by hand for many months. But as she began the task she found herself growing calm. She leant her head in the time honoured fashion, against the plump, well polished flank of one of Farmer Brierley's pedigree Jerseys, and pulled gently on the well filled udder, gaining confidence as a froth of milk squirted forth.

Oh, she thought, what a delightful little cow!

Her animal had huge kind eyes with long white lashes and a sweet neat little muzzle. Her legs and hoofs were dainty and fine-boned, like an antelope. At that moment a love affair dawned for Mary with this breed, which was to remain with her for the rest of her life. In addition, the milk was a delightful thick creamy yellow!

Next the girls moved onto a question and answer section. Mary did so well that it was announced that she had achieved joint first with another land girl, Miss Peggy Fruin.

"Well!" said one of the girls, patting Mary on the back. "Whoever would have thought I was working with a genius!"

Mary was delighted when her photo and details of the contest appeared in the local paper the following week.

"Fame at last," said Harry, pleased that his farm had got a mention in the article. "Now Miss Dairy Lee... You can go and muck out that there cowshed!"

Ah, thought Mary. Back to normal!

CHAPTER EIGHTEEN

OUTINGS AND A VISIT TO THE PALACE!

Mary remembers that throughout the war the aristocracy tried to do their bit for the land girls. Occasionally they organised tea parties at their 'family piles'. It was one of these 'do's', which led to a strange coincidence for Mary. Her branch of Young Farmers was invited to Tewkesbury Park, where her mother had worked as head parlour maid for Lady Violet, more than thirty years before.

A specially chartered bus took them there, and a guide ushered them into the lofty flag-stoned hall with its vast stone fireplace and coat of arms. An awed hush immediately fell upon the merry throng as they mustered under the ancestral portraits.

"We've got some of that stuff at home," whispered Mary, indicating the precious china in the cabinets. "Only broken bits though!"

She had told her friends about her mother working in the house as a young woman, and they were keenly interested.

"Gosh" said Jean, "you've certainly got connections!"

Mary looked around the hall. A beautifully carved central gateleg table supported an enormous vase from which spilled a perfusion of garden flowers. There was a strange but immensely pleasing smell compounded of dust only just kept under control, lavender polish, old stone, wet dogs and the overpowering perfume from the flowers. Mary drank it in, imagining her mother's feet clattering over that very same floor, perhaps bearing a message on a silver salver, or a gown delivered from the dressmakers.

As the girls waited for the lady of the house to meet them, a low chatter broke out and a few high spirited giggles. These were the girls of a brave new age and they were not easily subdued by grandeur.

Suddenly a heavy oak door at one end of the hall was flung open and a smartly dressed butler appeared, announcing the arrival of her ladyship. She may have been Lady Violet's daughter, but Mary remembers her simply as a tall, youngish woman, dressed in an elegant tweed skirt and heather-coloured twinset, with a rope of pearls at her throat. She gazed at the gathering of girls, gave them a nervous smile and ushered them into the drawing room for tea.

At first the girls were tense but, as they gazed at the assemblage of fusty and haughty ladies of the aristocracy, a few giggles broke out. Jean's eyes were half closed and her mouth twitched at the corners. Mary decided it would be safer not to look her way again!

The ladies did their best to appear interested. They asked the girls about their work, and listened politely, but no one was fooled. The girls knew they were just 'doing their bit'.

For Mary it was a strange experience, sitting in the very room where her mother had spent so many years working. She knew that Lady Violet had been a kind mistress and that her mother had been happy. She thought anew of the little treasures sitting in her mother's china cabinet.

But young Mary dismissed it all. Her heart was drawn to a simpler life, spent in the fresh air, and the fulfilment born of hard work. She was a farmer to the core and had scant regard for airs and graces.

Later the girls spilled once again into the fresh air and freedom of the grand courtyard, and excitement and chatter broke out with relief. Sunburned faces broke into laughter, and strong brown hands, with nails roughly chipped and broken, swung their young, healthy owners into the bus for the bumpy, merry ride back to Gloucester.

Soon voices were ringing out. "What did you think of them?"

"My! Weren't they funny old things?"

"Do you think they really knew one end of a cow from another?"

"I bet none of them has had liquid muck splashed on her face!"

"I'd like to see that lot get up a four in the morning!"

"Mary! Your mother actually worked there! Did she have to bow and scrape? Oh my! You wouldn't catch me tripping about and touching a lacy cap in that place!"

The girls were all so uncompromisingly modern! A thousand miles from those times of serfdom! Although, in the thirties and forties there were still many in service, the domain of the supremely wealthy crashed into disarray at the end of the war, when a new era of freedom and equality came rushing on the winds of change.

Mary smiled back at her companions, warmed by the gaiety of their laughter and that sense of belonging, which comes from the company of people with a common purpose. She was glad to put Tewkesbury Park behind her and return to the life she loved.

But there was another excitement in store for Mary, and an occasion far grander than tea at Tewkesbury Park.

As she came swinging into the kitchen after finishing the milking one bright morning in the early summer of 1943, she saw that a letter had been placed for her on the kitchen table, leaning against the marmalade pot. It didn't look particularly exciting, just a plain white envelope, so she picked it up casually, tore it open and took out a small white card. At first glance it seemed unremarkable, but then her eyes took in the crest on the top and the stark printed words BUCKINGHAM PALACE!

She swiftly read the spidery copperplate which followed: *The Master of the Household is commanded by The Queen to invite Miss Oakley to an Afternoon Party on Saturday the 3rd of July, 1943 at 3 o'clock. RSVP*

In a panic Mary ran through into the scullery, waving the card in front of Rhoda. "Look! Look!" she thrilled, "I'm going to a garden party... with the Queen!"

Rhoda quickly rinsed her hands and wiped them on a small strip of huckaback towel, then grabbed the card.

"My, oh my!" she said, her face askew, "It's not much of an invitation for such a grand occasion. Just a little bit of cardboard with black printing on it. One would never have known it came from the palace. Well, well! I suppose it must be genuine!"

"Of course it is," said Mary, grabbing it back. "Its wartime so the card's utility. They wouldn't go wasting money on things like gold ink, would they?"

Mary was gripping the card and gazing at it in amazement. Rhoda began to smile and laugh too. She was fiercely fond of Mary and delighted to see her so excited.

"Well," she said, "I suppose you'll be wanting the day off!"

"Gosh!" said Mary, "Oh Lord! I mean... well... I can go, can't I?"

"Of course you can!" laughed Rhoda. "I was only teasin'!"

Mary immediately rushed off to a phone box down the lane to tell her father.

"Dad!" she yelled in excitement, "You'll never guess! I'm going to meet the Queen!"

After a seconds silence the familiar 'Oo-ah', came down the phone-line.

"Oh Dad! For heaven's sake! Can't you get just a bit excited?"

"It's a garden party Dad! At Buckingham Palace!"

Back at the farmhouse she fished out a sheet of paper, which was enclosed with the invitation and read it with some dismay.

"It says I'm to go in full Land Army uniform," she said, "corduroy trousers, sweater and boots, woolly socks an' all!"

"Phew! We better be hoping it's not too hot a day, then," said Rhoda.

The 3rd of July dawned sunny and bright, with a cloudless blue sky and the promise of one of the hottest days for years.

Harry drove a tense and nervous Mary to Gloucester Railway Station.

"Strewth!" he exclaimed as they clattered onto the platform. "Look at this lot!"

The place was swarming with land girls! It was a sea of brown and green.

Their eyes took in the special Land Army train, emblazoned with the royal crest, and disgorging excited and bewildered-looking girls as it waited at the platform. The girls were in little groups, standing beneath banners proclaiming the title of their county. There were only four girls chosen from Gloucestershire, but the train had come all the way from Cornwall, picking up girls on the way.

Mary was delighted to see that Mrs Bathurst was there, flushed and excited. Her old mentor from the Usk Agricultural College was marching round the platform yelling at the top of her lungs: "NOW GALS! GALS! PLEASE!" as she tried desperately to impose a semblance of order on the noisy and unruly throng.

Mary finally found someone who had been allocated to the Gloucestershire girls and the four of them were ushered on board the train. As she was jostled along the platform she saw the word 'LONDON' on the front of the train and knew that it really was going to happen. She was going to meet the Queen!

She looked round to say goodbye, but poor Harry had become lost in the crowds.

The first thing the girls did once they were on board was strip off their thick green woollen jerseys and remove their boots. They were all gasping with the heat.

Who on earth, wondered Mary, had decreed that full uniform should be worn in the height of summer?

Mary also had to cope with a small suitcase as, directly after the garden party, she was going to travel to Cambridge to stay with her old school friend, Kay.

As the train rattled through the London suburbs there were signs of war damage and the Blitz everywhere. It was a sobering reminder that their country was engaged in bitter battle.

"It's terrible!" Mary breathed to her companions. "We are so lucky, working away in the countryside."

"I've not been so lucky," retorted one of the girls. "My parents lived in Hammersmith. They were bombed out!"

And another said that she had lost her uncle and his entire family.

Mary was consumed with guilt.

"Don't look so down at mouth," comforted the first girl. "You're doing your bit working on the land. We all are. We have to make the most of it!"

When they arrived in the city the Gloucestershire girls were met by Mrs Morris, the wife of the wartime Minister of Agriculture.

"Well now gals," she said as they stood on the platform,

"best foot forward! You'll all be famished no doubt. I'm taking you for lunch at the Carlton Club!"

The 'gals' marched in obedience, carrying their brown felt hats, which had been battered by the crush of the journey.

The foyer of the Carlton club swallowed them like a plush, softly-lit cave, and they found themselves brushing shoulders with sophisticated and glamorous women who spoke with exaggerated Oxford accents, and drifted past in a sea of silk and chiffon.

Mary turned to her young companions and whispered, "This place certainly has atmosphere!"

The women stared at the 'gals' dressed in their full winter gear, wondering what on earth was going on.

"It's the Land Army!" Mary heard one hiss behind a be-ringed and exquisitely manicured hand; "I believe they are going to a garden party, at the palace, don't you know!"

Another, floating by in a swirl of flowery muslin asked, "Why on earth are the poor things got up like that?"

"It's their uniform," said another. "Poor pets! But they're probably used to it."

The 'gals' were beginning to feel conspicuous.

Mary was acutely conscious of her chipped and unsightly fingernails. She had done battle with them the evening before, furiously working the nailbrush whilst soaking in a luxurious bath at Wallsworth Farm, but a rim of ingrained dirt remained.

"Well now gals," said Mrs Morris. "No doubt you'll want to freshen up, powder your noses etcetera!"

She led them to the 'Ladies' Powder Room' which was about the size of a ballroom, and told them to be quick, as lunch was soon to be served. The powder room was lined with pink marble, and the girls looked anxiously at the row of gleaming basins with their chromium-plated taps.

"I don't think we should use these," said one of the girls, "We'll make them dirty!"

"Oh! I just have to have a wash!" gasped Mary as she filled a basin with cold water and splashed her flushed face. A pile of the thickest, most luxurious towels stood on little gilded tables at each end of the row of basins. She seized one and buried her face in it.

"Absolutely gorgeous, gals!" Her voice came, muffled, from within the towel. "I feel a little cooler now!"

"Would that be a *milk* cooler?" joked another.

They emerged from the cloakroom, and Mrs Morris, who had come to hurry them up, chivvied them along.

"Come on gals! We simply MUST eat lunch!"

The 'gals' walked nervously across the restaurant, leaving an interesting track of impressed boot prints in the plush carpet.

Mrs Morris told them to sit down at a large circular table, spread with a gleaming white cloth, upon which expensive-looking cutlery had been placed.

"Wow! I reckon this stuff is solid silver!" one of her companions exclaimed.

"Of course it is," hissed Mary. "They wouldn't have rubbish in a place like this!"

She thought fondly of Miss Butt's handsome silver cutlery, attractively worn and dented. Far nicer than this posh stuff!

The waiter brought a whole flotilla of dishes and Mrs Morris helped each 'gal' to a portion of chicken, potatoes and garden peas... a splendid meal for wartime London!

After lunch a taxi took them to Buckingham Palace.

Disappointingly, the Royal Guardsmen were not in their bright red uniforms, but wore simple kaki battle dress, a further wartime measure.

The girls were told to wait in long corridor-like anterooms. It was terribly forbidding... several hundred girls all lined up and presided over by rows of sombrely dressed footmen. It was announced that the Queen was within a chamber at the far end, and that each girl would be called in turn for her audience. Despite the large numbers, there was almost total silence, broken only occasionally by nervous whispers.

Slowly, the lines moved along and Mary's little group drew nearer to the royal chamber. She was suddenly overcome by panic and whispered to her neighbour, "Oh Lord! I've always been overwhelmed by the aristocracy, and this is the QUEEN of them all!"

As they came closer they could see, through a pair of very grand double doors that the Queen Mother was standing on a little dais in the midst of a lofty chamber. At last they were at the doors, and they had to hand their invitation cards to the usher, who then announced them individually. Mary felt the card being taken from her hand and then heard her name read out. She walked twenty yards to stand in front of the Queen Mother, who stepped down to meet her and held out a white-gloved hand, asking her if she enjoyed working on the land.

Mary could only nod with a nervous smile and then she and her three companions had to attempt a curtsey, which was ludicrously difficult, wearing corduroy britches and boots. Then they had to walk backwards for a few steps, as they had been instructed, before turning and leaving the chamber. In silence, they made their way to an enormously long drawing room where tables were set for a tea-party.

One of Mary's companions let out a long sigh of relief. "Oh gosh!" she exclaimed, "Wasn't the Queen just too beautiful?"

"Oh yes!" agreed Mary. "Those eyes!"

The girls swiftly turned their attention to the food. It was of course a wartime tea, with quite simple little sandwiches and dainty cakes without too much sugar in them, but what impressed Mary most, was the huge ornate silver teapots which were so heavy that they had to be hung in silver stands, to precipitate the pouring. A fleet of butlers poured tea and assisted the 'gals' with hushed politeness.

Behind the tables were great ranks of French windows, running the entire length of the room. The girls could see that they led to a terrace and then out into the beautiful gardens beyond.

Mary and her friends helped themselves to a selection of the dainty eatables, and then stepped into the glorious sunlight of the July afternoon, where a band was playing.

Oh the relief to be free in the gardens after the tense ordeal of their audience with the Queen! Soon everyone was chatting and mingling, and Mary and her Gloucestershire friends walked across the great lawns, down to a little lake with its fancy ducks and geese.

A ripple of excitement was caused by the news that the Princess Marina, who had planned to attend the occasion, had been involved in a car crash. Fortunately it proved to be only a minor knock and the princess was not badly hurt, but it was a disappointment to the girls that they would be unable to meet her.

As they wandered through the gardens they noticed delightful little domestic touches, which told that this was not just a palace, but a family home. The odd rope dangled from a tree, knotted for climbing, and tucked in among the shrubs was a perfect little 'Wendy house'. The gardens had a wild, countrified air, so unexpected in the centre of London. But Mary was unbearably hot in her uniform!

As they walked back across the lawns one of her companions caught her arm and said breathlessly: "Look... the two princesses are in the garden!"

Mary looked up and saw Princess Elizabeth and her sister, Princess Margaret Rose, standing in the shade of the trees. She noted with a twinge of envy that they were both dressed in cool-looking, flowery print cotton frocks.

Mary's friend touched her arm again. "Look," she said, "they are going round talking to everyone!"

Suddenly, the princesses turned and came across the lawn towards them. As they drew nearer, Mary noticed that they had the same violet-blue eyes as their mother, and then, just as she was taking in this fact, they walked up to Mary and her Gloucestershire friends.

Princess Elizabeth asked, "Have you ever made cheese?"

Mary shook her head, but one of her companions swiftly answered that she had. The princesses listened and it struck Mary that they were, in many ways country girls. They swiftly passed onto another group and Mary watched them in admiration.

The land girls were free to spend more time in the gardens, but after about an hour Mary found herself being gently ushered through the palace rooms again, and then suddenly, she was on the train. Everyone was stripping off their jumpers and joining in with the babble of laughter and noise.

All too soon Mary had to say goodbye, for she was alighting at Cambridge to stay with her old school friend Kay who was at university, reading mathematics. There she was! Her darling Kay, waiting on the platform as the train pulled in.

It was a very tired and weary land girl who stepped down

from the railway carriage and fell into the arms of her dearest friend.

"Oh Kay!" she breathed, "I'm so glad to see you!"

"And how is my grand pal then?" teased Kay. "Fresh from hobnobbing with the Royals, no less!"

"Oh I just can't begin to tell you all about it!"

"Oh I bet you can!"

And Mary did!

CHAPTER NINETEEN

MARY THE UNDERGRAD, AND MORE LAND ARMY LIFE!

Kay and her fiancé, Ken owned a small car which Kay had left waiting outside the station. Mary had met Ken previously in Gloucester, but now her dear friend was wearing a beautiful engagement ring and had her own mini-flat inside the university.

"Well, here we are," said Kay after they had climbed several flights of stairs to her accommodation.

Mary looked round the room. It was quite small but furnished in modern style. There was a single bed, dressed with a cover and cushions set along the wall so that, during the daytime it could double as a sofa. A large cupboard and chest of drawers held Kay's eclectic collection of clothes, and a desk-come-table was set under the window, with two chairs tucked beneath it.

"There was only one chair when I arrived," informed Kay, "but I purchased another in a junk shop. There're loads of second-hand shops in Cambridge! I just love going round them!"

Mary admired it all. She liked the walls painted in the fashionable eau-de-nil, and the table, spread with a jazzy cloth, was decorated with a small vase of garden flowers.

In the corner she could see a cupboard on which stood a single gas ring so that beverages could be heated, or even a simple meal. The cupboard contained plates, cups, cutlery and tins of soup. Mary thought it all wonderful!

"Whilst you're here you are going to live the life of an undergraduate," smiled Kay. "We'll have such jolly fun! We even managed to... um... fix up for you, the right kind of company, if you know what I mean!"

"I'm sure I don't, Kay," said Mary, but it was clear from the look on her face that she knew what this meant.

"Oh you know Mary, dear old thing, some *male* company. *The opposite sex!* Ken and I love punting on the river and we couldn't have you tagging along as a gooseberry, could we?"

"Does this mean I have to attend tutorials as well?" Mary frowned.

"Oh no! We'll let you off them! You're just going to do the fun bit! But now darling, you really must get out of those ghastly clothes and put on something more summery. What have you got in that little case of yours?"

Without any kind of by-your-leave she snapped open her friend's suitcase and rummaged through its meagre contents.

"Goodness! It's not a lot is it? But I suppose you'll manage. "Come on, I'll show you the bathroom and you can freshen up."

Mary went through into Kay's own private bathroom. It was quite a large room with a bare linoleum floor, a huge bath and a very old-fashioned washbasin and lavatory. The window was open to the warm summer evening and a scrap of muslin curtain billowed gently in the breeze. Mary couldn't help thinking it must be a chilly place in the winter.

She stripped off her hot clothes and left them in a disgruntled heap on the floor as she stepped into the luxury of a hot bath, extravagantly perfumed with Kay's bath oil.

As she lay back blissfully, Mary watched the drips plopping from the enormous bronze taps, and listened to the soothing sound of the church bells ringing out over the city. It suddenly seemed a peaceful place, in the hush of sunset.

"Are you alright in there?" yelled Kay from the next room.

"Oh yes, answered Mary dreamily, "Capital, thank you!"

Later, refreshed and dressed in a simple frock with a cardigan over her shoulders, Mary allowed Kay to show her round the immediate part of the city, and they found a super little café where they ordered a simple salad meal. There was precious little meat and the pudding was a plain custard, but it was enjoyable none the less, and best of all was Kay's excited chatter, relaying all the pleasures of life at the university.

Later they returned to Kay's rooms and Mary sat, nodding off as they shared a cup of cocoa. At last the cushions were flung from the bed and the cover folded back carefully so that it should not become crumpled and look untidy when the bed was returned to its function as a sofa in the day time, and the girls climbed gratefully in. It was quite a crush in the narrow bed, but Mary, wearing a pair of luxurious silk pyjamas bought for her by her mother the previous Christmas, lost no time in falling into an exhausted slumber.

It had been quite a day!

The next morning Kay took Mary down to eat breakfast in the huge, echoing dining hall. It was jam-packed with students and reminded Mary of the noise in the communal rooms at Usk Agricultural College. Mary said as much!

"It's worse than the shed where we had to inject squealing piglets," she added.

Kay elbowed her way through the crush to the servery where the girls were offered a choice of porridge, or the new corn flakes, a breakfast dish recently introduced from America.

"The GI's love this stuff," said Kay, shaking a stream into a cereal dish.

Mary loved it too!

Kay caught the eye of her fiancé, Ken, who was standing up beckoning them over to his table. Soon the girls were seated and joining in the chatter and clatter as Mary renewed her friendship with Ken.

She thought him a brilliant chap, extremely brainy. Later he would obtain a professorship and employment at the famous Cavendish Laboratory, and work alongside scientists involved in splitting the atom.[6]

But on that bright July morning which held such promise of a perfect summer's day, Ken was content to put himself at the disposal of the two girls. Seated by his side was a sandy-haired pleasant-looking young chap called Clegg, who, Mary soon learnt, was to be *her male company* on their outings.

"And how is life down on the farm?" smiled Ken. "How on

---

[6] *Author's Note: Very shortly after leaving university, Ken obtained a professorship in Toronto, Canada, and they moved there. But they did not like Canada and, within two years they moved to Philadelphia, where he worked at the University of Philadelphia for the rest of his working life. The couple bought a lovely house near the Washington Memorial Park. Ken died many years ago but Kay still lives in same house.*

earth are they managing without you?"

"Oh, it's all hands to the teat-cups during my absence," laughed Mary, "but they'll survive!"

It was such fun! They took Mary round most of the city's colleges. Her shoes clattered on the flagstones of great cloistered ways, and she stood in silence in oak-panelled halls, or gazed in awe at row upon rank of tomes in libraries. It was all very impressive but Mary was not a lover of cities or great architecture, and she was glad when it was decreed that they should go punting on the river.

Here she was blissfully happy, leaning back against canvas-covered cushions whilst the athletic and graceful Clegg deftly steered their punt onto the peaceful waters beneath overhanging willows.

Mary watched him, squinting against the sun, which wrapped his slender form in a pale golden halo. She hoped that he did not mind her scrutiny. She was reminded of the story her mother had told her, about another young man, a carpenter called Fred, who had taken the young Edith in a boat on the river and cemented the deep love which was to bring forth Mary's being. Only, Mary reflected, she herself was in love with another, and could not feel the stirrings of romance towards the handsome man so skilfully guiding her among the ripples. She felt a frond of willow brush her face in a tender echo of that other young woman, so many years before.

Later that evening it was suggested by Kay that Mary should go into Clegg's room for 'an innocent snog'. Mary agreed, for she was a passionate girl, and the prospect was mildly pleasing.

She sat down awkwardly on Clegg's single bed, which was rumpled and not decorated with cushions in the form of a sofa, as Kay's. He took her in his arms and gave her a tender kiss. Mary responded eagerly, hungry for the passion, which she knew, lay in this good looking young man. The bed became further rumpled and the pillows slid to the floor. Then, quite suddenly Mary pulled away and sat up awkwardly, pushing back her disarrayed hair. She felt cold and a little unwell.

"I'm so sorry," she murmured, looking at Clegg. "I shall have to stop. I'm practically engaged you see… to a nice young farmer back in Gloucestershire."

"Kay told me as much," said the embarrassed Clegg. "Look! I'm the one who should be apologising!"

Without rancour he scrambled to his feet and made two cups of cocoa, which they drank sitting stiffly side by side on the bed. He picked up the pillows and shifted them behind Mary in an attempt to make her comfortable, but she remained tensely upright.

"Come on," he said when they had finished their cocoa. He took Mary along the corridor and returned her to Kay. Before he left her at the door he bent and dropped a tremulous little kiss, as light as a butterfly, on Mary's neck. Despite herself, Mary felt a thrill of pleasure.

All too soon her glorious sunlit time with Kay came to an end, and Mary found herself standing once again on the platform at Gloucester Station. *Goodness! Such a lot had happened since she had left and she suddenly felt down at heart and lonely.*

Then she saw Rhoda, Harry and Jean, all gathered to meet her. She felt like a film star as they swept her away to the waiting car.

"Well!" exclaimed Jean, "You better tell us all about it! What was the Queen Mother like? How did it feel wandering about in the palace?"

"I didn't wander," laughed Mary, "but it was wonderful! And I had such a good time with Kay!"

"It's been hell here without you!" teased Harry, "All the milkings were late, that hoeing you promised just never got done, and as for the dairy! Well! That's a filthy slum! I don't intend to be giving you so much leave in future! Don't go thinking that now you've met the Queen you can go swanning it around at Wallsworth!"

He sounded convincing but couldn't keep it up. At the sight of Mary's blanching face, he broke down into helpless laughter and said, "Don't worry, Miss. We've managed."

"Anyway," said Rhoda, "you look ever so well, and we're all pleased as punch to see you."

"Oh," sighed Mary, "I had a great time, but I just can't wait to see Harold!"

She was soon 'back in harness' at Wallsworth, and the

212

grandeur of the garden party became a pleasant memory. Nothing could match her joy in the life on the farm!

"I'd never change it!" she laughed to her friends. "Not for a million palaces!"

But one spring day, towards the end of the war she had an adventure, which could have ended her life. It started out as just a bit of fun. The boss had purchased a young riding pony for Rhoda but it had given her a few scares. Harry decided that it was just too young and he would have to try and recoup his costs by taking it to market. He thought that it would be a good advertisement if one of his land girls rode it into market in full Land Army kit. Mary was immediately keen on the idea.

She wasted no time in telling Harry that she had been told she had 'a natural seat'.

Harry said it would be perfectly safe, because she would only go at a very slow pace, and he and Rhoda would follow behind in the car.

The market was on Saturday morning in Gloucester. At first all went well. From the farm the Tewkesbury Road led straight into Worcester Street, which was a wide road about half a mile long. Mary and the pony negotiated this and eventually arrived in Market Square.

All went well, except that the pony was a little restless and inclined to side-step and pull on the bit, tossing his head around. Mary just sat tight, trusting implicitly to her 'natural seat'.

The little procession was almost at the market when suddenly, from the opposite turning, an American Jeep with five or six Yanks aboard, came careering out.

The pony, eyes and nostrils flaring, reared up on its hind legs and Mary's feet were jerked from the stirrups. She grasped the reins and made a frantic attempt to hold onto his flying mane but it was no use. She was thrown from the saddle, and suddenly found herself on her back on the road, with a fury of iron-shod hoofs thrashing above her. One of these brushed her top lip, causing a cut, but by a miracle someone grabbed the pony's head, and Mary managed to roll clear. With relief she saw that the menacing hoofs were gone and she was still alive. Shakily, and blushing with embarrassment, she attempted to scramble to her feet.

The jeep came to a grinding halt and the GIs were immediately upon her, picking her up, brushing her down and supporting her as they led her to the side of the road. A small crowd had gathered.

"Gee Miss! We're sorry!" the GIs kept on, as they examined her shaking form for wounds, but apart from the cut on her face and a small rip in her britches, she seemed unharmed.

"Gee Mam, we're so glad you're OK," they said. These snippets of American slang had infiltrated the English language.

At last they were persuaded that she was not badly hurt. They climbed back into their jeep and went on their way, but sadly still at breakneck speed!

It was decided that Mary should return home with Rhoda, and the boss would take the pony to market. Mary never heard the outcome, but was convinced that the incident had backfired, and the price was not a good one!

CHAPTER TWENTY

A WEDDING IS PLANNED

As the British and allied soldiers fought their courageous battles on the blood-stained beaches of Normandy, Hitler's reign of evil was drawing to a close. Every family waited in a state of expectancy, listening to the news reports on the radio. And then it came! The wonderful news that the war was over! Suddenly everyone was celebrating!

Mary joined in joyfully, but the end of the war brought her serious issues. She now knew what she wanted to do with the rest of her life. She had to farm! Harold shared her passion. He came from a farming family, which went back many generations, and she could look into his grey-green eyes and read a kindred spirit. She admired his cleverness in carving for himself a niche in the war effort. But best of all she liked the big strong solidness of him. It felt so good to be enveloped in his arms! Mary knew that she was finally in love!

So when, in the final days of the war, with all Europe going crazy around them, Harold took her in those arms and popped the question. Mary had no hesitation in answering 'Yes!'

Harold knew she was a passionate young woman and whenever she was near him he felt his head spinning!

"Do you think we can make a go of it?" he breathed against her soft blonde hair.

Mary nodded and they kissed and kissed, whirling away on the wings of their mutual love and desire!

***

Later Mary stood before her father at 'Oakboro'. He was relaxing by the fire in his usual chair, with his feet on the mantelpiece.

During the war years he had lost this habit but now he was himself again. As he saw her he swung his feet down.

Mary came straight to the point.

"Harold's asked me to marry him and I've said yes," she said.

"Oo-ah," said her father. Poor Fred, as usual it was a struggle to find the words but he took a long deep look at his daughter, raised an eyebrow, and then said simply, "Are you sure?"

Mary met his eyes. What did he mean? Did he have doubts about her marrying? Did he feel Harold was not right for her? Was it because he felt that she was, at twenty-three, still too young? But the whole world was doing it. These were the heady, madcap days immediately after the war. Sweethearts were tying the knot by the hundred!

All these thoughts flashed through her mind as she answered simply, "Yes Dad."

"Well then, I have a little something to tell *you*," replied Dad with a twinkle in his eyes, which Mary hadn't seen for several years.

He told Mary that, for some time he had been looking around, trying to find a small farm for her. He had known only too well that the ending of her Land Army days would be devastating for his daughter.

He said he had a place in mind. It had thirty-two acres of good Gloucestershire land, a nice farmhouse, and a range of farm buildings. Some of the buildings were in need of a bit of renovation, but then, he had always fancied doing up an old place. It was called Tan House Farm, and now that she was planning on getting hitched he would be delighted to give it to the couple as a wedding present!

It was a very long speech for Fred!

Now it was Mary's turn to use the mantelpiece. She put out a steadying hand.

Since she had grown up the relationship between herself and her father had grown even warmer, but not overly demonstrative, so it was with some surprise that Fred suddenly found his daughter all but sitting on his lap with her arms round his neck, hugging him.

216

"Oo-ah!" he said, untangling himself.

Later that evening Mary told Harold the news. For some time they had worried what they should do. His parents had to leave Middletown Farm, and there was nowhere for the young couple to go. Mary was relieved that Harold's future was now assured, as well as her own. She made up her mind that they would be equal partners in the farm, and that although it was a gift from her father, they should own it jointly.

"We can fix the date for the wedding," she said. Then, as an afterthought she added, "I shall have to organise my dress!"

The next morning Mary sought out her mother. The two women smiled knowingly at each other.

"I really must go up to see Kay," Mary said brightly. "I need to tell her the news, and also to ask her to be my bridesmaid."

"You go, Mary", Edith said lightly. "This is such a happy time for you... of course you want to be sharing it."

Her friend had since married Ken, and they had bought a little house in Cambridge. Mary phoned and said she was coming, and that she would stop a few days. Then she packed a few simple things and caught the train to London. These were utility days, many items were still rationed and luxuries were hard to come by. London wore a bleak look with the war-damage everywhere. Mary was distressed to see the bomb sites as the train slipped through the city. But already there were signs of rejuvenation. The rubble was being cleared away and new homes were going up. Also, there was an atmosphere of gaiety and relief everywhere. Times had been terrible, but Britain had come through!

Mary changed trains and was soon on her way to Cambridge. Kay was on the platform to meet her, and the two friends hugged.

"How is the wonderful Harold?" Kay asked.

"He's fine," replied Mary. "By the way darling, will you be my bridesmaid?"

"Of course," said Kay.

"Oh dear," said Mary, serious now, "This wasn't the way I planned to ask you. I was going to put it to you at exactly the right moment. But I'm too excited to hold it in!"

217

"Let's go to Kerswell's for some tea," Kay said sweetly. "You must be positively parched after your journey. Poor dear! Was it grim?"

"No, not at all. It's just that, well, in a way I feel guilty. The war passed me by, being buried at Little Wallsworth Farm."

"Oh but Mary!" Kay reasoned, "you did your bit! You worked jolly hard! Keeping the country fed and all that!"

"I know, but I enjoyed it all so much!"

Kay burst into infectious laughter: "And whatever's wrong with that? Really Mary! Do I detect you've become a little too serious these days?"

"It's not rubbing off from the oh-so-dependable Harold I hope! Come on and I'll buy you a Kunzle Cake!" With this she took her friend by the arm.

Later, as Mary sipped her tea from the rose-patterned cup, it occurred to her that some things never changed. Sitting there whilst her dear friend plied the teapot and fussed around with a napkin; it was just like old times!

There was no petrol so the two girls had to walk across the city to Kay's cosy little red brick semi-detached house in the suburbs.

Of course, everything had to be admired... the decoration, the furniture, the pictures."

"You've done well for yourself," said Mary, as she was led from room to room to view the wonders.

"I'm very happy," enthused Kay. "But we may not stay in England very long. Ken has plans for working abroad. America perhaps."

Mary was appalled. "But Kay... I couldn't bear it if you lived so far away!"

"Oh for heavens sake cheer up," said Kate, a small false laugh in her voice, "it probably won't happen! Anyway... I'm certainly enjoying this darling little house whilst I have it.

"Let's go downstairs. You can talk to me while I fix dinner."

Mary enjoyed her few days with her friend. As ever they slipped without effort into their natural, easy ways. They went shopping together and did some sightseeing, including a visit to the cathedral. Mary stood in the huge central aisle, tilting her head back to gaze at the soaring fluted pillars and the sweeping arch of the roof.

"Goodness," she marvelled to herself. "Soon I shall be in church making my vows to Harold." The thought was a happy one, but serious too.

On her last afternoon, Mary went out alone to the shops in order to buy a small gift to take home for her mother.

Just as she was thinking about returning to Kay's house she noticed a length of pretty blue crepe fabric in a shop window. Mary looked at it intently.

Yes, she thought, that's the sort of fabric that would drape nicely!

Once inside the shop she asked the assistant to show her the material. She ran her hands over it, imagining it made up into an attractive, long-sleeved dress. It was showy, but not extravagant... just the sort of thing for a post war, utility wedding.

"I'd like enough to make up a long-sleeved dress," she said to the assistant.

"For yourself madam?"

"Yes." Mary's clear gaze did not invite comment.

"Long, or the new mid-calf-length, madam?"

"Mid-calf please."

"For a special occasion madam?"

"Yes. Reasonably."

"Reasonably special madam? Well, I hope it will prove enjoyable."

Mary nodded and watched fascinated as the assistant's large, sharp scissors slid across the fabric, neatly dissecting enough for the dress.

"Do you require a pattern madam?"

"No thank you. My dressmaker will have one."

"Ah."

The assistant, knowing she was beaten, gave up the battle. Silently, as if performing a sacred ritual, she folded the fabric, smoothing down each fold with the flat of her hand, and wrapped it with utter tenderness in tissue paper and then packed it into a large carrier bag made from quality paper. It was, after all, a quality shop.

"There you are madam," she said as she handed it across the counter.

Mary meticulously counted out the amount in payment and handed it to the poor woman without a flicker of change in her expression.

The silent transaction completed, she turned to go, bearing her fabric.

Just before she clicked the shop door shut behind her, Mary turned to the assistant and said in a tiny but confidential voice, "It's for my wedding dress!"

**

Mary was too excited to keep her engagement from their friends at the Young Farmers' Club, and she insisted that she and Harold break the news at once. Everyone congratulated her and indicated that Harold was a 'good catch'!

Later there was a special Young Farmers' Dance at the Guild Hall, Gloucester with the newly famous Joe Loss Band. Mary put on her glad rags, a silk checked blouse and long velvet skirt, and with her young man beside her she mounted the steps to receive a cheque for twelve guineas from the chairman, the result of a collection made for the happy couple.

Shortly after this the Nortons invited Mary to stay overnight at Middletown Farm, so that they could get to know her better.

She washed her hair and fashioned it into the latest style, and put on her best brown tweed suit. Her father drove her there as Harold did not, at that time own a car.

Harold's parents welcomed her kindly and she sat at the big kitchen table drinking cups of tea and eating some of Gladys Norton's fruitcake. The kitchen was warm and comfortable and, surrounded by the homely clutter of farm life; Mary began to feel more relaxed.

Farmer Norton was a short, distinguished-looking man dressed in the manner of a gentleman farmer, with neatly buttoned gaiters and gleaming boots. Mrs Norton informed Mary that she always polished her husband's boots for him the evening before market day!

She was a small, rounded woman with a pretty little heart-shaped face set off by a halo of greying coppery-coloured hair. She was very talkative and energetic.

She took Mary on a tour of the farmhouse, proudly showing her the pleasant and well-furnished rooms.

Mary remarked on a particularly fine flowery chintz which hung at several windows, and was informed that the fabric came from some curtains which had graced the Norton's last farmhouse, a huge place, called Ashlewell Court.

"I bought yards and yards of the stuff," Gladys explained. "The drawing room windows were so vast, my dear!"

The grand tour finished, Mary was shown back to the kitchen. Feeling a little overwhelmed, she looked around for Harold, but was informed that he was out in the fields, 'doing some jobs'.

"Never mind, dear," said Gladys: "Perhaps you would like a little something to do. To keep you occupied till he gets back?"

Mary could not understand what was meant, but nodded amiably, anxious to please.

Gladys arose and went through into the scullery. "Here you are dear," she said as Mary followed, bewildered.

She took a little basket of socks from the floor and set them on the wooden draining board by the large Belfast sink.

"Some of Harold's socks, dear," she said. "Perhaps you'd like to give them a wash."

It was all said so naturally and with such evident good humour that Mary felt unable to refuse. Gladys padded away, leaving the bride-to-be to contemplate the task.

Mary ran some hot water into the sink, but the tap was splashy, and she looked round for a pinafore. She was not used to doing household tasks in her best suit. There was no apron, so she tried to stand back a little from the sink, unrolling the soiled socks and dropping them into the water. She added some 'Rinso' from a packet on the windowsill and swished the socks around in the sudsy water.

Mrs Norton's cleaning lady had arrived and all the time Mary could hear the two women talking and laughing in hushed voices in the kitchen. She had an uneasy feeling that she was being 'tried out'!

Well damn it! She thought to herself. I better wash the

wretched things!

When she had finished she took them, in their basket back to the kitchen.

"The line's out there, dear," indicated Gladys.

Mary was relieved to be out in the yard with the warm sun on her neck. She felt a little tearful and wanted to run for home, but at that moment Harold appeared.

"I've just washed your socks," Mary said.

"Well, that's champion!" said Harold, smiling. She noticed that he looked puzzled too.

He opened his arms and Mary ran to him. He practically lifted her off the ground in his strong encircling hug and then they were kissing. It was a long kiss, full of passion, and it just swept her away, banishing her anxiety and filling her with joy!

At some point she was aware that Mrs Norton was watching them. But she didn't care one bit!

Jolly good! she thought. Let her watch!

CHAPTER TWENTY-ONE

A COUNTRY WEDDING

Mary will never forget the day that she first saw Tan House Farm. Harold's father George came along too, to offer his advice and opinion. Mary sat in the back seat cuddled up to Harold with her hand snug and warm in one of his. There was nothing she enjoyed better than being close to Harold. They were so keen on kissing and cuddling that their friends had dubbed them the 'love birds'!

Fred drove through the pleasant little town of Berkeley, with its castle and hunt kennels, and the tiny hamlet of Ham set around its pleasant Green. About a mile further on he drew up in the quiet lane and pointed to a farmhouse and buildings on their left. It was Tan House Farm, easily visible from the road.

They bumped over a long track dividing two flat fields, and drew up in the untidy farmyard. The place wore a sad, neglected air, but the old cream-rendered farmhouse looked solid enough, and most of the farm buildings were of substantial brick and tile.

"It seems quite run down," Mary said to her father. "It will take a fair bit of work to bring it up to NAS standards."

Her father smiled. "Oo-ah," he said.

They crossed the yard to look at the buildings. Mary stood in the neglected cowshed. There was space for twelve cows to stand in a row for milking but the floor was earth, no doubt soaked through with years of cow dung. In her mind's eye Mary could see the shed in good repair with a concrete floor and fitted with yokes and modern milking machines.

She knew it was not going to be easy. Thirty-two acres was not a lot of land with which to make a living.

But Harold was keen to bring in the radical ideas outlined by his high-up friends in the NAS. He planned to farm by the fence and strip method. This involved planting high quality grass in narrow strips of land, sectioned off by electric fencing, which was moved daily. This method of farming had its roots in far-off medieval times but the electric fencing was a brand new method just being explored by the Ministry of Agriculture for small-scale dairy units. The country still needed food and everything possible was being done to increase production. It was an exciting time to be in farming!

Mary also cherished a dream to build up a herd of lesser sized pedigree milking cows, suited to their small acreage. She remembered the Jersey cow, which she had milked in a dairy contest during the war, and she had read that the breed was docile.

Her father was giving them the farm jointly as a wedding present. Mary was insistent that she and Harold should be partners in all aspects, not just sharing the work, but ownership of the farm. They were even to share a joint bank account, a very radical idea for those post war days of the 1940s. Mary was one hundred per cent confident in Harold's abilities and his farming ideas. Without them she knew, they would be unlikely to make a good living from such a small acreage. The farm was neglected and run down, but together they would turn it around.

The previous owner had been a good farmer in his younger days, but in his latter years failing health and the harsh life had led to him becoming a little too fond of his tipple at the pub in Ham.

Hand in hand, Mary and Harold explored the farmhouse, which was to be their first home. It was a good house with well proportioned rooms. The entire ground floor was stone-flagged with the exception of the large, gentrified drawing room, which had a magnificent floor of wide elm boards. As Mary and Harold viewed this vast space for the first time they both agreed it was too grand and cold for them. Mary walked round looking at the cavernous inglenook and peering from the large window.

"It's too big," she said. "We'd have to have huge fires just to get the chill off."

"I doubt if we'll have the time to furnish it," said Harold, "let alone sit in such a big room."

So they chose instead to set up home in the cosy dining

room, with two easy chairs by the fireplace and a large dining table and chairs. Harold's words proved prophetic, for during their eleven years at the farm they never did furnish the elegant drawing room, and it remained empty. The only time it was used was the occasion of the birth of their son, John, when Mary spent her confinement on a bed, which had been dragged into the room.

Upstairs were four big square bedrooms, each with views over the farm. The couple's feet echoed on the bare boards as they went from room to room.

"We'll sleep in this one," said Mary, "and furnish another for our parents. You know how keen they are to come and stay and help us."

The lovers stood in the room enjoying a long delicious kiss before exploring the house any further.

In the attic were two more rooms, which had been used for hanging cheeses, but Mary did not plan to produce cheese, and so the rooms were left, and would later come in handy as the family grew and the couple took on hired help.

"It's a good house," Harold said as he led Mary downstairs.

They both knew that in the early days at Tan House Farm they would have to go back in time, half a century. It was going to be tough. There was no electricity, so they would have to make do with candles and oil lamps, and the water supply for the farm came from a well. There was a huge pump with a stone trough located on a flag-stoned area close to the kitchen.

The kitchen also was pretty bare. There was a large Belfast sink with a wooden draining board, and for cooking Mary had to use a forbidding-looking 'Valour' oil stove.

"My word!" she exclaimed the first time she saw it, "what a fearsome looking thing!"

The stove had three burners with grids on top for saucepans, and an oven set to one side. There was an inlet for fuel to be poured in, and another for ventilation.

"I'll be too scared to use it!" laughed Mary. "I might blow us up!"

There was also a large iron range, fired by solid fuel. This would have to be kept in during the winter to provide hot water, but the couple had been told that the oven was very slow, and only good for casseroles. For anything needing faster cooking Mary would have to use the Valour.

There was a large brick-lined cavity in one wall of the kitchen, which her father was keen to fit with a galvanised mesh door so that she could use it as a larder. There were also other deep cupboards where she could store her groceries and the jams which she planned to make from her own fruit trees which grew on the farm.

The kitchen floor sloped and was made of large flagstones. It could be washed by pouring buckets of soapy water, which escaped at the bottom end through a hole in the wall. Mary had never seen such an ingenious arrangement!

The couple walked back out into the sunshine. It seemed very bright after the chill of the empty house.

Close to the kitchen was an old washhouse. When Harold opened the door they both stood back in dismay! It was full from floor to ceiling with empty bottles!

"We'll have to clear that lot out," said Mary, "I suppose the old copper is in there beneath it somewhere."

They left the washroom and went to examine the small, run-down dairy.

"Getting this up to date will be a priority," Harold remarked. "We'll also need a milk cooler. This place doesn't come anywhere near meeting the current regulations!"

They both knew that it was possible, in those days, to make a good living from producing milk, but they also realised that they would have to work very hard to achieve this. Furthermore, the land was semi-derelict. And there was one all-pervading enormous problem, which had to be tackled before any serious farming could begin.

The farm was mainly divided into small, hedged fields, sloping away from the farmhouse and its buildings. But, over two hundred huge elm trees were growing in the hedges. Mary stood under one, peering up into its vast tangle of branches. Even bereft of its leaves it threw a huge circle of shade upon the ground – *and there were two hundred of them!*

"These are our biggest headache," Mary said in dismay.

"It'll have to be our first job," said Harold, "It's too big for us. I'll get a contractor in!"

Mary knew this would not be a problem. Moving in his high-up agricultural circles Harold was bound to know someone.

"This is good land, but the trees have poached it. We're going to need a mountain of muck!" he said.

Mary smiled. She was no stranger to muck spreading!

As yet, there was no livestock on the farm, but Harry's father had promised them some Shorthorns, the last vestiges of his herd.

The couple also had plenty of offers of furniture. Harold's parents would soon be leaving their large house at Middletown Farm, so there would be plenty surplus.

The Nortons were planning to retire on a small but comfortable pension. Until they found a suitable home they had arranged to move in with Mrs Norton's sister Kate, at her home at Cutterne Mill, and some of their furniture was already stored there. Mary and Harold were told to take as their own anything which would be of use to them.

A week after their visit to see Tan House Farm, Harold turned up at 'Oakboro' to take Mary to a dance. As she walked down the path toward the garden gate, Mary noticed a smart little black Ford Eight parked at the kerb.

"Whose is that?" she asked.

"It's ours," said Harold, a broad beam spreading on his face. "I bought it for a hundred quid from my friend Geoffrey at the garage at Newent. He assured me it's a good little runner!"

Mary had been taught to drive by her father and she was delighted that she and Harold now had a car of their own. She hitched up her evening skirt and stepped gracefully in. They really were up and coming!

***

In the days before her wedding Mary had much to do. She took the pretty blue crepe fabric to her dressmaker for a fitting. The kindly woman decided to add an unusual touch to the back of the dress... a small panel of delicate hand-smocking, which would be visible as the bride stood at the alter. From the same material a little Juliet skull-cap was fashioned, and Mary bought a piece of pretty pale brown net to use as a small veil.

The wedding was to be held at her very own Church of St Barnabas, which had been newly built on the vacant plot next door to 'Oakboro'. No cars would be needed to transport guests to the reception, because that was to be held at home.

Mary had two young cousins, Betty and Maisie who lived in Liverpool, and who had been pastry cooks. A few days before the wedding, they moved into 'Oakboro' and set to work to prepare the wedding feast for thirty guests. The house was soon alive with activity and the smell of baking, as the piles of food were swiftly produced and moved to the pantry. Plates were piled high with savouries and little cakes, all swathed in clean white cloths. Mary was excited and kept lifting the cloths to have a peep.

"Mary!" scolded her mother. "Leave those eatables alone!"

Great tables lined the dining room, covered by all her mother's best white cloths, in readiness for the feast, and the centre-piece was to be the great white iced wedding cake with a silver knife laid beside it. All was ready for the most exciting day of Mary's life!

Saturday the third of March 1945 dawned bright and clear. It was a perfect spring day, with primroses and the last of the snowdrops blooming in the garden. Downstairs in the sitting room a huge bouquet of spring tulips lay in a long cardboard box, alongside another for Kay, Mary's bridesmaid.

Mary was told firmly to stay in her bedroom where she was to dress. The window was as usual, thrown wide open. Suddenly, the little scrap of brown net, which was to be her veil, blew away into the garden below.

"My veil! My veil!" Mary screamed down the stairs and soon there was pandemonium as everyone ran round the garden, searching for it.

"Stay up there!" her mother shouted as Mary stood at the top of the stairs, distraught. At last the veil was located in a flower-bed, and returned to the bride.

Then, before she knew it, the moment arrived, and Mary swept down the stairs in her beautiful dress, her golden hair brushed and gleaming beneath the dainty cap, the veil lending her face an air of mystery. She was bursting with love for her Harold and longing to marry him, and her joy gave her a stunning beauty. Her father was waiting at the bottom, and he let out a little gasp as he saw her. Now he was really lost for words! His usual 'Oo-ah' became a long drawn out, "Ooooo! My word!" as he gently laid the bouquet in her arms.

Suddenly, they were out in the welcoming sunshine, and Kay, her friend of a million years, was behind her as, supported lightly on her father's arm, Mary walked the short distance across the garden to the church next door, and into her brand new life!

They came from the sunlight into the cool darkness of the church, and Mary's breath caught in her throat as she saw Harold standing at the front with his best man, good old Frank Dunn from Young Farmers, standing stiff and anxious beside him.

Harold looked so tall and straight and strong. His bright red hair, caught in a stream of sunlight from the windows, shone a rich gold, and he looked so smart in his dark suit. Mary thought him a farmer to the core, and the thought thrilled her, because that was what she desired!

All at once her father's hand was gone from her arm, and for a fleeting moment she felt alone, but then Harold was beside her, and her heartbeat began to slow. She was quite calm as the vicar welcomed them.

She heard the time-honoured words. "Dearly beloved..."

She did not join in with the hymn, although she would have liked to. Then she was facing Harold, holding one of his hands as they made their vows to each other. "In sickness and in health..."

Goodness, there was no time for ill health running a farm! Mary was looking deeply into Harold's eyes, and he was slipping the ring upon her finger.

Suddenly she was back at 'Oakboro' amongst a hubbub of chatter. Cards, telegrams and presents seemed to be piled everywhere. Someone put a sandwich into her hand. It was her mother with a concerned whisper. "Better eat something, darling. It will steady your nerves."

Frank, looking so dashing in his Sunday suit called out that the cake must be cut. It was covered in white icing. Many friends must have chipped in all their sugar rations to provide it, and Maisie had made a grand job of the decoration!

Harold's hand covered Mary's as the knife slid through the cake, and afterwards, when the cake had been cut into portions Mary called out, "Come on everyone! You must have a piece!" Her eyes were sparkling and she was enjoying every minute!

When no one was looking she picked up the little silver shoe, which had topped the cake and slipped it into her pocket. Sixty years later, Mary has it still!

She was surprised to find she didn't have any nerves. As she stood in the garden for the photographs, she and Harold could have been two Vikings, so striking was their colouring. They were surrounded by loving souls, and it was all wonderful; but Mary was longing for the time when she and Harold would be alone.

Later, she went up to her bedroom for the last time and changed into her oh so dependable smart brown tweed suit for the going away. Such things that suit had seen... the Usk Agricultural College, a world war, sightseeing in Cambridge, trips to market in Gloucester, and now it was to go with her to Tan House Farm! The blue dress was folded into her suitcase. It would be useful if a dance came their way on the honeymoon.

As the sky bled into a glowing splendour of red and gold the hire car drew up to take them to the station for the journey to their honeymoon in Torquay. Mary took her father's hand and led him into the relative privacy of kitchen. She wanted to give him a kiss.

"Thank you," she said.

"Oo-ah! What for?"

"For everything Dad!" she said, "the wedding, the farm, my life!"

"He'd better look after you." That was a grand speech for Fred, and Mary could see that he meant it.

Then there was her mother, standing in the doorway trying to pretend there were no tears in her eyes. They briefly touched hands, but it was an awkward moment. Sadly, there was still that strange reserve between them, that indefinable distance which had come upon them after Edith had returned from hospital so many years ago, and which was to rob them of warmth in their relationship right to the end of Edith's life.

"I wish you well," she said.

And then they were in the front garden, and Mary and Harold were being helped into the car. There was no confetti, for such fripperies were not to be had in post-war Britain. But everyone was cheering and shouting and waving them off.

The car pulled away, but a few yards up the road Mary looked down into her lap with dismay.

"Harold!" she cried, "I've forgotten my handbag!"

The poor driver had to return to the house, the handbag was found, and the waving off had to be done all over again!

As she settled back in the luxurious seat, Mary wanted to giggle, but Harold could not see the humour of it. How she wished in her heart that he could! Still, it felt good to snuggle close to him in the back of the car.

The couple boarded their train for Torquay just as twilight was falling upon their perfect day. Their suitcases were heaved to the netting rack above them, and Mary was soon cheered by Harold's strong arm about her. They sat in the happy huddle of those in love, often looking into each other's eyes. Occasionally Harold took her hand and squeezed it, and knowing looks passed between them.

There was an elderly lady sitting near them in the train, and when they arose to alight at Torquay, she said meaningfully, "I wish you all the best."

Mary and Harold looked at each other. "Oh no!" they said together, *"Are we really that obvious?"*

They had booked into a nice little boarding house. Most of the hotels had been commandeered for war work as government and military offices, and they had not yet been restored to their normal use.

Mary wanted to see the sea... immediately! Living as she always had, in the centre of England, she was always excited by the ocean. Harold grumbled a little about the weight of the cases, but smilingly agreed. They stood for a happy ten minutes on the seafront, looking across the harbour to the dark waters. It was a chilly night, but neither noticed. A little ripple of breeze ruffled Mary's hair. She stood, so much shorter than her husband, and with her slender form she felt almost like a child beside him.

He'll take care of me, she thought, as they kissed, and then added in her mind, but he needn't worry! I'm not afraid of hard work!

After a short while they went in search of their lodgings and the enveloping night.

***

The honeymoon was a great success. They were blessed with the most delightful spring weather. The nights were frosty, and in the morning there was always a sparkle of rime on the little lawn outside the guest house, but the days were sunny and warm with clear blue skies.

The couple spent their days walking, either taking a simple picnic or enjoying sandwiches in little tea shops. Food was still mostly simple in those days of post-war rationing and many places were shut down because it was out of season.

Sometimes they climbed the cliffs and walked, over-looking the sea, or took the paths inland to ramble through pretty, violet-studded lanes. Sadly, there were few primroses. The cold spring frosts in that part of Devon had held them back.

One day they managed to hire a little rowing boat and went bravely out on the sea. But it was very choppy and Harold was no great oarsman, so they quickly came back again! One evening Mary put on her wedding dress and they went to the theatre to see a variety show. But most of all they enjoyed the walks, and each other's company, and the unaccustomed pleasure of snuggling up in the big double bed at nights.

On their final morning Mary awoke early and padded over to the window. It was a golden spring dawn with frost lying thick under the hedge.

"We're so lucky," she said as Harold stirred and sat up to see her, "a March honeymoon, and not a single drop of rain!"

They knew they must leave the little guest house, but neither minded. They were excited at the prospect of moving into the farm!

When they returned to Gloucester they spent a fortnight with Mary's parents at 'Oakboro', sleeping in the big guest bedroom.

On their first night, Mary's mother fussed around, making sure they were comfortable. Once, she looked in on them, her face full anxiety, but when she saw that they were happy she went away, looking relieved.

One evening Mary peeped in at her dear little room. It remained, as always, with its coverlet and curtains, and her old familiar dressing table, which had once held her brushes and toiletries. Now it looked bare. She tip-toed in and opened her wardrobe door. Not a thing was left inside, except an empty coat hanger.

Oh well, she breathed, things move on!

Outside on the landing she met Harold coming up the stairs. He was wearing his evening jacket and his hair was brushed, gleaming.

"Come on," he said. "Have you forgotten? We're going to a hop tonight with Young Farmers. It's a special band. Someone famous! I think it's Joe Loss!"

Childhood memories put aside, Mary went gladly to change for the evening, but she knew that she would never truly forget her young days in this house, and all that her parents had done for her.

CHAPTER TWENTY-TWO

TAN HOUSE FARM

In the 1940s, Lady's Day, the 25th of March was the traditional day for moving into farms. It was a date respected by owner and tenant farmers alike, so it happened that, as Harold's parents moved out of Middletown Farm, the newly-weds were moving into Tan House.

"Father will milk the Shorthorns for the last time this morning," Harold said to Mary as they opened the farmhouse door, "and then he'll bring them over to us later in the lorry. From then on they are ours."

The day was bright and clear, with a blustery March wind sending small white clouds scudding across the hills. But Mary was far too busy to think about the fresh spring weather. She was just relieved that it was not raining.

Their furniture arrived by van and was hauled into place by Dad and Harold whilst Mary and her mother swept and dusted and cleaned. As usual Edith had flung all the windows wide. She was hanging some curtains in the living/dining room and Mary was upstairs, making the big double bed.

Mary was pleased with the well proportioned room. From the window she could view her land, including the big meadow, which sloped away to the little River Pill.

I'll be able to see a great deal better once the elms are gone, she thought.

The couple would be stepping back almost into Victorian days. There was no mains electricity at Tan House, and she would have to depend on candles and oil lamps until they could afford to have it connected.

The previous occupants had turned a bedroom into a bathroom. It was fitted with a hand basin and a lavatory, but it contained only an old galvanised tin bath, which had to be filled, and emptied by hand, using an enamel slop bucket. All water had to be pumped up into the house from a well under the flagstones of the outside yard and heated by the old iron range in the kitchen. A further lavatory had been squeezed into the cupboard under the stairs, but it was dark and uninviting!

It's just as well, thought Mary, that we will be too busy to linger!

They would have to manage with the house as it was because the priority was to update the cowshed and dairy.

The laundry arrangements also were Dickensian. Mary had given it considerable thought. First a fire would have to be lit beneath the big copper in the washhouse, and the washing hauled in, sheets and towels first, then their clothes, and finally their milking smocks. Afterwards, the 'soup' of water, would be used to wash the stone-flagged floors of the kitchen and washhouse.

When dry the laundry would be ironed, using old-fashioned flat irons heated on the kitchen range. It was all a big step back in time for a young woman used to the home comforts and modern amenities of 'Oakboro'.

I'll just have to get on with it! This was now Mary's familiar maxim in the face of adversity!

She heard Harold's father in the yard below, and from the window she saw him lifting out a sack. Mary knew it contained a big grey cat given to them by the Nortons to help keep down mice and rats. Eager to set it free, she rushed downstairs and grabbed the sack.

"Careful! It might scratch you!" warned Harold's father.

Mary grabbed a sharp knife and was cutting through the rope, which bound the sack when she slipped, and sliced the tip clean off her finger.

Blood spurted, and the grey cat shot out of the bag like lightning. Mary delicately picked the little tip of severed finger from the dusty sack and popped it back onto the bleeding wound.

"Mum!" she called out, "I'm in a bit of bother!"

Edith came running.

"Oh my goodness!" she exclaimed, her face blanching,

"what have you done?"

Harold also heard the commotion and came over.

He took one look at Mary's finger.

"Oh dash it!" he said: "Now we'll have to go to the doctor's. You better get into Dad's car!"

Edith produced a tattered length of bandage and wrapped it round, holding the piece of severed flesh in place. Mary watched miserably as the blood immediately came seeping through. She was beginning to worry that it might be a few days before she would be fit for all the hard work which lay ahead. It hurt too but Mary would not complain.

The front seat of the car was piled high with folded sacks and feed bags, so she had to climb into the back. She sat in silence as Harold drove her into Berkeley to Dr MacDonald. Looking at the back of her husband's neck she sensed he was disgruntled at this inconvenience, but he sounded kindly enough as he helped her out and escorted her into the surgery.

Fortunately the doctor was at home, but he proved to be a dour Scotsman, and he frowned as he undid the makeshift bandage.

"Well young woman, what have you done to yourself?" He surveyed the wound with its morsel of flesh perched on top. It had stopped bleeding but it throbbed. Mary bit her lip.

"How did this happen?" asked the Scot.

"I was letting the cat out of the bag," said Mary, with a suppressed, nervous giggle.

"We're moving into our farm today," said Harold, "and my wife was using a knife to undo the sack which held our farm cat."

The doctor and Harold shared a long meaningful look. Mary could hear them thinking: *How inconvenient!*

But Harold said kindly, "Well, accidents happen at the worst of times. The important thing is to get it fixed."

The doctor indicated to Mary that she should go over to the sink in the corner and hold out her hand.

"This may sting a bit," he said as he took a brown bottle from a shelf. It was iodine, and as he poured it over her injured finger the pain was so bad that Mary nearly fainted.

The doctor told his blanched patient to sit down and she

turned her head away whilst he stitched the piece of finger back in place and applied a clean bandage.

"Well, young woman," he said, "I've done all I can. We shall have to wait and see if it takes!"

"Oh it will!" said Mary sharply, rising to her feet ready to go.

Harold gently steadied her arm and as they left the surgery she was beginning to feel better. The thought occurred to her that she had been initiated into the farm by blood. She said as much to Harold.

"Hum" he said, "It's taken up a fair bit of time."

But he moved the sacks so that she could sit with him in the front of the car and, on the way back he gave her knee a quick squeeze and said: "Well done! You were very brave!"

Back at the farm Mary's mother had prepared a picnic of bread and ham; and a tin of home-made cakes stood open on the table. Mary, her sore finger stuck out of harm's way, battled for the first time to light the 'Valour' stove.

The kitchen reminded her of the saddle room at Little Wallsworth Farm, where she had seen the men eating their 'bate'. It was quite dark, lit only by one small-paned window, but the table had been spread with a cheerful red and white check oil-cloth, and the crockery was set out ready. Mary carefully poured some paraffin into the stove and lit it. A little flurry of black smuts came from of the ventilation chimney and settled greasily on the stove. A few even drifted over to the table. Mary wiped them with the dishcloth, but they left little black smears.

"Wretched things!" she said. "I'll clean them up later."

The kettle boiled quite quickly and Mary was just filling the teapot when her father stuck his head through the door, his sleeves rolled up, dirt to his elbows.

"Are you going to have a quick wash at the pump?" she asked.

Dad said his usual 'Oo-ah', and vanished. Mary reflected fondly that he had probably been working in the cowshed again. Until the concrete floor was laid they would be milking out in the field, and she knew the job would take months. The old earth floor had to be dug out first!

They all met in the living room to eat, but just as Mary was biting into her sandwich she heard the lorry arriving with the cattle. She and Harold ran out into the yard.

"Where do you want these?" It was George Norton, yelling through the wound-down window of his lorry.

Harold pointed to the field nearest the house and George reversed his vehicle against the open gate, leapt from the cab and struggled to let down the ramp. All three of them urged the cattle out with sticks, and the Shorthorns, nervous from their journey, lurched down into the field.

"They should be settled by milking time!" said George.

Mary hoped they would be. She was the one who would have to catch them and get them milked! And her finger was hurting more than ever!

The afternoon passed quickly, in a flurry of jobs. As twilight was falling Mary peeped into the kitchen. Her mother was there, setting out a supper of cold ham and bread and butter, which she had brought with her from 'Oakboro'. Two candles burned on the windowsill and Edith's hair shone grey-blonde by the light of the oil lamp. Mary thought it all very lovely.

Harold came in looking flustered. "I'd better do the afternoon milking," he said. "You can't do it Mary; not with that finger of yours!"

Mary felt a stab of guilt. She knew that Harold had been depending on her to do it alone, this first time.

But he was smiling. "Come on," he said. "Let's go together. It will be quicker anyway!"

He took hold of her uninjured hand and led her away into the gathering dusk. His hand felt warm and strong.

Mary brightened. She loved her husband when he was in these cheerful moods. He couldn't help being quick tempered. Being born into farming means a hard life, and after all, he had his wonderful flaming red hair. He was so handsome and hard working. Mary wanted to kiss him that minute but she knew it would have to wait.

They walked hand in hand to their little makeshift dairy. There was no milk cooler, and cobwebs hung in swathes from the windows and walls.

"We'll have to get this place up to date," grumbled Harold. "It's urgent!"

Mary smiled and Harold took his young wife in his arms and gave her the kiss she had been longing for.

"Now Mary," he said kindly, "Don't go getting that bandage mucky. We don't want your finger infected. There's too much to do!"

He popped a further gentle kiss onto the bandage, and despite his tiredness, Mary saw that he had a twinkle in his eye.

It's wonderful to be in love, she thought!

She handed him the stool and a milking pail. Into another bucket she dropped a damp cleaning cloth wrung out in 'Deosan', the new disinfectant for farmers. They also took a small bucket containing some concentrate, as a 'bribe' for the cows.

As they set out to the home paddock Mary's emotions were an odd mixture of euphoria and nervousness. Would they be able to catch the cows?

But she need not have worried. They were calm animals with full, swinging udders, and keen to be milked, and besides, they knew Harold. As the couple walked up to them the cows raised their heads and gave them both a long, hard look. Harold tipped the concentrates onto the grass and stood absolutely still. The cows shuffled around picking up the food, and he carefully approached one and sat down beside it.

"Alright, old thing," he said as he gently wiped the udder and teats, and began milking. The cow took absolutely no notice, evidently much pleased with the lush grass.

When Harold had finished he moved onto the next. As the buckets filled, Mary took them to the dairy and poured the milk into the waiting churn.

It was almost dark by the time she returned to the dairy with the final pail of milk, but she felt along the lintel and found the waiting box of matches which she knew had been placed there by her father. She lit the Tilley lamp and hung it from a hook just as Harold came in with the last pail. They were pleased with the yield and knew that they could expect even more at the morning milking. Harold sealed the lid on the very first Tan House milking!

There was an air of celebration as the couple walked through the spring twilight, back to the farmhouse. Edith had lit the oil lamps and cheerful golden light shone from the kitchen window, sending a homely glow across the yard, and Mary could hear her father clattering in one of the outbuildings, putting tools away. The wind had dropped and the first star was out, twinkling above the elms.

Later that night, when everyone had gone home, Harold drew the heavy iron bolts on both doors and the couple went up to bed. The room was dim with candlelight. It reminded Mary of the night she had arrived at her uncle and aunt's house after her mother had been taken ill at Aunt Sue's funeral, many, many years ago. There had been candlelight then too, in her Cousin Joan's bedroom. Dear Joan! Mary remembered how she had tickled her feet to make her laugh! How strange that she should think of it now!

But here she was, in a different life. The one she wanted so much. She climbed into bed and pulled the blankets snugly round them both as Harold snuffed out the candle. They were utterly tired and neither could imagine how they would have coped without the support given so generously by their parents.

"Well my girl," said Harold. "It's been quite a day, hasn't it? What with your poor finger and everything. We're all set now, and we're going to make a go of it!"

"I'm so dead beat I don't know how on earth I'm going to get up for the morning milking," said Mary.

"You've got to!" said Harold. "Time, tide and the milk lorry wait for no man!"

"Nor woman," said Mary, but her words were lost in a huge yawn.

"No canoodling tonight," smiled Harold. "We'll have to give it a break!"

It was delicious lying safe and warm, cuddled against her husband's broad back as waves of drowsiness swept over her. Just before she dozed off she heard an owl cry, somewhere above the elms.

Mary awoke to the sound of the alarm clock. Harold rolled out of bed with the alacrity of a trained soldier but she had to lie, blinking into the darkness for a few moments until her thoughts settled. She knew she was at Tan House Farm, and the realisation pleased her, but she also felt she could sleep for hours!

"Come on," Harold grumbled amiably. "We have to get the churns down on the stand before the lorry gets to us!"

This, Mary knew, was the truth, and it was to become the pivot of their lives, every day they lived at Tan House!

She was no stranger to the morning milking as she had done it for years at Little Wallsworth Farm. But she was still so dreadfully tired! She also knew that she and Harold had to make their own living, and there was no one to stand in for them if they felt tired or ill. The tyranny of the milk lorry had entered her life!!

They both tugged on their clothes and went downstairs, Harold leading the way by the light of a candle.

"We ought to call this Stone Age Farm," joked Harold. "I can't get used to creeping about by candlelight!"

"You don't creep *anywhere* in those great big boots," retorted Mary.

Outside there was the merest hint of light in the sky but the weather had changed to a cold, dreary drizzle.

Mary lit the oil lamp. The kitchen was cheerless. The big iron range stood unlit, the coke in the hopper, and roughly chopped logs stacked against its side.

Harold was poking around in a box he had just taken down from a shelf.

"Ah! Here it is!" he said, withdrawing a drooping leather object.

"It's a finger stall," he said. "I knew we had one. If you put this over your bandage, it will keep it protected. I rather thought you might start the milking!"

They had agreed that they would always share the morning milking; so it came as a shock to know she was to do it alone on this first day, and with the added problem of her injured finger.

Mary watched as he popped the leather stall over her finger and knotted the two tattered-looking straps around her hand.

"It's fine," she said.

She noted that the drizzle had turned to rain, which was now beating against the window, driven by a cold March wind.

"I'll get the range going," said Harold. "I think we should run it all the time. It will give us some warmth and you can put in stews and things to cook whilst we are out in the fields."

241

Mary nodded.

She didn't dwell on the fact that the testy old range would be, for a long time, their only source of heat; and she did not know that on cold winter days they would lie down on the rug in front of it for their love-making, as it was the only warm place in the house.

"I'll just light the 'Valour' and put some bacon in," she smiled. "Mum said it would be an idea, so that when we come in from milking our breakfast will be cooked."

"Sounds good!" agreed Harold, who was busy screwing up newspaper and poking it into the range firebox.

Mary opened the galvanised mesh door of the cupboard her father had made for her in the wall, and laid four thick rashers on a tin baking tray.

"I'll do the bread and butter when I get back."

"Go on Mary, get going. We must have the milk down by eight!"

Mary put on her oilskins and went out into the rainy dawn. Soon she was in the field, wiping the udder of the first cow. She laid her cheek against the animal's side, grateful for the warmth. The milk began to splash into the pail, and the familiar rhythm of it brought a feeling of calm. The rain dripped from her nose and streamed down her rubber overalls, but Mary was impervious. This was her routine, the life, which she loved. It might be uncomfortable, but she could watch the dawn wash the clouds in soft grey light, and the feel of the rain on her face would wake her up.

It wasn't long before she saw Harold striding down the field to help. He lugged the milk to the dairy whilst she milked the final cow. They had a method, which they used, from the very start. As they worked, the yield from each cow was tipped into a larger bucket, with a lid over it. This was a precaution, which prevented double wastage if the next cow managed to get a foot in the bucket and soil the milk. Every bucketful meant money and was vital to their economy!

Mary joined Harold in the dairy. He clipped on the lids and man-handled the two churns into the trailer to take them down to the stand by the farm gate. Their first produce was on its way!

Mary rinsed out the pails and cloths in the trough on the

stone-flagged walkway by the kitchen, and set them in the make-shift dairy to dry.

She went back into the kitchen. The range was burning, but it did little to take the damp coldness off the room. There was a wooden airing rack over the range, which could be let down by means of two rope pulleys. She rubbed her overalls quickly down with a towel, and then draped them over the rack to dry out. She peeled off the grubby finger stall and hung that there too. She was pleased to see that the bandage was still dry.

The kitchen was full of the smell of crisp bacon. She took the rashers from the Valour oven, slid them onto two plates and put them on the range to keep hot whilst she made big mugs of sweet tea, and buttered the bread.

The rain was lashing at the kitchen window as Harold came in, wet and dripping. She helped him out of his overalls and they both sat down at the wooden table for their breakfast.

Both sets of parents were coming over to help again and they all planned to spend the time working on the outbuildings.

"I'm afraid it's you for the rest of the milking today," said Harold, using a hunk of bread to wipe the bacon grease from his plate. "There's too much heavy stuff to be done. How's your finger today?" he added as an afterthought.

"It's fine," Mary lied.

"I might start shifting some of those empty beer bottles from the wash house," she said, thinking it would not be too difficult to keep her finger out of harm's way!

"It's a damn nuisance that we have to milk in the field until we get the cowshed floor concreted," said Harold. "The old boy might have been alright doing it in there with all the mud and muck, but it won't meet today's regulations."

Mary nodded. During the war farming had been literally 'cleaned up'. All manner of rules and regulations had come in to improve hygiene and increase production. It was imperative for them to modernise and vital that they buy a milk cooler for the dairy.

"Dad says the cowshed is going to be his first job," she replied.

She was already on her feet again, putting their dishes into the stone sink. The range had done nothing to heat the water.

She had to shake 'Vim' onto the dishes in an attempt to remove the grease. Such primitive living conditions meant extra work, and she had to do it all with one hand, trying to keep her wretched finger out of the way.

"I'm getting the contractors in to fell the elms next week," Harold said. "It's our first big job."

He glanced out of the window: "Thank God, the rains stopped!"

It was fully light now, and a weak, watery sun was trying to break through.

Just as Mary was putting away the dishes she heard her parents' car drive up in the yard.

Thank heavens, Mary thought, now we'll have some help!

CHAPTER TWENTY-THREE

TAN HOUSE TRIALS & TRIBULATIONS

The tree-fellers arrived the following week, just as Harold had promised. Mary watched as more than a dozen men spilled out of two lorries.

"You keep well away," said Harold. "It's going to be dangerous!"

The men began work on the elms in the nearer field, and later Mary ran down there, bearing flasks of tea and slices of cake which her mother had baked.

It was a brutal scene. The men had set up an iron winch and were wrapping a tree in chains. The air was full of shouts, the clanking of the links and the whine of the winch, whilst all the time a dismal rain fell, turning the land beneath to a sea of mud.

In the battle between machine and mighty tree there could only be one outcome. The elm, shuddering in its death throes, toppled over, its roots ripped out of the ground in a tangle of soil and stones. Mary gasped at the speed of it and how all at once a space had opened up in the hedge. The men leapt onto the fallen giant with chainsaws and began stripping it of its branches, attacking it like a pack of wolves.

The governor suddenly noticed Mary and shouted out to her, "Keep well out of the way! Stay back, Miss!"

Then he saw that she was carrying flasks and he added more cheerfully, "Break time Lads!"

The sound of the chainsaws died away and stillness fell, broken only by the men's quietened voices and the steady patter of the rain all around them. From a little way off a blackbird resumed its April song.

As the men sat around eating and drinking, Mary went over to where the tree lay. She touched its splintered branches and noticed that the tips were swelling with buds, just like the oak tree, which had towered above the broken body of her Aunt Sue in the ill-fated car. That was another April, so many years ago.

Harold had struck a deal with the tree-fellers, that they could have most of the timber in exchange for a keen price for doing the job. The best of the long straight wood was loaded onto the lorries, and sent off for the furniture trade. Logs were made with the rest, but Harold did not want to lose *all* the timber. He arranged that a good quantity of logs was stacked in one of the Tan House barns. This fuel was to see them through many winters.

The great elms continued to fall. Sometimes the weather was quite hot, and the men stripped off their shirts. Mary stole admiring glances at their fine physiques and hoped that they didn't notice! Soon nothing was left of the two hundred ancient trees except a few broken twigs and rough circles of sawdust on the muddied ground where the fallen giants had lain.

At last Mary and Harold found themselves alone again. This was how they liked it. The lovers were free to delight in each other's company!

They walked round their farm to see the improvement. It was a lovely spring day and a shower had left the hedges sprinkled with diamonds. Harold slipped an arm around Mary's shoulders, one hand affectionately fluffing out the strands of her blonde hair. He thought she looked very sweet in her dungarees, with the sleeves of her jumper rolled up. Already her arms were browning from days spent in the open air.

"Well," he said. "They've done a good job!"

"I can't believe how quick they were!" replied Mary. "It's a different farm now."

She turned to slip her slender arms around his neck and was delighted when he gave her a kiss.

"It feels as if we've gained a lot of acres," she smiled.

"I ought to start putting them to good use," Harold said, drawing her close to him. He was thinking of the work to be done. A mountain of fence posts and drums of wire awaited him.

"Yes," said Mary, "and I've that awful dairy to scrub out. Our washing's piling up too. I have to face the washhouse and that dratted boiler soon!"

But in the balmy sunshine the work seemed a long way off. It was such a lovely warm day and they were so in love. They were standing beneath a hawthorn. Mary looked up into its froth of blossoms and the clear blue sky above.

Harold gave her one of his special looks, which always thrilled her. His eyes became a soft grey-green and it seemed as if he gazed into her very soul. They were united in a pure clear oneness by their passion for the farm and the life, which they had chosen; two people melding into one through a mutual dream.

"Let's lie down for a bit," he smiled.

And they did.

***

Over the next few months the couple adjusted to their new lives and their routine of toil. Their acres were thick fertile clay and there was already some excellent pasture, but Harold wanted to improve it. Behind the cowshed was a seven-acre field, which sloped slightly upwards towards Ham Green. He ploughed two acres of this for planting with kale and mangolds, and a further half-acre to grow vegetables for their own food.

He also wanted to plant a strip with high grade timothy and rye grass to provide a silage crop. They planned to have one of the very latest silos, a breast-high wooden contraption shaped like a vast open-topped barrel.

Shortly after the war, the Agricultural Executive Committee had been disbanded and the National Advisory Service (NAS) set up to help farmers modernise. Harold was 'well in' with these people and determined to follow their advice to the letter. The NAS officials were frequent visitors to the farm.

Harold was very friendly with an official called Mr Jones, whose chosen dictum was to travel all over the West Country, advising on potato growing. He was an expert on all the varieties and how to gain the best yield by growing them on the most suitable soils. Harold was not sold on the idea of potato farming for a living but he planted a few, and the expert was a frequent caller at Tan House Farm for a cup of tea and a chat. Mary saw him so frequently that she had dubbed him 'Potato Jones'.

She often had to run out to the fields in search of her husband with Potato Jones puffing behind her, his face red with exertion, and his soul bursting with some vital new potato fact.

Once, as she waved down her husband's tractor, she caught herself yelling: "Potato Jones is sprouting again!"

Sometimes Mary resented the NAS officials. She felt her own ideas were often overruled. She still nurtured a dream of build up a herd of pedigree Jerseys, but the officials insisted that Friesians were the cows to have. The breed made maximum use of the grazing, their yield was unbeatable, and their genes were so dominant that, when put to other breeds, even first-crosses came out virtually Friesian. This offered a cost-effective way to build up a herd, fast.

Mary could see this was true, but in her opinion the milk was inferior.

The officials had another new gambit up their sleeves. There was no need to own a bull. Artificial insemination (AI) was just coming onto the scene, and the officials would turn up with their little phials of Friesian semen and do the whole job for you!

"They're coming to do the cows, tomorrow!" Harold yelled on the first occasion.

Mary worked especially hard to get her jobs done so that she could watch. Matters did not proceed with as much speed and efficiency as predicted. Successful AI depends a great deal on speed of application, and George Norton's Shorthorns, intensely quiet but set in their ways, did not take kindly to the men in white jackets approaching them from the rear with their nasty little bottles! Mary heard a quiet 'thump' which indicated a well-aimed kick, and the air turned blue with some exceptionally expressive swearing!

Mary decided she had heard enough and retreated to the kitchen to make the tea. From the window she had a clear view of the big meadow, which sloped down towards the Berkley Pill. It was always calming to look on this pleasant view. Harold and the officials later came in, heading for the sink. In view of the matter they had just had in hand Mary was not pleased!

"Use the stone trough in the yard, gentlemen please!" she frowned.

The officials turned tail and headed obediently out of the kitchen.

But these events were in the future, as the couple toiled for their first months at the farm. And it wasn't all weariness. They found plenty of time for their canoodling in those heady days of their passionate love!

Every weekend Mary's parents came to help with the chores. Edith climbed out of the car with her big feather bed in her arms (she would not sleep without it), and the car was invariably loaded with tins of cakes and biscuits she had baked. Whilst the women worked indoors Fred laboured in the cowshed, digging out tons of the ancient mud and muck, which made up the floor. This was piled on the strip of land at the back of the barn. It seemed to grow unendingly, despite Harold's efforts at every spare moment to drag it away with the tractor and spread it on the fields.

Edith set up her treadle sewing machine and very soon a slice of the Norton's highly esteemed 'drawing room chintz' was converted into bedroom curtains. In between sessions with the Singer she baked and cleaned and mended, and the two women caught up on their gossip. Although over the years their relationship had become a little strained, these times in each other's company were enjoyable. Both she and Harold were 'only' children, so they benefited from a great deal of help and attention from their parents.

There was no vacuum cleaner at Tan House and Mary hated the clouds of dust, which filled the air whenever she attempted to clean the carpets with a dustpan and brush and Edith was often quick to grumble about the housekeeping standards at the farm. One practice upon which she particularly frowned was the young couple's method of disposing of their bath water.

They were still using the galvanised tin bathtub, which had no drainage, and after enjoying their soak they found it too arduous running up and down the stairs with the slop bucket, so they simply threw the dirty water out of the window!

"It just runs away over the flagstones," Mary pleaded when pressed about the matter. "It gives them a good old flush!"

Edith could not agree, and every time she had to walk over the watershed area she scowled at the soapy stains.

"Look at all this residue!" Edith complained. "And it's a right slippery mess every time it rains!"

Mary did not relent. Her daily grind was so constant that she had to take every possible shortcut.

By their first autumn things were much straighter. Fred had almost finished the dairy. He had laid a large area of the floor with new concrete and replaced the rickety old shelves with good strong ones. Knowing that the milk cooler was a legal requirement, Fred had lent them the money to buy one. The task of disinfecting the dairy was just one more for Mary to fit into her hectic day!

They were still milking the cows in the field and the autumn rains made everything so muddy. One morning Mary overslept, and this, as so often happens, set the mood for a difficult day. The situation was made worse by the fact that Harold had two important NAS officials coming to hear his latest report on their strip grazing scheme.

She put their usual rashers of bacon into the 'Valour' oven and they both went to fetch the milking things. On the way over to the field Mary tripped and one of the 'Deosan' cloths fell out onto the mud, so she had to go back to the dairy for another. She searched frantically.

"Oh blow!" she hissed, remembering, "I took them all up to the washroom yesterday!"

She had to run over to the washroom, pick out a cloth, fill a bucket from the stone trough, add the 'Deosan' and rinse out a cloth, all the time with one eye on her watch. It was getting late, and the milk lorry always came at eight!

At last she joined Harold in the field and they finished the milking. Harold was in a bad mood, frantic lest they should miss the milk lorry and lose a whole day's income.

They fled to the dairy. "We're running so late," he frowned, his hands clipping the lids down on the churns. "You know the NAS bods are coming. I've left all the paperwork in the kitchen. Make sure it's shipshape for me, would you Mary!

"For heavens sake, get a move on!" he added, as she stood there, flummoxed.

She fled to the kitchen, leaving her husband to rush the churns down to the milk-stand.

The thought of the bacon cheered her but as she opened the kitchen door she noticed a strange oily smell; and then her eyes took in the scene. A thick pall of sooty smoke hung in the air and everything in the kitchen was covered in smudgy black smuts. The 'Valour' had malfunctioned. It often did this, but not on such a mammoth scale.

Worse still, there was Harold's neatly written report lying on the table, blackened with soot.

Poor Mary didn't know what to do first. She was standing there panicking when Harold came in, wet from the drizzle.

"Good Lord," he said, taking in the chaos. "What have you done now?"

Mary bridled. It was so unfair!

"It's not my fault," she said. "The ventilation's gone wrong on the 'Valour'. The chimney must be blocked or something!"

"Well, we better try and get cleaned up." Harold was already searching around in a cupboard for the cleaning things while Mary threw open the door to let out the smoke.

The smuts were greasy and difficult to shift. As the couple tried to wipe them away they left dirty looking smears. It took a lot of elbow grease, and every surface in the kitchen had to be cleaned. Even the cups and plates on the dresser had to be taken down.

Suddenly Mary remembered the bacon. She opened the oven door and a further pall of black smoke poured out, just as the NAS officials announced themselves at the kitchen door!

Somehow Harold managed to stay calm and the meeting proved successful.

"Jolly rotten luck, old chap..." one said as they peered through into the kitchen before departing, "You're 'Valour' making such a damn mess. I've heard they often play up. You'll have to invest in one of those newfangled AGA things. I can send a salesman round if you wish. Jolly good report though. Carry on like this you two, and you'll be making a damn good living!"

After the officials had gone, Mary and Harold breathed a sigh of relief. They still had a bit more smut-clearing to do but they never did find out what made the 'Valour' malfunction. It worked perfectly the next time they lit it. Unfortunately it misbehaved again, every few months or so.

They had not yet saved enough cash to buy an AGA but the couple decided it should come pretty high on their priorities! Life was so hectic on the farm that they could not spare the time needed to keep cleaning the kitchen.

"It's a bind," Mary said.

"We've a living to make," scowled Harold. "You'll have to grin and bear it a bit longer!"

CHAPTER TWENTY-FOUR

SILAGE, CHICKENS AND 'FRIESIANS ARE BEST!'

The couple's grazing system was working well. Harold had fenced off a strip of pasture about 200 feet in length. A further electric fence was put across this, sectioning off about twenty feet, and this was moved, virtually daily as the cattle ate down the grass. When they reached the end, Harold sectioned off another 200-foot strip, and the cows ate their way along this. In this manner the pasture was slowly rotated, ensuring efficient grazing and allowing the grass time to recover. It was almost a return to farming methods used in medieval days, but with the addition of electric fencing.

Mary became adept at judging it. If the cattle were lying down chewing the cud she surmised that they were satisfied, but if they were gathered, peering at the greener grass over the fence, it was a fair bet they were hungry!

"Harold!" she would shout. "The fence needs moving again!"

In the spring they had planted small areas of kale and mangolds, but these would not be sufficient for the winter and the couple knew that they would have to buy in concentrates. The two acres they intended to plant in the autumn would ensure a much bigger crop for the following winter.

Harold had wasted no time in planting a large plot of vegetables for their own use. These germinated well, but so did the weeds!

The couple went out into the field to hand hoe the kale and mangolds, but the early summer weather was so wet that the soil soon churned to a sea of mud beneath their feet. As they uprooted the weeds with their hoes they found they were treading them back in with their boots.

"Harold!" Mary said in despair. "We're planting the rotten things again!"

Harold looked at his wife, thin and diminutive, with the rain streaming down her face, and her dungarees and mackintosh topcoat plastered in mud, and thought what a tough little thing he had married.

He said, "We'll just have to do the best we can!"

Mary nodded and got on with it. There was only an hour to go till the afternoon milking!

By May they were ready to experiment with their first crop of silage. In the autumn Harold planned to plough up another strip and plant it with high quality grasses, but for the first year he decided he would cut a crop from the existing pasture.

Silage making was another new innovation for farming, and the silo was duly delivered and hauled by Harold's tractor into the field. A few days later the NAS officials arrived to offer support and advice.

The weather had cleared up and it was such a lovely May day that Harold and Mary were in fine spirits. In fact they were inside the silo enjoying a passionate kiss and a cuddle when the officials turned up, unannounced!

"What's this, then?" laughed one of the men. "It's like the bloody Garden of Eden here!"

Mary blushed and smoothed down her hair and tucked it back under her headscarf, whilst Harold commented what a nice time of year it was.

"Um... yes indeed," said one of the men. "Depends what you're up to!"

After the officials had intoned their advice and departed, the couple collapsed in laughter.

"We better watch ourselves in future!" said Harold.

"Yes indeed," said Mary. "It could be Potato Jones next time... and you know what a hawk eye he is."

"Shall we finish what we started?" said Harold with a gleam in his eye. Mary knew he wasn't referring to their silage making!

But it was not such a laughing matter over the next few days. The weather turned unseasonably cold with a biting wind. Mary was positioned inside the silo spreading the grass around and treading it down as Harold pitchforked it in to her.

It was alright whilst the crop was still low. She was quite sheltered inside the wooden walls. But once she reached the top she was blasted by the full force of the wind. She stood aloft the heap, the grass flying past her in the gale, her eyes streaming. The silage had to be built up with intermittent layers of molasses, and this sticky substance added to the mess on her boots and hands. They were both glad when the job was done and it could all be covered by a large tarpaulin.

"Now it just has to cook all summer," said Harold with satisfaction.

"Jolly good luck to it!" said Mary.

There was a henhouse at the farm and the couple invested in a flock of ten Rhode Island Red/ Leghorns.

Mary loved to see the birds pecking around in their large run, and it was the sweetest of pleasures to search in the nesting boxes each day for the lovely fresh eggs. One soft summer morning Harold followed her out to the home paddock and stood watching. She plucked an egg, still warm from its bed of straw, and pressed it to her cheek, looking back beguilingly at him. She was beautiful! Her skin was so bronzed by the sun that it made her eyes appear turquoise-blue.

One morning in August Mary made the hens a mash of vegetable peelings and bran. She spooned in a little molasses, a special treat much loved by them. The milking was finished and Harold was at work in the fields. Feeding the hens was always a special time for Mary, like a little ritual. She walked briskly through the paddock to the henhouse, light of heart and spirit.

When she saw what had happened she let out a cry of horror and threw up her hands. The pan of mash went spinning away on the breath of her screams.

The fox had raided the coop. Mary remembered locking the chickens into their house the evening before but the varmint had dug under the wire. His scratches and piles of earth told the tale.

One hen had been carried away but the other nine lay around in a scene of carnage! Feathers, entrails and mangled bodies lay everywhere. Mary went down on her knees and scrambled under the torn wire, hissing with rage as she counted the remains of her beautiful birds.

She ran out into the fields to Harold, flagging him down in his tractor.

"What on earth's happened?" he yelled.

Mary's face was streaked with mud and tears.

"Our hens!" she sobbed. "Such an awful sight!"

Harold had little sympathy. He knew all about the problem of foxes and poultry. To him it was just another farming frustration. But he had a few words with one of his NAS officials and a little while later a crate arrived, containing thirty, one-day-old chicks.

Mary peered at the fluffy yellow creatures, fascinated.

"They're a commercial enterprise," said Harold. "Keep 'em warm, feed 'em, and when they reach point of lay, sell 'em on. We'll make a tidy profit!"

The chicks were placed in a large cardboard box on top of the old iron range, and Mary nurtured them, feeding them chick-meal at first, and then choice kitchen scraps and mashes. They were growing well so Mary moved them into the henhouse. Her father had strengthened it by digging down around the run and burying more wire netting underground.

'Oo-ah', he had said when Mary remarked that the fox would never manage to dig under it.

He had also fortified the coop, putting thick timber spars across the door and securing the nest boxes with metal latches. It looked invincible!

Mary was jubilant. The hens continued to grow and their adult plumage began to come in. She planned to keep ten for herself and sell the other twenty. She already had customers waiting.

But then the fox struck again. He found a weak point where the wire butted against the hedge, and then he slashed at the house, exploiting a place where a piece of timber had rotted unnoticed.

Mary discovered her beautiful point of lay hens, massacred. After that, the Berkeley hunt was called in to kill the fox but it was a long time till the couple decided again to keep commercial hens. They kept just a few for their own eggs, and Mary checked the henhouse constantly.

During the Autumn Harold ploughed his two acre strip to

plant a bigger crop of mangolds and kale. He then went over it with the chain harrow, flattening the furrows and preparing the land for the seed.

The couple knew that, for their first year at the farm they would have to use a hand-drill for sowing. This contraption consisted of two wheels with rotating metal cups at two-inch intervals. The cups contained the seed, and a spike in front made the groove as the drill was pushed along the ground. It was slow, back-breaking work trudging up and down the field with this primitive, outdated machine. Harold planned to buy a modern seed drill which could be pulled by the tractor, as soon as they could afford it.

They owned the farm outright so there was no rent to pay, and their milk was bringing in regular cheques, but all new items of equipment had to be saved for. They were still hand-milking and Harold knew it would be many months before he could install modern milking machines.

One by one the Shorthorn cows ran dry and needed putting into new lactation. Each cow was turned out to graze on nutritious new pasture for a month before being impregnated by artificial insemination, using Friesian semen. In addition, they bought in some Friesian cows to increase their output.

"What about my Jerseys?" Mary moaned.

"NAS says Friesians are best," replied Harold. "You know it's true! Nothing yields half so well!"

"But Jerseys would increase the cream content," Mary reasoned. "Then you might get the extra five pence subsidy."

Harold grunted. He knew this was true.

"Well, perhaps later!" And that was all he would say on the subject.

CHAPTER TWENTY-FIVE

GOODBYE 'VALOUR' & A NEW USE FOR CURTAIN DOCKETS!

By spring Harold and Mary were well settled at the farm. Gradually the days lengthened and more daylight was available to work by. It was a life of almost unremitting toil, but Mary never complained.

Better get on with it was her philosophy! Her love and dreams were on the wing and she and Harold were both completely wrapped up in the farm and their passion for each other.

The mangolds and kale, which Harold had planted the previous autumn, had come through well, but once again, so had the weeds!

Mary was dismayed when she first stood in the two acre field looking at the rows stretching away before her, and knowing that just the two of them must hoe the lot!

"We'll never do it," she wailed.

"Yes we will," Harold insisted. "We can get in four hours before the afternoon milking!"

Mary bent her back to the task, working her way down the first row, but the thick clay stuck to her boots, and as she moved on she knew she was treading the weeds back into the mud, and like the season before, many would survive. She had done this work many times at Little Wallsworth Farm but never on such a daunting scale.

The weeks slipped into each other in an unbroken round of milking, cleaning and hoeing. But as the days grew brighter the sound of the birds and the beautiful rosy dawns were compensation. And it was always a relief at weekends when her parents came and Mary could ease off a little to spend time with them.

At last Fred had finished the cowshed. It now had a good solid concrete floor, and drainage channels to take away the water and muck. He had split the shed into twelve separate stalls with strong wooden partitions and a long manger, which ran the entire length of the building.

It was a great relief to milk inside. Harold and Mary filled the long manger with hay and soon the cows knew their own stalls and rushed in at milking time. The couple then clipped the cows into their restraining yokes and worked their way down the row, wiping udders and then milking. They took it in turns to track backwards and forwards to the dairy, filling the churns.

Whilst Harold was taking the churns down to the milk stand Mary had to release the cows from their yokes and drive them back to their allotted strip of grazing. Her last task was to flip back the electric fence and secure it. Only then could she and Harold meet up for breakfast.

After her bacon or porridge it was back to the dairy for Mary, to clean all the milking equipment, whilst Harold headed out for his morning's work in the fields.

Her other morning tasks depended on the time of year but there was always plenty to do! It could mean working out in the fields, hoeing, planting or muck spreading, or labouring in the house, cooking and cleaning or sweating over the washing in the old-fashioned outhouse, using Dickensian methods.

The couple always had their main meal at lunchtime, so this had to be prepared at some time during the morning hours. This entailed Mary running in and out, sometimes from the furthest boundaries of their land, so that she could prepare the vegetables, or check on the stew. She felt it was a good job they were up so early, or there would never have been enough time in the day!

But there were compensations. One spring morning, as she was washing the dishes, looking out of the kitchen window at the long meadow which sloped down towards the river, Harold came running in.

"Come and see!" he exclaimed, grabbing her and dragging her outside, her hands still wet.

He took Mary to the home paddock.

"I was going to get her in last night," said Harold: "I knew it was near her time. But look, she's calved all on her own in the field!"

There in the meadow, standing beneath the shade of a sycamore, stood one of their Shorthorn cows, and at her knee tottered a perfect little black and white calf, looking for all the world, like a pedigree Friesian!

"That's the Friesian genes for you," Harold laughed: "Dominant! And there'll be another four soon! That's the NAS semen package! Bang on time and true to form!"

Mary nodded, but she was still dreaming about owning some pedigree Jerseys.

April brought a spell of bitter cold, chilling rain. It made everything so difficult. The washing drooped miserably on the line under the veranda, the stove sulked, and out in the fields the thick clay turned to mire, spattered with endless kaki coloured puddles.

Mary set her jaw, pulled her hat down over her eyes, and simply endured. The thick mud found its way onto the paving stones on her walkway, and trips back and forth from the dairy, carrying the heavy pails, became a slippery business. Her boots were loaded with the stuff from the hoeing, and the bottoms of her trousers were stiff with it.

Farming intensively on such a small acreage brought endless problems. During spells of wet weather they could not risk the cows turning the pasture to a sea of mud, so they had to bring them in each night and leave them in their stalls in the cowshed.

One morning the milking took twice as long because the cows' rear ends were coated with dried-on mud. Mary lost count of the number of times she went back to the dairy to wash out the pails and rinse the udder cloths. Harold grumbled that they would miss the lorry.

"It's the blessed mud!" Mary hissed; and Harold could see from the look in her eye that he better not complain again!

They made the lorry, with only three minutes to spare!

"It was a close shave," grumbled Harold as he met Mary in the yard and went in for breakfast. It was raining so hard they longed to be in the dry, but as they opened the kitchen door they both let out a mournful: "OH NO!"

The wretched 'Valour' stove had malfunctioned again, and the kitchen was covered in black smuts. The filth lay, thick and oily on every surface. Even the plates Mary had set out on the table were blackened.

"Get your wet things off," she ordered, tugging at her own: "We're both starving. We'll eat first, and then clean this mess up!"

She quickly produced two more plates from the cupboard and they ate in grim silence.

Just as Harold was downing his second mug of tea there was a knock at the door, and on the step stood Potato Jones and a colleague from the NAS.

"Oh Hell!" said Harold, scraping back his chair. "I forgot they were coming!"

"Stove trouble again?" asked the official. "Or haven't you managed to clean it up since our last visit?"

With a mumbled expletive Harold vanished into the living room followed by the two men.

Tears streaked Mary's face as she dissolved some soda crystals in hot water and started on the mess. It was going to be a long job, and they would have to make do with boiled eggs for lunch.

Later, Harold joined her with a sheepish look on his face.

"Bit of luck them turning up like that," he said, but before Mary could explode, he threw a brochure down on the table and added: "Thought you might like one of those!"

It was Mary's turn to be wide-eyed.

"It's one of those AGA things," he said. "The very latest in country cooking. Potato Jones just happened to have a leaflet on board!"

Mary held it in one hand, reading it whilst wiping the table top.

"I thought you said it would be ages till we could afford one!" she said.

"Well," he said, "you've waited long enough!"

The big cream AGA arrived in due course and was assembled in the kitchen. Mary loved it at once. And shortly after, they had enough money for milking machines too. The couple's days of hand-milking were at an end. Of course, the machines were no use without electricity, so they had to be connected to the mains. Their oil lamps and candles were also consigned to the past.

"It's alright," said Harold. "The milk cheques have been regular and good. It's hard work I know, but we're up and coming, Mary."

Although their work was relentless, they liked to play hard too. They both loved dancing and so it became a point of issue to go to every NFU hop.

They also went to the cinema with Barbara Cane, Mary's friend from the Land Army days. Barbara had married and was living at Dursley, where there was a cinema. Her husband, John was still in the forces so she was glad of extra company.

Harold and Mary motored over on Saturday nights. Cuddled up in the warm cinema it was wonderful to escape the rigours of farming for a few hours, and enter the romance and glamour of the silver screen. Usually poor exhausted Harold dozed, sending the girls into fits of giggles at his tranquil little snores. If the snores grew louder they had to dig him in the ribs. He always woke up with a start, saying, "This film's terribly slow!"

"No it isn't, you silly whatsit!" the girls hissed in loud whispers. "You've been asleep!" Poor Harold usually dozed off again.

Jean & George Warren also stayed in touch and the two couples met at the NFU dances.

But her social life was causing a problem for Mary. The fashionable wardrobe of her pre-war days had long since shrunk to a few summery frocks and winter skirts. Her evening wear consisted of an out-dated sateen gown covered in fiscu net with huge puffed sleeves and rosebuds at the neck (which she had always detested anyway!) There was also her wedding dress, but Mary no longer liked its shade of blue. She decided that to make a change she would have it dyed a deeper blue, but it was not a success. It turned out more a sort of charcoal grey! She took it out of its tissue paper and discarded it in disdain.

"I have absolutely nothing to wear to the mid-summer ball," she announced to Harold, "and clothes are still rationed. What am I to do? I can't wear my velvet skirt and checked blouse any more. They've seen it since our engagement days!"

Harold looked up from his copy of Stockbreeder and said disinterestedly, "Potato Jones's wife gets dockets for furnishing fabric, and makes it into evening clothes."

"Harold! What a wonderful idea!" Mary exclaimed. "I never was much interested in curtains and I'm perfectly happy with the ones mum and I have made. But an evening dress is an entirely different matter!"

"You'll find time for making that, then," Harold said dryly.

"Of course I will!" Mary blazed.

She was as good as her word and, on their next trip into Gloucester she took her furnishing dockets and purchased a nice length of bottle green velveteen, which she soon made into a lovely gown.

On the night of the summer ball she swept down the farmhouse stairs to a slow whistle of appreciation from Harold. He was looking pretty smart too, in a black evening jacket and bow tie.

They were both carried away on a wave of euphoria! It was wonderful to be young and in love and enjoying their chosen life! They went out into the yard and Harold helped her into the car. He almost messed up her hair by insisting on a kiss.

"Not now!" she hissed with a wicked smile. "I want to stay glamorous!"

Their laughter soon died away. The Ford wouldn't start. It had become temperamental of late. "You'll have to get us going with the tractor again!" Harold said, flinging aside the starting handle.

"Oh, but Harold! My new dress!" moaned Mary, looking with dismay at the grease and muck on the tractor.

"Hitch it up, woman! I can't get the dratted thing going till you give it a jolt forward!"

Seeing it was useless to argue, Mary attached the tow rope, and pulling up her skirt, she scrambled on board the tractor. To prevent the folds of her gown swishing against the dirt she stood on the metal tow bar and skilfully reversed, looking back over her shoulder.

"What a woman!" yelled Harold above the din, as the car shot forward and the engine spluttered into life. "A circus performer too!

"Good girl!" he added. "Now get in quick before it conks again!"

Mary obeyed, undid the rope, dusted down her beautiful gown, and within minutes they were on their way to the ball. They left a lamp on in the farmhouse window to welcome them home. It gave out a cosy glow, a celebration and one more proof of their success on the farm.

As their second winter closed around them the couple could look with satisfaction at their improved circumstances.

The amount of feed they needed to buy in would be minimal. The rows of kale stretched away in the two acre field, and part of the mangold crop lay in a heap by the gate, clamped up with straw to keep off the frost, and the rest remained in the ground. The kale was cut daily; a wet job if it had been raining overnight. They also had a fair crop of their own hay and silage.

Their herd of cows had more than doubled and they had to do the milking in two shifts. Twelve took their places in the cowshed whilst the rest waited patiently outside in a little yard fenced round with electric wire.

In the house the hated 'Valour' stove was gone and the new cream AGA cooked their food efficiently, and dried and aired their clothes. They were also now connected to mains electricity and water. They still kept the 'old' iron range, as it heated the water and cost nothing to run, since they had such a good supply of logs.

Their apple crop was laid out in trays on the attic floor, and Mary's jams and pickles, prepared by her from their own fruit in the golden days of high summer, lined the pantry shelves in jewelled rows of garnet and gold.

"We're making a go of it, Mary, girl," Harold said.
And Mary knew that they were!

**History in the making! The Victory Parade in 1945 in
Gloucester! Mary's father is 3rd from front (nearest row.)**

Mary and Harold on their wedding day, March 1945.

Tan House Farm. Mary is seen far left.

Well-bred, Mary with one of her first calves.

Mary and Harold milking in the field at Tan House Farm before the cow shed was renovated.

Camping holiday in Cornwall. Poor Harold's legs sticking out of the tent became painfully sunburnt!

The children from Finlay Road Nursery School make a visit to Tan House Farm.

Holiday at Blue Anchor with Fred, Edith, Margaret and Linda.

Harold with Margaret and Linda at Bournemouth.

Linda's Christening with Margaret Grey (Godmother) in her 'new look' left, Harold (centre) and Mary (right.)

Fred Cooper, who kept bees and wanted to be a farmer.

**The Coronation Parade! Margaret on tricycle in front, Linda
on her trike, behind.**

A happy day at Weston-Super-Mare.

Mum's busy! Margaret and Linda have to amuse themselves!

**Harold and Mary, winners of the
Gloucestershire Grain, Root and Fruit Farmers
Competition for the Best Small Farm.**

The reality! A photo taken at around the same time, showing the strain of their relentless life of hard work.

Mary today, living on Exmoor with Barney her dog.

In his grandmother's footsteps! Mary's Grandson, Mark with his pigs.

Mary's Uncle Albert Oakley, the High Sheriff of Gloucester.

Mary's brother James, who died aged eight, before Mary was born.

CHAPTER TWENTY-SIX

A HARD WINTER

In the July of 1947 there was a short break between haymaking and harvest, and Harold suggested they might go away for a few days.

"Oh Harold! A holiday would be wonderful!" Mary said, "But what about the milking?"

"Dad and Mum will move in and look after things," he said. "We could probably be away about five days."

The couple headed for Wales. To save money they decided to sleep in the car, on a mattress, which was kept rolled up during the day. Any romantic notions that the holiday would be a second honeymoon were soon vanquished. Poor Mary had to sleep with her portion of the mattress jammed over the steering wheel!

It was a strange, unearthly experience to wake in the mornings with the mist and heather stretching away around them.

One day they decided to climb Mount Snowdon. They ascended by one of the more difficult paths but their busy lives had made them so fit that they reached the summit in just three hours. They stood by the cairn of stones gazing at the glorious view and swigging water from their bottles. They felt vastly superior to the trippers in their sandals and sunhats, who had come up by means of the rack-and-pinion-railway.

They started on their descent, which should have taken them far less time than the ascent, but their energetic climb had tired them out so much that it took just as long.

At last the car was in sight, in the car park below. Relieved and exhausted they rolled out their mattress and both immediately fell into a deep sleep. It was still daylight when they awoke.

"Goodness!" said Mary, rousing herself to tidy her dishevelled hair. "Whatever will people have thought of us? Sound asleep in the middle of a car park!"

"They can think what they like," said Harold, reaching for the primus and kettle.

***

1947 brought one of the most severe winters ever recorded in Britain. By late autumn the temperatures were dropping and every afternoon Mary lit the fire in their living room. She banked it up with coal and lugged in logs to burn throughout the evening. It meant they would have somewhere warm and cosy when they came in from the fields at the end of the day.

Just before they went up at night Mary switched on a small electric fire in their bedroom, and because the vast chilly bathroom was so uncomfortable the couple resorted to using a china jug and bowl in their room. Mary toiled up the stairs with the jug of hot water and a kettle so Harold could have a shave. They took it in good part, saying they were back to their first days at the farm!

"Shall we get out an oil lamp?" teased Mary. But Harold was not amused. She wished sometimes he saw the funny side of things. She often felt a little silly, reduced to giggles by something which amused her whilst Harold looked on, uncomfortable and straight-faced.

Well, Mary reasoned, No two people are ever completely alike, and I must take the rough with the smooth!

A continuing bone of contention between them was Mary's wish to build up a small pedigree Jersey herd.

"NAS says Friesians are best," said Harold in the now familiar argument. "And you know it's true!"

"But, at the very worst we could mix their milk in with the rest, and it would improve it," Mary once again insisted.

Harold couldn't deny this fact. The extra cream content might bring them in line for the government's subsidy of five pence extra per gallon. Mary knew her argument was sound and in the end Harold relented. They began to watch the stock reports for sales of Channel Island cattle.

Two weeks before Christmas some very highly bred pedigree Jerseys were listed to come up at Bristol market.

"Alright," Harold sighed: "We'll go. But my bet is they'll be way too expensive! We can't really spare the time, but if you insist!"

Three days before the sale the weather turned bitterly cold. The air crackled, and fern-like fingers of ice spread across the window panes. Harold brought the cattle into the cowshed where they pulled at their hay and stamped in the straw, their breath misting the air.

On the second morning the sky turned leaden and a devastating blizzard swept down on the whole of Britain. Feeding and milking the cattle became a nightmare. Mary, warmly padded with scarves and woollens under her coat, buffeted her way to the cowshed, with Harold grunting and moaning behind her. Even the heat from the cattle did little to warm the building. The wind howled in the rafters, tugging at the ancient roof and whirling driven snow beneath the tiles.

"Bloody hell!" said Harold. "I hope this little lot doesn't do too much damage!"

The milk froze in the churns and a thick white rime built up on the bare trees and hedges. Harold cleared a rough path across the flagstones but it was so slippery that Mary feared she might lose her footing. She was terrified of breaking a leg, because Harold would never manage without her! The farm's economy depended on her being in full work. She also worried that the pump would freeze and cut off their water supply. Harold lagged it with strips of sacking, but the weather was so bitter that Mary was still anxious.

"Don't worry," said Harold, "The well's a good way underground."

No matter how hard they worked to clear the snow, it built up again. The mangolds and kale were buried underneath it in the fields, and the couple had to use their emergency supply of concentrates to keep the cattle alive.

On the night before the sale the temperature rose a degree or two, but an evil wind made it feel twice as cold. As Mary stood at the bedroom window wearing two thick sweaters under her dressing gown, she heard snow driving against the glass, the tight, zinging little crystals of bitter cold.

"There's no way we'll make the market in Bristol," she moaned to Harold.

It was a great disappointment. Mary really wanted the Jersey cows.

"The weather forecast is for it to get a bit warmer in these parts, but it sounds pretty bleak for the rest of the country," said Harold. "For God's sake woman! Get into bed!"

Mary set the alarm clock as usual. The milk lorry hadn't made it through for two days and they had lost their income, but it just might come in the morning.

She awoke in the night to a deep silence. The wind had dropped and the windows had cleared of ice. She could see the moon scudding between clouds. Somewhere an owl was crying above the fields, and then she heard the soft pattering of rain.

By morning the rain had turned most of the snow to slush!

"Can we go?" she begged as she climbed into her clothes.

"It might be on. You get the milking done. I'll see to the feed and bedding," said Harold.

Outside the slush was a slippery mess but Mary fought her way to the cowshed. It was so much warmer that it almost felt balmy.

Some of the cows were drying up and waiting to be put into calf again, so the milking didn't take long. Harold dished out hay and concentrates, and pitchforked the steaming straw onto the midden.

Whilst Mary cooked breakfast he took the buckets to the dairy and poured the meagre contents into the churn. The rest of the milk had thawed to a mush. He hoped the lorry might make it now that the weather had improved.

"There's not much money in that little lot," Harold grumbled to himself. "And now we're buying pedigree Jerseys!"

Mary was in the kitchen, packing sandwiches and filling flasks with hot coffee, whilst Harold built up the range. She had prepared a large casserole of beef and vegetables with sliced potatoes on the top, which she would leave in the warming oven to cook slowly. Harold loved this sort of dinner!

Harold went down to the lane and when he had heaved the

churns onto the milk stand, he took a good look at the conditions. Even in the semi-darkness he could see that the snow was vanishing. Water was rushing everywhere in the fastest thaw he had ever seen. It was flowing away like a stream down the road towards the Berkeley Pill.

"We'll have a go," he said to Mary over breakfast. "This rapid thaw may just be local. We might have to give it up, but let's try anyway."

Mary was delighted! It seemed like a miracle that the snow could disappear so rapidly.

Soon they were in the Ford, and the dawn was streaking the winter sky as they drove out of the farm towards Bristol.

There was still plenty of snow on the roads, but it was wet and sloppy, and the Ford swished through it easily. They arrived at the market in good time, to find it almost empty. A few trailers and lorries stood around among the banks of piled up snow, and their owners were stamping in the cold.

"It's pretty sparse," Harold said to the man in the registration office.

"It's the weather," the man replied. "Everywhere else has got it really bad. We've had a bit of a thaw locally, and a few have managed to get through. What are you after?"

"Oh this and that," said Harold, never a one to give anything away. He was always afraid the price might go up!

The couple made their way to the cattle ring.

"Look! Over there!" Mary hissed, pointing to a lorry with its back down. "It's the Jerseys!"

They watched as two cows were unloaded.

"Look!" said Mary: "See how easy they are to handle. Just little rope halters! No need to drive them at all!"

"I've heard the bulls are a different story!" Harold grunted.

There was quite a lot of stock up for sale, from the surrounding farms, but precious few bidders. The roads were bad and many had kept away.

This could work in our favour, thought Harold with satisfaction. The owners will already have paid to have the cows shipped across the channel and they won't want to pay for their return! I might get out of this Jersey business a lot cheaper than I expected!

There were a few lots to go, and Mary watched as they were sold.

"Now it's us," she said, nudging Harold's arm. But she need not have worried. He wasn't asleep, just dreaming of a good deal!

There was only one other bloke interested in the Jerseys. He stood leaning against the railings, watching.

They're nice little cows, thought Harold.

They weren't a type which particularly interested him, but he could see the breeding in them, from their slim, straight hocks, neat little muzzles and well-set flanks. Both cows possessed tidy udders, empty, but taunt and delicate beneath them.

Mary stood tensely at his side.

Oh well, he thought. Might as well get 'em for her. She's her heart set. Besides, we might get the extra five pence a gallon subsidy for the extra cream.

The other chap bid against him a couple of times, but he didn't have his heart in it, and Harold got them for an unbelievably low price.

Mary smiled with pleasure, but kept her cool. A market was no place for emotion.

They walked back to the office where Harold paid and organised a lorry to bring the cattle over that afternoon.

Mary picked up their papers and leafed through them.

"Ispagula and Snowdrop," she said. "What lovely names!"

Well that was alright, thought Harold as they drove home. The inclement weather had done him a good turn!

The break in the weather proved a mere respite. It was a hard winter and it took all their efforts as they battled the frost and cold.

One morning Mary awoke to find their fields once more buried in snow. She pulled on her clothes as Harold made his usual grumbles about having to clear the milk stand.

They completed the milking and Harold went off with the tractor to try and retrieve some of their kale from under the snow.

"Feeding all this hay and concentrates is eating into our profits," he moaned, "especially with the blasted yield down as well!"

Mary was worried too. They desperately needed their milk cheques or they would soon run into difficulties.

Later that morning Harold came into the kitchen, his face chapped red with the cold, and his ginger hair standing on end.

"Geese!" he cried, grabbing his gun. "They're coming over in skeins! Must be from Peter Scott's place at Slimbridge! Come on! Get your boots on!"

Mary left the dishes and fled with her excited husband, out into the snowy cold. As she looked up at the scattered V's of birds overhead, thin snowflakes began to fall from the leaden sky, dissolving on her lips and lashes.

Harold took aim and fired.

"Damn!" he said as he missed.

He fired again and this time a bird came swirling down from the sky in a flurry of feathers and snowflakes.

Mary was thinking rapturously of golden roasted goose with apple sauce.

But the bird was injured, and fluttered along the ground.

"Damn!" snapped Harold again. "Can't leave it like that!"

They set off in pursuit, floundering through the snow, but just as they drew close the bird took to the air again.

"Oh no!" wailed Mary in disappointment.

Then the bird fell to the ground once more and the couple resumed their chase.

This went on for some time, with the bird repeatedly taking flight and then falling, and always keeping just ahead of them as they struggled through the thick snow-covered vegetation.

At length they had to admit defeat. They stood facing each other in the white landscape, their breath coming in gasps. It had stopped snowing but the sky was leaden grey, heavy with more.

Overhead the vast skeins had vanished. Mary fell against her husband's chest, not knowing whether to laugh or cry.

"We'll just have to call it the one that got away!" said Harold, against Mary's froth of golden hair, which had come loose in the chase. Hand in hand they struggled back to the farm, often breast high in snow.

By the time they reached the buildings the temperature had sunk a few degrees and they were both feeling cold.

"We can't get much done today," Harold grumbled, looking round at the snow-covered fields.

Then he had an idea!

"Come on," he said. "We need the cider room for storage. Let's go and dismantle the old cider press!"

Beat it up would have been a better description!

They grabbed crowbars and set about breaking the ancient press apart. The air screamed with crashes, and sparks flew as metal pounded metal. The couple yelled like savages, whacking it with fiendish enjoyment!

Their faces streamed with sweat as they stood back to survey the wreckage. Only the huge wooden screw remained, and Harold beat this to bits with a pickaxe!

Fifty years later Mary was to feel a flicker of shame at their destruction of the historic press!

But in those days on the farm, survival was all that mattered, and Fred soon had the room fitted with neat shelves. Sacks of feed and drums of fuel took over the space as if the press had never existed.

The couple's wild goose chase and the battering of the cider press became just two memories of that long, cold winter of '47.

CHAPTER TWENTY-SEVEN

STARTING A FAMILY

The following spring the young couple had a surprise. Mary was pregnant. Her pleasure was tainted by apprehension as the work of the farm left little spare time. How would she cope with a baby as well?

Mary purchased a manual entitled, *'How To Bring Up A Child!'*

She was sitting in bed, leafing through it whilst Harold finished his ablutions.

"This book's jolly good," she said. "It says you must not spoil the baby. You have to look after it and see to its needs, but NO FUSS! It says you must not rush to give in to all its demands. If we do it properly we will have a happy, contented and well-behaved child! What do you think Harold?"

Her husband took off his slippers and climbed into bed.

"It sounds sensible to me," he agreed. Then, leaning towards her he added. "Don't worry about this pregnancy business. There's nothing to it you know. The cows do it all the time."

Mary was a little taken aback but thumped her pillows into shape and settled down with the eiderdown over her ears.

Pregnancy might be a breeze, she thought, but having a baby was a pretty major life change. She intended to follow the book to the letter! And she was going to get some help in the house whilst she was carrying the child! That way she was sure she would be able to keep going with all her farm work.

Mary engaged a widow called Mrs Truman who lived in nearby Ham Green. She was a cheery woman with a small daughter called 'Sandie', who had a lame leg. Sometimes the little girl came too. She was a sweet-tempered child who played quietly on her own.

Mrs Truman was a great gossip but not in a malicious way. She just liked to keep up with all the happenings in the area.

Sometimes Mary worried that more talking than work was going on, so she made sure that her helper had something to occupy her, such as peeling the potatoes, before a chat set sail. But the relationship was a formal one. It was always 'Mrs Truman ', and 'Mrs Norton'. They *never* used Christian names.

Mrs Truman came twice a week, first on Monday to boil up the copper in the washhouse, and then later in the week to give the house a thorough clean.

Mary hated the dust, which flew every time the carpets were cleaned with a dustpan and brush, and was only too pleased to pass this job on to her helper.

But Mrs Truman had other ideas "It be time you gotten yourself modernised," she grumbled in her soft Gloucestershire dialect as the dust flew around her, infiltrating eyes and lungs. "I never have known anythin' the like of it. You be back in Victorian times, Mrs Norton!"

In those days vacuum cleaner salesmen were regular callers at country houses, but Mary had always sent them away, feeling unable to stretch the finances, but she finally gave into Mrs Truman's pleas and purchased a brand new Hoover. What an amazing thing! The flying dust became a thing of the past.

The first time she used the vacuum cleaner herself she was thrilled.

"I be a ballet dancer, gliding over the floor," she said aloud in a mock up of Mrs Truman's country brogue.

Why on earth, she thought, have I never bought one of these wonderful things before?

But it had always been Mary's way – to make do! She is just the same today!

***

The baby was due at the end of November. Mary was determined to carry on with her work on the farm with scarce regard for her pregnancy.

When she first went to Dr MacDonald, her dour Scottish

GP in Berkeley for confirmation of her condition, doctor and patient faced each other across his desk.

"Should I expect any problems?" she asked.

"Goodness no!" exclaimed the doctor. "There's nothing to worry about at all! One day the baby will just pop out!"

When Mary later relayed this conversation to Harold, he said confidently, "Didn't I tell you? It's a perfectly natural process! Look at the cows!"

In fact, throughout her pregnancy, Harold often compared her condition to that of the bovine reproductive system!

She and Mrs Truman laughed about it while they were enjoying their morning coffee break.

"I'm certain," said Mary with a giggle, "that he regards me as one more bit of livestock!"

"All farmers be the same, Mrs Norton," the other laughed. "They be so used to it, you see!"

On one occasion Harold walked unexpectedly into the kitchen whilst they were giggling.

"What are you two laughing about now?" he asked, serious-faced.

"Oh nothing," replied Mary, dabbing at her eyes. "We were just having a little conversation about calving!"

Harold strode off in a huff! *What on earth could be funny about calving?*

But Mary was so fit and well that she did indeed carry on as usual. She suffered a little morning sickness, but this soon passed and she saw no reason to mollycoddle herself. She still took her full turn at the milking and continued to work in the fields at planting, hoeing and cutting kale. And she looked a picture! She blossomed, her eyes aglow and her limbs bronzed by the sun as the months progressed. Her only concession to her condition was to drive into Berkeley each week to collect her post-war government issue of cod liver oil and orange juice.

Her parents continued their weekend visits and Edith tried to make a fuss of her daughter, but Mary would have none of it!

"I'm fine!" she insisted.

And Harold would invariably add his comment: "The cows do it all the time!"

Mary's mother did however have one piece of advice,

which was to prove invaluable.

"What you need," Edith insisted, "is a Welsh flannel baby sleeping bag! You can run one up on your sewing machine in a jiffy!"

Edith came from a Welsh hill farming family, and this traditional piece of baby equipment made work easier. Whenever the farmer's wife had to leave the baby in order to carry out chores, the little one could be popped into the bag in the knowledge that it would be safe, secure and warm. The bag had wide shoulder straps, which were buttoned like dungarees, but the essential secret was that the buttons must be sewn on extremely strongly, so that the mother would not be haunted by the thought of her infant pulling them off and swallowing or choking on them! The other requirement was that the bag *must* be made from real Welsh flannel.

Mary made several of these bags, in different sizes, and stored them away in readiness.

In the summer, mindful of their brief holiday the previous year Harold suggested they take another short break.

"Oh yes!" enthused Mary: "It might be the last for a long while, once the baby's born!"

A frown crossed Harold's face. He hadn't seen things that way!

"But I won't sleep on that mattress in the car again!" said Mary.

"We can't afford to go too mad!" said Harold as he strode out of the house.

Later that day he came in whilst Mary was busy peeling vegetables. He tossed a large canvas bag onto the floor.

"There you are!" he said. "Better than a five-star hotel!"

Mary investigated. Inside the bag she saw a small tent, and a jangle of poles and pegs.

Soon everything was organised and the couple decided to go camping in Cornwall. On their first night they reached Countisbury Hill, near Lynton, in North Devon, in the middle of a tremendous thunderstorm. Harold drove the car off the road onto a suitable-looking flat stretch of moorland saying tartly: "This will have to do!"

It was a nightmare getting the tent up but at last the couple crawled inside, soaking wet and miserable. The rain was so torrential that using the primus was out of the question, so they stripped off their wet clothes, climbed into their sleeping bags and munched on chocolate bars and a bag of apples to the accompaniment of thunder and lightning. Harold was not in the best of moods. He moaned continually that he wanted a cup of tea.

At last, as daylight faded and the thunder clouds rolled away, a few birds perked up sufficiently to sing. It was a sound of infinite sweetness and Mary drifted off to sleep, her arms around Harold. She felt warm and snug. But as darkness fell the rain started again, and it continued all night. Answering the call of nature was unpleasant, struggling in the gale force wind and torrential rain.

In the morning Mary awoke, aware that thin daylight was penetrating the tent, and that she was being smothered! Something stiff and heavy was over her face, but with all her struggles she could not throw it off. Then she heard Harold beside her. He was lashing out too, and swearing "BLOODY HELL!"

"The blasted tent's collapsed!" She heard his strangled voice.

They managed to free themselves and crawl out onto the turf, clad only in pyjamas. Then the glory of the view engulfed them! All trace of the rain had gone, the sky was a clear sharp blue and the sea was dancing with light, whilst all around them, slipping into the distance like a second ocean, the heather and gorse were in bloom. In that moment Mary fell in love with Exmoor! It was a love, which would last a lifetime!

Fortunately Mary's cousin Nora and her husband were also holidaying, in a rented cottage at Lynmouth, so the couple were able to bundle the wet tent into the car and drive down to ask their help.

Nora was still in bed when they arrived. As she looked at them standing, bedraggled on her doorstep she let out a cry: "Good heavens! What on earth has happened to the pair of you?"

She and her husband soon dried the tent out and gave them a good meal, and then sent them on their way to Cornwall.

But the holiday was doomed! Whilst staying near Bude,

Harold fell asleep in front of the tent. He was clad only in shorts, without even shoes, and when he awoke he was terribly sunburnt. He had blisters up his shins and on the tops of his feet. He was in such pain that he could not walk. Mary, full of concern, smothered him in calamine, and for the rest of the holiday she drove her chalky-pink, wraith-like husband around Cornwall. It was almost a relief to arrive back at the farm.

***

In the late summer Harold drew up details for improving the hedges and ditches on the farm.

"It's no good," he said, "I can't do it on my own."

Mary rested her hands on her husband's shoulders. She knew that sometimes, even in those early days, the work of the farm was getting him down.

"It's too big a job," he stated. "I'm going to ask the NAS for advice."

This was Harold's accustomed reaction to adversity, and Mary nodded.

A few days later one of Harold's ministry friends arrived. Mary placed the tea tray on the table and went out to finish loading their crop of mangolds onto the trailer.

Later Harold joined her. He was smiling.

"I've solved it," he said as he came up to her: "We're getting a team of German prisoners of war."

"Goodness!" Mary stepped back in alarm.

"It's a government scheme," he said, "putting them to work on the land."

"Aren't they being repatriated?"

"Eventually, yes, but things are still up in the air. We might as well take advantage of the scheme while we have the chance."

Mary threw the last few mangolds into the trailer. They dislodged the heap and trickled down with a rumble.

"What will it cost?" Mary asked.

"Let's go indoors. I'll tell you the details."

A few days later the Germans arrived in a lorry with their armed guards. They were billeted in a location midway between Gloucester and Bristol, at an experimental 'open' prison.

296

They did not seem in the least downtrodden or defeated, and most were pleased to labour on the land, although very few spoke English. Mary, by this time was so heavily pregnant that she kept herself out of sight. The prisoners had all their refreshments in the lorry, under the watchful eyes of their guards.

The work was completed in less than two weeks and the prisoners went on their way.

"I'm very pleased," Harold related. "They've done a damned good job!"

That might have been the end, but one rainy night at the beginning of November Mary received a disturbing surprise. She was in the kitchen preparing tea when she heard a knock on the farmhouse door. Wiping her hands, she went to open it. On the doorstep stood a man with rain streaming from his clothes. The light from the doorway illuminated his face, and Mary could see that he was handsome, blond-haired and in his early thirties. He stretched out his hands in entreaty.

"Please, Fraulein," he begged in a thick German accent. "Let me come and stay with you. I will work very hard on the farm, I promise."

Mary backed away, covering her stomach in a protective gesture. She knew he was one of the German prisoners.

"Please do not be afraid," he begged. "I come to ask for your help to save my life. They say I must go back to Germany, but I helped the Resistance, and I know I will be shot as a traitor! Please Fraulein, let me stay!"

Mary looked into his handsome face and saw that he was crying, or maybe it was the rain. For a brief moment they stared at each other in silence. She was filled with pity for him, but also with dismay. Her whole heart wanted to help him but she knew it was impossible. Although undoubtedly they needed help on the farm, this handsome young officer would cause all kinds of complications. In a blinding flash she could even imagine herself falling in love with him!

"No! No!" she said: "It is impossible! You must go! NOW!"

The man seized her hands in a burning grip. "Please," he said. His voice had fallen to a husky whisper and there was desperation in his eyes.

Mary shook her head. "Impossible," she said, stepping backwards into the hall.

The young officer turned and walked away through the teeming rain. Mary regretted her decision for many weeks. Even the excitement of her newborn child could not completely erase the soldier from her mind and she knew she would feel pain for the rest of her life. She would forever wonder what became of him, and indeed, how many other Germans had been against the war and had made the ultimate decision to help the allies.

Just two weeks later Mary went into labour. She was seated at her sewing machine when she felt the first flicker of pain. She ignored it and carried on.

At nine o'clock that evening she was still sewing. Each time a contraction came on she gave in to it with a groan, but as it died away, back went her foot on the treadle and the needle whirred again.

At ten o'clock, when the pains were coming every few minutes, Mary finally gave in. "Come on!" said Harold with determination. "I'm driving you to the hospital. NOW!"

Mary went upstairs to their room. She had prepared a small suitcase. Inside it, along with her nightclothes and toiletries, was a little set of baby clothes. Mary smiled. It really was going to happen! Soon they would have their first child. For the time being the childcare manual remained on her bedside table.

"Come on!" called Harold from downstairs, and soon Mary was in the car, still protesting that there was no need to hurry!

He drove her to the cottage hospital in Berkley where Mary found everything most welcoming. She was put into a pleasant room with another young mother, who was sitting up in bed, nursing her baby son.

Before the two women could introduce themselves another pain struck and Mary bent over gasping. Harold fled the room!

"Poor you!" said the other young mum: "But you'll find it was worth it once it's over!"

"I daren't make a fuss," Mary giggled once the pain had ebbed away. "I have to perform as well as my husband's cows!"

Just then the nurse came into the room and swept Mary away to the labour ward.

The doctor was waiting and as the next contraction struck he placed a chloroform mask over her face.

"It will help ease your pain," he said soothingly.

"Give me plenty!" said Mary.

Indeed she drew so much on the chloroform that she was only semi-conscious throughout the birth, but she did remember the precious moment when the doctor said, "You have a baby daughter!"

So her child would be called Linda, the name which she and Harold had agreed upon should the baby be a girl. It was just a few moments to midnight on the 30th of November, 1948.

Mary lay back exhausted and watched as her baby was held aloft and given a sharp smack on her back. Lusty cries filled the room.

Poor little soul, thought Mary, remembering a comment she had heard often at chapel: We are brought kicking and screaming into this world.

She was anxious to hold her baby but the nurse insisted on giving the newborn a bath. Mary lay exhausted, but contentedly listening to the gentle splashing sounds. At last Linda was wrapped in a shawl and laid into her mother's arms.

Mary held her for a few short minutes, then the nurse took the baby away and put her in a small cot by Mary's bed.

Betty Yardley, the other young mum in the room turned to Mary and whispered: "Was it very bad?"

"I can't remember much," replied Mary. "I think I overdosed a bit on the chloroform!"

"They told me," said Betty in a hesitant voice, "that at one point you tried to rip the doctor's gown off!"

With these words Mary at last fell asleep.

She awoke at four in the morning with the nurse bending over her.

"It's time to feed your baby."

Mary took her daughter in her arms whilst the nurse gently directed her how to breast feed. Now at last, Mary had plenty of time to admire her infant. One tiny hand was curled into a fist and the other was laid softly against Mary's breast. The little face was contorted with the effort of feeding and although Mary could see that her baby had a crop of soft ash-blonde hair, she could not make out her features, or the colour of her eyes. For the moment it was good enough just to feel her in her arms as they both enjoyed each other's company in the semi-darkness of the room, where another young mother and baby so quietly slept.

The next day Mary felt exhausted. For a lot of the time she lay back on her pillows watching Betty Yardley with her baby son, Paul. How adept she was at handling him, and how confident!

At four-hourly intervals the nurse lifted baby Linda from the cot and handed her to Mary to feed. Mary was pleased, as the precisely timed intervals also featured in the childcare manual!

Later that morning Harold came bounding into the room with an unaccustomed nervousness, and his face alight with happiness. He was as pleased as punch to be a father!

All the same, his first comment was, "Hell Mary, I missed you at the milking this morning!"

Then he saw the baby in her cot and bent to look at her.

"Oh Mary!" his voice was almost a whisper. "She's ours!"

Then his huge hands were in the cot, lifting her out and holding her in his arms to take a closer look. Mary relaxed. Harold was so used to handling young animals that he didn't give it a second thought!

"It's hard to say who she takes after at this moment," said Harold. And Mary, watching him, giggled.

"She's called Linda," she said happily. "The name we agreed."

At that moment Linda awoke and after a few convulsive gurgles, let out a yell.

"Good Lord!" said Harold, and handed her swiftly to Mary.

"She's hungry," explained the other mum from her bed. "By the way, I'm called Betty."

"Pleased to meet you," said Harold in formal manner, almost drowned out by his daughter's screams.

It was a relief for all when Linda was at last pressed against Mary's breast.

"How was it?" he asked.

"It wasn't too bad," Mary replied. "Not too bad at all, except for the doctor's gown!"

When Mary explained they all broke into laughter.

Of course Harold could not stay long. He had to race back to the farm. But he handed her a box of chocolates saying, "I thought you might prefer these to flowers."

A quick kiss, another rapturous look at Linda, and the exultant father was gone!

Later that afternoon Edith arrived.

"Goodness Mary, you look so tired," she said as if this was unusual after giving birth.

Then she handed Mary a little parcel containing pretty baby clothes, which she had knitted.

But to Mary's surprise her mother would not look at the baby. She kept circling round the cot in a most peculiar manner. Mary felt uncomfortable with this strange behaviour, but at last her mother stood still and took a quick glimpse. Poor Edith, even after so many years she had not recovered from losing her son, and was frightened to confront this new member of her family.

Mrs Norton on the other hand, had totally the opposite reaction on *her* first visit. She picked Linda up without so much as a 'by your leave', and sat for a while holding her in her arms and saying: "Oh the little dear. She's so sweet."

Mary was relieved when she went.

Betty explained that she ran a small sweetshop in Berkley and she and Mary soon became friends. The two women kept in touch for the rest of their lives but Betty never gave birth again. Paul was to be her only child.

In the 1940s it was normal for a new mother to stay in bed in hospital for two weeks after her confinement. For Mary this was an enchanted time, resting, reading and getting to know her baby in the pleasant little cottage hospital where everyone was so helpful and kind. She learnt how to bath and dress her baby, and how to change nappies!

Harold came to see her every day. He tried hard not to mention how he was missing Mary on the farm, and assured her that Fred and George were 'managing wondrously well'!

In quiet moments Mary read and reread the childcare manual, which she had requested Harold bring in for her. The advice in the book seemed tailor-made for a young farming mother. It recommended that the baby be the subject of a rigid routine.

'Never', it advised 'pick up the baby each time it cries. This is simply teaching it to cry. A young mother needs her rest and should not be woken frequently during the night by a demanding baby'! *Wise words, indeed, thought Mary.*

Mary knew that the going was about to become tougher with a baby to care for as well as all her tasks on the farm, and she was determined to follow the advice in the book. She told Harold that Linda was to have her own room.

"I won't be woken by her crying then," she said sharply. "The book says that as long as the baby is warm and fed and has a clean nappy, she will only be crying for attention, and if we don't come running she will soon learn to be happy and contented!"

Harold approved, and Mary continued: "It's a very good book, written by a team of doctors and baby experts."

"Well that's alright then," said Harold.

He had brought in a smart cream carrycot, a gift from Potato Jones!

On her last night in hospital Mary lay awake thinking that she was grateful for the kindness and rest. It would be tough returning home. In the morning she packed her few things, wrapped Linda in the shawl, which Granny Norton had knitted, and with her husband's arm around her, walked out of the hospital into a brand new stage of her life!

CHAPTER TWENTY-EIGHT

FAMILY AND FARM!

Mary knew from the moment she took Linda home that things would never be the same again. She now had to juggle her commitments between the farm and her baby.

There were two parallel priorities... Linda's four-hourly feeds and nappy changes, and the relentless routine of the milk lorry. Both had somehow to be juxtaposed.

The first day was a miserable muddle with people calling in, Harold trying to get on with the chores, and Linda screaming for her feeds.

By ten o'clock that night Mary was truly tired for the first time, and missing the peace of the hospital.

She took Linda up to their room and climbed into bed with her for the late-night feed. At last everyone was gone and she was able to lean back against her pillows and cradle her baby in her arms whilst looking round at all the familiar homely surroundings. She had been so happy in the hospital that she hadn't realised she had missed them.

Harold came up just as Mary was changing Linda's nappy. She dropped it into a lidded bucket, which she had placed there for the purpose. There was another bucket under the sink downstairs and Mary was beginning to panic at the alarming way the wretched things were mounting up. Boiling, washing and drying them was a time-consuming palaver. Mary gave Mrs Truman most of the household chores but she decided to do the nappy washing herself.

Linda had slumped into the blissful sleep of the sated infant, a dribble of milk trickling down her chin.

"I'm going to put her back in her carrycot for the night," Mary said as she lifted her sleeping baby and took her into the adjoining room. The room did look bare with just the cot in the middle, and the low nursing chair against the wall.

When she returned Harold was in bed, winding the alarm clock.

"Is she alright in there?" he asked: "I mean, it's the very first night."

"We're starting how we mean to go on!" Mary replied. "The book says this is the best way. I must have my sleep Harold. It's nearly eleven thirty now and I have to be up by five to feed her before we do the milking!"

"It's alright," Harold assured her. "I think it's sensible."

In the grim December dawn Mary awoke with a start. The alarm clock was screaming, and so was the baby in the next room. Mary leapt out of bed. Linda was red with rage and sopping wet.

Quickly Mary whipped off the nappy and threw it onto the floor.

"Damn!" she said aloud, "another one!"

Within minutes Mary had her baby wrapped in a shawl and at the breast whilst she sat in the low nursing chair and stared at the dark square of window. It was pitch black outside. How she envied Harold his extra hour of sleep!

By six thirty Linda was back in her carry cot, securely buttoned into her Welsh flannel bag, and Harold and Mary were starting to milk the first batch of cows. By the time the second lot was underway Mary's eyes were drooping with tiredness. Only the coldness of the cowshed kept her awake.

They made the milk lorry with less than ten minutes to spare, and as Mary took their bacon from the AGA she was realising just how hard she was going to have to work. Her eyes took in with some dismay the nappies piling up by the sink!

She rushed through the work in the dairy eager to get back to Linda.

She had told Harold very firmly that at ten o'clock each day she would take two hours which she had dubbed her 'baby time', during which she would feed and bath Linda. This routine had been taught to Mary at the hospital and she was determined to enjoy it.

After the feed Mary carried her baby up to the nursery and

laid her in the carrycot whilst she spread a towel on the cot and filled the baby bath with warm water. She put her elbow in to check the temperature as she had been shown in hospital, and laid the new tablet of baby soap alongside.

"Come on little one," she said as she lifted Linda gently and wrapped her in another towel. Then leaning her over the bath she gently soaped her tiny head, rinsed it with warm water from a jug, and then plunged her into the bath. Linda kicked out with her tiny feet at the pleasure of being dandled in the warm water and Mary smiled at the surprised expression on the little face. Her two-week-old child was remarkably unwrinkled and pretty!

As Mary sat in the chair with her on her lap she gently patted her dry with the towel and smoothed the ash-blonde hair into a fashionable little 'quiff' on top of her head. *Oh what a delightful little thing! How lovely to have a baby!*

Soon Linda was in the sitting room asleep in her carrycot and Mary was busy preparing lunch. When Harold came in later he took a look at the baby.

"She does look grand," he said. "She feels so warm."

"Yes," said Mary. "She's well tucked up!"

When he had finished lunch Harold asked Mary if she could come and help cut the kale.

"I can't," she said. "I've got to wash nappies!"

Harold went out, looking a little sulky but Mary knew he had to give her time for the new tasks in her life. They both needed to adjust. Feeling suddenly miserable she turned her attention to the nappies. The pile had grown so swiftly and it was such an unpleasant job that Mary wanted it over.

She had found an old galvanized bath in an outhouse and the nappies were put into this to boil in soapy water on the AGA. Mary had decided against using the washhouse and copper for this task. The turnover was too great!

The steaming and soapy nappies then had to be hand washed in the sink and hung up to dry. The weather outside was too cold and wet, so they were draped on a clothes-horse by the old iron range. Keeping on top of this task was to rule Mary's life for many months.

When she had finished it was time for the 2 o'clock feed, which had to be fitted in before the afternoon milking.

By the time Mary had struggled through the 10 o'clock feed at night she was tired fit to drop, but as she climbed into bed she heard Harold winding the alarm clock and knew that in less than six hours, it would all begin again!

Relentless as it was, Mary was soon settled into her new routine. Harold was her ally because he adored the baby too. He was always peeping into the pram and, whenever he could spare the time from his now even heavier load of farm work he lifted her out and dandled her on his knee, making faces at her.

The routine, strictly as directed by the childcare manual was a big success, and Linda did indeed turn out to be for the most part, a surprisingly easy and contented baby. But at first Mary came in for a few hard words from her own, and Harold's parents.

They were all shocked that Linda slept in a separate room. Edith, mindful of the great coddling and spoiling which she had inflicted on Mary as a child, was especially upset.

"The poor little thing!" she protested, when she first saw the lonely cot in the centre of the bare nursery: "What happens when she cries in the middle of the night?"

"Hopefully, I don't hear it," Mary replied.

Edith took a quick increase of breath: "But Mary!"

"She really just sleeps right through! Exactly as the book says!" argued Mary.

"How can you bring up a baby from a book?" chided Edith.

"Quite easily," said Mary, a dangerous gleam in her eye. She knew her system was working and that Linda was happy.

"But my dear," continued Edith: "When you were little – well – you slept in our bed most of the time. You used to have those night terrors!"

"Well Linda doesn't! She's as contented as a lamb."

"Does seem to be," said Harold. "Mind you, she has a good set of lungs and can scream the place down when she has a mind to!"

Fred looked on in dismay. He hated arguments of any kind. When the going became too rough he would simply say: "Oo-ah," and retreat into another room.

Edith very soon saw that Mary was determined to do things in her own way, and she gave in and left her to it.

Harold's parents did not interfere. They had a healthy respect for their strong-willed daughter-in-law!

But Gladys did show concern when she saw the cot upstairs in the nursery.

"Why!" she exclaimed. "The poor little mite's in a room all on her own!"

"That's right," said Mary.

"But my dear," Gladys said mildly. "Shouldn't she be at your side at night? It is tradition, you know. For farmers' wives, I mean."

"I'm not a farmer's wife," said Mary. "I'm a farmer! I have to do *both* jobs!"

Both sets of grandparents quickly accepted Mary's routine, and there was no denying that the baby thrived!

Mary put Linda in her pram in the garden every day. It didn't matter how cold the weather, the baby, wrapped in cosy clothes and tucked up tight, slept peacefully and was as warm as toast when Mary lifted her out for feeding.

When she was five months old Linda sat up for the first time in her pram and looked around, her eyes wide at this new perspective.

"Look Harold," said Mary, and they were both delighted at this new stage of their baby's development.

The fact that Linda could now sit opened new possibilities.

"We can take her to the cowshed with us," Mary said. "It will be much better than leaving her in the cot while we do the milking."

So, some mornings Mary wheeled the pram across the yard and, once the cows were safely in their yokes, Linda, bouncing in the pram, watched from one end of the building. Sometimes if she grew fretful the pram rocked like a ship in a hurricane and the yells grew louder. Poor Mary and Harold sometimes had to continue the milking to the most deafening roars. But they had to get on. There was a job to be done!

Mary was grateful for the bright spring mornings. It was much easier to shake her tired body out of sleep for the five o'clock feed, with the sunshine and birdsong.

The pram was even wheeled out to the fields whilst Mary slogged up and down the rows of kale and mangolds, hoeing. It was a hard life! But at least Mrs Truman was still coming and did most of the housework, although of course there was still always some for Mary.

In the early summer Mary had a pleasant surprise. She received a letter from her old friends Molly and Margaret, the two teachers who had befriended Mary in her days at the Finlay Road Nursery School. They were going to pay her a visit. But there was an even greater surprise! They were bringing fifty children with them, to see the farm!

Mary was a little taken aback at entertaining such numbers, but could not refuse. She remembered fondly how the two kindly women had taken her on holidays with them.

"Don't worry about a thing," said Molly in her letter. "We shall bring our refreshments with us!"

On the great day the party arrived in a coach, which was parked in the farmyard alongside the cowshed, and the children spilled out, delighted and making a great deal of noise!

Everyone crowded round to admire Linda in her pram.

"How lovely!" enthused Margaret: "You're a mother at last! And what a gorgeous little girl!"

Linda loved the attention and smiled and cooed to order.

Harold had been persuaded to take the children on a tour of the farm, and he arrived in his tractor, anxious at the sight of the little ones milling all over the yard.

Molly and Margaret rounded up the children and restored order, and Harold reluctantly set out with them and the bus driver in tow.

Mary and her two friends followed at a respectful distance, laughing. "Just like the Pied Piper of Hamlin!" Mary giggled.

First the children crowded into the cowshed to see the yokes and milking machines. Then of course they had to put some hay in the long manger, and a great deal of mess was made on the floor. Harold took this with reasonable good humour.

"Now dears, would you like to see the moo-cows?" said Molly, and the children became even more excited. Harold began to look distinctly worried as they all traipsed outside.

The Pied Piper then led them across the fields to see the cows grazing on their strips.

"Don't touch the fence!" yelled Harold, above the din. "It's electrified!"

But of course a few did, and anguished wails were heard, until Molly and Margaret pacified them, and the party moved on to see Mary's Jersey cows.

"Oh how sweet!" said Molly, and all the children joined in rapturously.

Next the Pied Piper led them back to the yard, so that everyone could have a go at the big iron pump. The children were very little and so nobody managed this, but Harold obliged energetically and everyone got wet.

Then it was time for lunch and they all traipsed across the fields to the allotted spot, with Harold pointing out the kale and mangolds on the way. By now he was enjoying himself, and Mary walked alongside, jolting Linda over the ruts in her pram.

They all sat down on the grass for the picnic, which the kindly teachers had prepared. It was a feast of ham sandwiches, chocolate biscuits and sponge cakes. Molly and Margaret didn't enjoy much relaxation as they had to be constantly wiping sticky faces and retrieving food from the grass!

Harold and Mary leaned against each other, munching their meal whilst Linda cooed with interest in her pram. It was such a lovely summer day and the countryside was looking its best.

"I couldn't be happier," said Mary as she looked into Harold's eyes.

"I'll be a great deal happier if we get the afternoon milking done on time," Harold muttered.

After the picnic the children tumbled over the soft grass, thoroughly enjoying themselves. But soon the bus driver pointed out that it was time to go, and everyone returned to the yard, hugging and saying thank you.

At last they were all aboard and Harold lifted Linda in his arms to wave. Fifty little hands appeared out of the coach windows, waving back, and the farmers watched as their visitors drew out of sight.

"Well that was nice," said Mary.

"Yes," said Harold. "Half a bloody day wasted!"

***

One morning when Linda was six months old Harold laid aside his copy of 'Farmer and Stockbreeder' and said: "Shouldn't you be weaning her now, Mary? You look a bit peaky. I think all this breast feeding could be wearing you down. I need you in good health, you know!"

Mary raised an eyebrow. Although she welcomed her husband's concern, she was taken aback by his motives!

"As a matter of fact I'm going to get her some Farex," Mary said. This was a cereal especially for babies, which she had noticed in the chemist shop at Berkeley.

Then Mary began mashing up small portions of dinner (there were no little tins or jars of baby food in those days), and Linda ate it all! But Mary continued to breast feed until the baby was nearly a year old, as it was far easier than mixing up bottles, and she was always so short of time.

Linda was a sturdy infant and soon became very mobile. In the mornings Mary buttoned her into the flannel sleeping bag and left her in the cot whilst she went to do the milking. When she returned she invariably found her daughter red-faced, gripping the cot side and bouncing furiously to an accompaniment of robust yells. But at least she did not have to worry about her getting cold. The Welsh flannel bag did its job!

Linda grew so big and strong that she could rock the pram ferociously if she had a mind to. Sometimes she did it for fun, but at others it became an effective new weapon for gaining attention. Back and forth the pram plunged, in time to the screams!

Sometimes she did this in the milking shed, and Mary was terrified that the pram would tip over, throwing her daughter onto the concrete floor. The fact that Mary always came running was not lost on Linda, who rocked the harder, with a triumphant look on her face.

One Sunday Harold, Mary and her parents were enjoying their roast lunch in the dining room. Linda had been put out to enjoy the warm summer air and could be clearly seen through the window. Unfortunately, she could also see them, and wanted to be brought inside!

The adults were treated to the sight of the pram rocking

ever harder, whilst a puce-faced Linda gave vent to screams, which could have raised the dead.

"Damn!" said Harold, laying aside his roast potatoes in annoyance. "She'll tip the blasted pram right over!"

"Finish your lunch," said Mary. "She'll probably give up in a minute!"

But as she spoke the company was horrified to see Linda give one more mighty bounce. The pram capsized, its wheels spinning in thin air, the baby beneath it. The screams stopped abruptly.

Edith went chalk-white. "Good God!" she screamed. "She's dead!"

Mary also turned pale as she flew out into the garden, followed by Harold.

He swiftly righted the pram to reveal Linda, upside down on the grass with her bottom in the air, silent and immobile. Mary feared the worst. But as Harold picked his daughter up, she gave a choking gasp of rage, and broke into screams of a truly gargantuan nature!

"That's why she went quiet," said Mary. "The little horror was filling her lungs!"

"Cover your ears!" said Harold as he brought Linda into the house, still screaming fit to bust. Physically she was unhurt, but the incident was a huge blow to her pride!

"It's a pity," said Harold above the noise, "that Mary's childcare manual does not offer any advice about pram rocking!"

CHAPTER TWENTY-NINE

ANOTHER BABY, DRUNKEN CATS & A BULL FROM HELL!

In September Mary discovered that she was pregnant again. When she told Harold he took it in good heart, but they both knew that life was going to become even harder. Unfortunately a further shock was in store.

One morning Mrs Truman turned up with some news of her own.

"I be fearfully sorry, Mrs Norton," she said as she fished a clean pinney from her bag and proceeded to put it on, "but I'm afraid I shall be leavin'!"

"Oh," gulped Mary. "Why's that? I thought you were happy here!"

"Oh I have been, Mrs Norton! Have no fear of that! But the truth is… I've gotten married again!"

Mary was so surprised she sat down with a bump in the elbow chair.

"But Mrs Truman! We never even knew you were courting!"

Here's a right old turn up for the books, Mary was thinking. She kept this lot quiet!

"Is the lucky man anyone we know?"

"It's the postman, Mr Dangood!" said the newly-wed. "He has a nice little cottage in Berkeley.

"We kept the wedding a secret. No one knew till after we'd done it! I do hope you don't mind, Mrs Norton."

Mary drew a breath. I'm very happy for you and I'm sure Harold will join me in giving congratulations. It's just that, well, it's come as a bit of a shock!"

"Well I'm sure you will understand that I can't work for you anymore. Well, there's no need for me to be doin' another's housework now, is there? That's why I be givin' you a week's notice!"

Once Mrs Truman had departed Mary gave way to tears.

"Oh Harold!" she wept at lunchtime. "I'm still breast-feeding one infant, pregnant with another, the harvest is looming and here I am with no one to help in the house! And you know what it's like in winter. It can take a whole morning just to cut the kale for the cattle; and it has to be done EVERY DAY!"

They looked at each other in dismay.

"Well," said Harold. "We knew at the start it'd be hard work working a small farm, using intensive methods."

"I think it's harder than working a larger acreage," said Mary, disheartened. "And we're on such a tight budget."

This was certainly true. They had to produce their own cattle fodder in the form of kale, mangolds and silage because they could not afford expensive concentrates.

"What am I to do?" she asked.

"You'll have to find someone else," Harold said.

When he had finished eating he marched out of the kitchen. He never took part in domestic affairs! Mary sat with Linda on her lap.

But he must have had the matter on his mind because suddenly he burst in again, his face red. He came straight to the point.

"Listen Mary!" he said: "Don't worry that you're pregnant again! It's just a natural process! You'll be fine! What we need is a son to grow up and help on the farm!"

"I don't think I can do it to order, Harold!" Mary gulped.

He could sometimes be harsh like this. Phlegmatically she took the view that as she had been so cosseted and spoiled as a child, perhaps she had to go through this process of emotional hardship to forge herself into a better person. And Harold was such a good man, and a wonderful father! He was just tired and anxious and always had to race on with the next job! She looked at him tenderly despite his face reddened with frustration.

Seeing her so upset but uncomplaining made him feel ashamed. "Listen, I'm sorry," he said: "I know it's hard!"

"I'll have a word with the NAS. I told them you are expecting again and how worried I've been about having to manage without you."

"I'll still be able to give you some help," Mary said meekly. And I'll work all through my pregnancy."

"I don't want you risking yourself," Harold said kindly. "And listen. Someone at the NAS said we might be able to take on a student. Farming's so buoyant now that there're hundreds of youngsters wanting to get into it.

"A lad could sleep in the attic, and in return for a small wage and some training, he'll help me on the farm. That will give you more time in the house. What do you think?"

"It might work," Mary replied.

Later in the afternoon Harold came into the house looking more cheerful.

"I've just seen Mrs Truman – I mean Dangood! Oh drat the woman! How am I supposed to remember she's changed her confounded name? She was coming up the drive to see you, but asked me to give you a message.

"She says she knows a young girl, Anne somebody or other, who might take her place. You see! Things aren't so bad. And you've been pregnant before! You know what to expect!"

Seeing her woeful face Harold wondered why his wife wasn't instantly cheered up. *Women! he thought as he strode out, anxious to return to his mangold clamping: I'll never understand 'em!*

They decided that even if Mary had help in the house, they would still need another pair of hands for the farm, so they placed an advertisement in 'Farmers' Weekly'.

They were swamped with replies. In the evenings, after a long day, they had to plough through the letters and make a short list to interview.

They chose a lad called Michael, and set to work turning part of the attic into accommodation for him. The top floor of Tan House Farm had once been used as a cheese store, and there was no glass in the windows. They had been left open to ventilate the cheeses. A carpenter duly arrived to fit glass, and Mary and her mother furnished the room comfortably.

The newly-wed Mrs Dangood recommended a young girl called Mary Sherman to help in the house, and it was arranged that she should start at the beginning of the following week.

Mary liked her at once. She was a pleasant-faced fifteen year old, who had just left school. Mary set her to work clearing the dirty dishes which had piled up since lunch the previous day.

The girl not only made an excellent job of it but once she was finished she scrubbed down the wooden draining board with fresh water, and scoured out the sink.

When Mary praised her, the girl said: "Oh, it's no problem Mrs Norton. I always do things properly. My mother taught me to be very clean."

Mary was impressed and a little ashamed when she thought of the quick flick and a dash, which was her own method of washing up!

She left her new helper to carry on with the housework, and went out into the fields to join Harold. It was hard labour covering the mangolds with straw and soil to protect them for the winter, and Linda had been grizzly all day. By bedtime Mary's head and body ached with tiredness. She didn't even hear Harold winding the alarm clock, and as she dived into a heavy slumber her last thought was, "I hope this student idea works!"

Michael arrived the following week. He was a city boy, seventeen years old, with blond hair. Whilst Harold was in the cowshed showing the lad how to use the milking machine, Mary was preparing a nice supper of bread and cheese. She wanted to make a good start and show him he was welcome.

Harold came in smiling. "You sleep in a bit tomorrow," he said: "Michael and I will see to the milking. I've given him Dad's old alarm clock. That should wake him well enough!"

They both laughed, for George Norton's old clock was as loud as Big Ben!

Linda had just learnt to walk and she was staggering round the room from chair to chair, chortling to herself. Both parents smiled indulgently.

Next morning Mary awoke to find Harold shaking her violently.

"For God's sake wake up!" Harold shouted: "Dratted Michael hasn't got up! We'll miss the milk lorry!"

With a furious gleam in his eye Harold explained what had happened as Mary frantically pulled on her clothes.

"I trusted him!" he said: "So down I went and started the

315

milking. But after twenty minutes I smelt a rat, so I had to come indoors and what do you think I found? The stupid idiot was fast asleep. He'd simply chucked Dad's clock across the room! It's on the floor, with its innards hanging out!

"For God's sake woman, hurry up! All I've done is to get the first lot in, and milked a couple. There're eighteen more to go!"

As they clattered down the stairs Linda started to yell. They heard the cot rattling with the fury of her bouncing!

"Ignore it!" Harold hissed. "The bloody milk lorry!"

In the cowshed Mary and Harold worked like Trojans. Harold's brow was dripping with sweat but Mary could see they were miles behind!

Ten minutes later Michael arrived, looking sleepy and bored. He didn't seem in the least perturbed.

"Right you great clot," Harold spat scornfully: "There's the udder cloths. Get that lot wiped." And he gestured to the row of cows still waiting to be milked.

But it was no use, for the first time in their lives they missed the milk lorry. Harold was furious. As they stood by the now useless churns he grabbed Michael by the shoulders and shook him.

Mary was afraid he would hit the boy, but instead he yelled: "Right then! You can tip that lot down the drain! You've lost us our entire income for the day!"

They watched as the first froth of milk splashed across the paving stones, and then both strode angrily away.

It was the start of a stream of problems. Some days Michael would pull his weight and things went well. But on others he was completely disinterested. He was a London boy and not used to the rigid discipline of farm life. And Mary had the extra burden of caring for him; washing his clothes and feeding him. Also, she never again had the confidence to sleep late, because on several occasions Michael had failed to turn up for the milking, and she needed to always be on hand in case it happened again.

Autumn and winter slipped away and Mary did not allow her pregnancy to stop her working on the farm. On frosty winter mornings Michael would complain about the cold as they cut kale for the cattle. He often did not feel well and said that he had pains in his stomach. Mary, hatless and determined, bent her back to the task, and cut twice as much as the young lad. Then, her maternity smock flapping round her, she would energetically throw the kale onto the trailer whilst Michael messed around on the ground with the rake.

He helped gather some more kale but cut it too far up, wasting the thick nutritious stems. Harold often became hopping mad!

Linda was almost a toddler now and she had to accompany Mary to the fields. Sometimes she sat in the pram, watching. But if the impatient rocking became too dangerous she had to be let out. Clad in a little brown corduroy coat which Mary had made from an old pair of her Land Army britches, and with her tiny Wellington boots caked with mud, she tottered up and down the rows, a wild, tough little thing full of sturdy health.

As spring spread its green mantle over the farm, Mary's pregnancy was coming to an end. And she was so weary.

Her parents thought their daughter had done amazingly well to carry on so long, but Harold made light of it. He had been so overworked himself that he hardly noticed. Michael was working much better but there were still upsets between him and Harold. His laxness and lack of interest frequently meant extra toil for Mary.

Then one day Michael announced that he was leaving and going back home to his mother. Mary and Harold were both relieved and anxious to try someone else.

Within a short time they had taken on another young lad, called Fred Cooper. Fred was a town boy but he loved the countryside and wanted passionately to be a farmer. His uncle farmed in Scotland, and Fred had pleaded to be able to move up there and help, but his uncle said that he could not afford to take him on.

"He says I've got to get some experience," Fred explained as Mary and Harold faced him across their kitchen table, "and then perhaps he'll reconsider."

He was so earnest that the couple took him on at once and, from the very first day he was a hard worker, and very seldom upset Harold.

On the 9th of April, 1950, Mary went into labour. In the evening Harold drove her to the cottage hospital as before.

The Labour Government had just brought in the National Health Service, and Mary found the hospital much changed. It had lost its relaxed, happy atmosphere and seemed to be short-staffed. In fact when she arrived the midwife appeared to be the only one on duty.

"Ah, Mrs Norton," the midwife smiled. "How are you dear?"

"Bearing up," she said, and then added with a giggle: "Well, I suppose I shall soon be bearing down!"

"You're a farmer's wife, I see."

"Well, not exactly. I'm more a farmer really. My husband and I share the work. That is why I must not make a fuss during my labour. The cows do it all the time, you see. My husband's been reminding me of this for nine months! I'm expected to produce a male calf soon. I've only managed a heifer so far!" Mary and the midwife giggled.

"I know what you're saying," laughed the midwife. "One young mum told me she was sure her husband had chosen her because of her child-bearing hips!"

"I still think the cows have an easier time of it than we women," gasped Mary as another contraction struck.

"Well let's make this time an easier one for you," the midwife replied.

She gave Mary a pethidine injection which almost knocked her out, and the birth was so swift that Mary could remember precious little about it. As before her confinement was followed by two weeks of bed rest in the hospital.

Back at the farm Granny Norton came early every morning to look after Linda. She and George had rented a cottage at Clapton, just two miles away.

Harold and Fred tried not to wake Linda as they crept down to the milking, but often the sound of their boots on the stairs would rouse the infant, and the men had to flee the house to the sound of furious yells.

Mary, trying to regain her energy in the hospital, heard terrible tales from Harold, of Linda screaming the house down. Gladys Norton was not as strict as Mary and soon Linda was playing her up, demanding constant attention.

"I'll have to sort her out when I get back," Mary complained to Harold, as he sat by her bed on one of his lightning visits, helping himself to her box of chocolates. They were not a luxury which they usually enjoyed, and Harold was very fond of them!

The couple called their second daughter Margaret. She was a very pretty baby with violet-blue eyes, which reminded Mary of the young princesses she had met at the Buckingham Palace Garden Party in her Land Army days.

At the very end of April, she placed her baby in the cream carrycot and Harold drove them both home to the farm.

Mary was immediately thrown into the hubbub! Linda was screaming her head off and Granny Norton looked red and flustered. Harold had let the AGA go out and was trying to relight it, whilst Fred was making himself a huge cheese sandwich to take out to the fields.

Poor, tired Mary looked round in consternation. Linda's screams soon woke Margaret and then there were two sets of lungs bawling lustily. Mary gave Linda a shake, but this just made the screams louder, and the feckless child ran over to Granny Norton, clinging onto her skirts. She looked round defiantly at Mary, huge tears of anger streaking her face.

Mary grabbed the baby and fled upstairs to her bedroom.

"It's her feeding time!" she muttered on the way.

Mary Sherman had kept the house beautifully clean and tidy and Mary was grateful. She drew breath as she looked out at the peace of the fields and then flopped onto the bed to breastfeed Margaret. She sat for half an hour, nursing Margaret and listening to Linda's wails from below. There was a sudden silence and Harold came into the room.

"It's suddenly gone quiet," said Mary. "Has Gladys murdered Linda?"

"No!" Harold replied sheepishly. "She's given in! Let her have some chocolate."

Mary screwed up her face. She knew from her own childhood what that sort of giving in led to!

"It's back to the childcare manual tomorrow," she said firmly.

Harold sat down beside her on the bed and looked tenderly at the baby.

"Oh she's a fine one," he said, touching her gently.

Harold was a wonderful father and adored the girls. Mary was grateful that he never complained that they still didn't have a son.

He had put another cot in the nursery and Margaret slept in it, in the safety of her carrycot. Mary was once again plunged into the routine of the four-hourly feeds.

It was obvious that this time she would not be able to enjoy her 'baby hour' each morning as she had with Linda. She now also had a demanding toddler to care for, and of course the burden of boiling and washing nappies again. The AGA never seemed to be free of them, draped around it or hanging from the airing rack.

On the two mornings a week that Mary Sherman came, there would be a little more time.

Mary was still occasionally needed to help with the morning milking. She left Margaret and Linda in their cots, both buttoned into their flannel baby bags; and by the time she returned bedlam reigned. Linda would be screaming blue murder and bouncing like a maniac in her cot, whilst Margaret was thrashing around in hers, red-faced and sopping wet! It was a right old duet!

As the weeks passed the routine worked more smoothly. What a blessing the childcare manual proved to be!

But by summer Harold and Mary were so exhausted that they decided they must have a holiday.

"How on earth are we going to achieve it?" Mary exclaimed.

It wasn't going to be easy with Linda now going strong on her legs, plus a new baby in a carrycot. But the heroic grand parents came to the rescue.

"Dad and I will come with you," said Edith, folding up nappies and piling them on top of the AGA. "And George and Gladys have agreed to move in to look after the farm. I thought Blue Anchor Bay might be a good choice. It's not too far away and the children will benefit from the sea air."

Edith and Fred stayed in the cream-coloured guest house,

but Mary, Harold and the girls rented a chalet in the grounds.

"It'll be better this way," Mary insisted. "Mum and Dad won't want to hear our pair yelling their heads off first thing every morning!"

The family met up for their days and at last the couple could relax. Fred and Edith sometimes looked after the girls, making it possible for Mary and Harold to go off on their own for a walk. But they could never take more than four hours because Margaret was still being breastfed. One day they went to Porlock and climbed Ley Hill. As they stood among the heather, looking down at the blue-brown waters of the Bristol Channel Mary cuddled into Harold's arms.

"I love Exmoor," she said, looking into his eyes. "I wish we could have a farm here one day!"

"It's sheep country," he said. "We are dairy people. But I agree that Exmoor is one of the most beautiful places on earth!"

All too soon the holiday was over and they returned to the farm. George was full of praise for the young Fred Cooper.

"The lad's cut out to be a farmer!" said George: "Keen as mustard!"

Better than Michael, thought Mary as she dropped another soiled nappy into the lidded bucket, still doing service in its place under the sink.

But a few days later she was to feel a pang of guilt. Michael's mother wrote a letter saying that her son had been rushed to hospital suffering from peritonitis.

"Oh," said Mary quietly as she handed the letter to Harold: "Perhaps the lad had a 'grumbling appendicitis'. He was always complaining about pains in his stomach. I hope we weren't too hard on him!"

"Humph!" said Harold with a grunt, as he pulled on his boots and stomped off to work.

***

Margaret's christening was planned for July. Linda had been christened eighteen months before, at Berkeley Church, and Mary's childhood friend, Margaret Gray had been the godmother. She had caused quite a stir by arriving wearing a coat in the new look!

But as it was now warm summer weather Mary planned to hold Margaret's christening party in the garden. Tables were moved out of the house onto the lawn and a festive spread prepared.

But one problem nagged at Mary. Their population of farm cats had reached explosion point. They were wild-eyed and unkempt and roamed the yard and all the outbuildings.

Mary stood at the kitchen sink watching one of them slink across behind the barn and wondering how to get them out of the way for the day.

These blessed animals prowling around won't enhance the occasion, she thought.

If only I could send them off to sleep for the afternoon!

A plan began to form in her mind. She went to the medicine cupboard and emptied the remains of a packet of aspirin onto a plate. There were not very many tablets, but perhaps they would do the trick! She crushed them to powder.

I'll have to be put them in something very tasty to get the cats to eat them, thought Mary.

She had just the thing; some nice fresh minced beef in the pantry. She swiftly concocted the tempting meal and set it down in the farmyard. It worked! Soon the cats were crowding round the dish, wolfing down the meat. As they began to look whoosey Mary scooped them up and put them onto the straw bales in the barn.

"You lot can sleep it off in here!" she said aloud as she turned away. Once back in the kitchen uneasiness seeped into her mind. She hoped that the dosing would not kill the cats!

A little later the guests arrived and they set off to the church for the christening service. The party was a great success and everyone enjoyed their food and drink in the warm sunshine. And there was not a cat to be seen!

After tea, whilst Mary and Anne Sherman were washing up, she began to have uneasy feelings in the pit of her stomach. Supposing she had poisoned the cats! None could be seen anywhere! Perhaps they were all dead!

She stole away to the barn in secret. All the cats were spread on the straw, in a languorous slumber, snoring gently!

Later that evening, when all the guests had departed, she saw the cats beginning to regain consciousness. One by one they awoke and staggered out into the evening sunshine. There never was such a band of hung-over felines!

**

One hot summer day, towards the end of August, Mary was in the kitchen ironing, when Harold came in looking very pleased.

"Come outside," he said. "I've a present for you!"

Mary obliged, with Linda trailing behind, excited at the word 'present'. In the yard stood a lorry with its back down, and two men were leading out a Jersey cow. She wasn't in the same class as Ispagula and Snowdrop. She was not pure-bred and there was a slight look of shorthorn about her, but Mary was delighted all the same. She watched Harold lead the new cow away.

Suddenly there was a commotion in the back of the lorry, and Mary could hear shouting and loud swearing, and the clattering of hoofs. The two men emerged, struggling with a small but incredibly lively Jersey bull. The men clung on to its halter as it pranced and dithered down the ramp, dragging most of the straw bedding with it.

Margaret was asleep in her pram but Mary grabbed Linda. One look at the boss's wife's glaring scowl was enough for the men to swiftly moderate their language.

They clung on, waiting for Harold to return, while the bull snorted impatiently and pawed the ground.

"For gawd sake hurry up!" one of them shouted as Harold came running, and all three of them tugged and pushed the bull into a sectioned-off portion of the barn. The two men let go the halter.

"God! I hope these'll hold!" Harold gasped as he rammed home two stout bars.

The bull took a look round, shook his head like a racehorse and settled down to tug at the hay in the manger. But he still maintained a shifty eye on things, and occasionally let out a high-pitched bellow.

"We must keep Linda well away," said Mary: "He looks nasty!"

"That's Jersey bulls for you," Harold retorted. "I told you they had a reputation!"

"Well thank you, Harold. I love the little cow, but I wonder, is it really necessary to keep a bull? Can't we use AI?"

"Costs a fortune," said Harold. "They're such a minority breed. But, I do admit, I'm jolly glad of that cream subsidy! Perhaps he'll make some nice calves. You're always saying how you want to build up a herd.

"Besides," he added, "these two didn't cost a mint. Potato Jones knew a bloke wanting to get rid of them!"

At that moment there was a clatter. The bull had finished his hay and was getting lathered again, tossing his head about and scraping the concrete floor with both front hoofs in sequence!

"I can see why," said Mary as she took Linda firmly by the hand and led her back into the house.

As Fred was young and nimble he had the job of cleaning the bull's stall. He became adept at whipping away the soiled straw from between the animal's heels with a pitchfork, keeping just out of reach of those itchy hoofs. Fred had given the bull the unlikely name of Fido!

One day, Mary was in the kitchen with the children when she heard whispers from the porch.

"Good God!" hissed Fred. "That was a close one! Did you see the look in his eye?"

"Yes, I bloody did!" snarled Harold: "I thought you'd had it! Those horns! Did he hurt you?"

"He missed, thank God!" said Fred: "Went straight through me shirt, though! Look at this! It's ripped to shreds! Another inch and he would have finished me off!"

"BLOODY HELL!" Harold's voice was shaking.

"At least we've got 'im back in the barn!" There was relief in Fred's voice. "What are you going to do now?"

"Sell 'im on, and bloody quick!" said Harold.

The two men came into the kitchen looking dishevelled.

"You two alright?" asked Mary, gesturing to their disarray, but feigning ignorance.

"We're fine," said Harold jauntily. "Just a bit of bother out in the yard!"

Try as she would, Mary never succeeded in extracting further information from them, and very shortly after, the Jersey bull disappeared!

CHAPTER THIRTY

A BIRTH IN THE DRAWING ROOM!

As Margaret grew, the thirty-two acres of the farm became her playground and she followed Mary out into the fields, as tough and sturdy as her sister.

The couple were proving that their intensive method of farming worked, and their milk yield was as high as much larger farms. Harold was still well in with the NAS and keen to try out their innovative ideas. One year it was 'haycocks'!

The Berkeley Vale weather tended to be wet, which made haymaking a chancy business. NAS had devised a novel method to raise the cut grass off the ground in rough cradles mounted on tripods, so that the wind could blow through, drying the crop quicker.

Their hayfield looked spiky and strange with these contraptions erected all over it. Mary and Linda walked through it hand in hand.

Suddenly Linda began to cry and point at one of them. Mary investigated and saw an extraordinary sight. There appeared to be several snakes poking out through the grass in the haycock.

"Oh Linda! This is horrible! Whatever's happened?" said Mary in alarm.

As she poked at one to see if it was alive she saw it had no head or tail!

"Err!" she said, swiftly stepping backwards. "It's a chopped up grass-snake! It must have been cut up with the grass!"

Linda began to bawl even louder and Mary quickly pulled her away!

The haycocks couldn't have been a great success because they were only used that one year. It was probably due to the amount of time it took making them.

Mary couldn't help resenting the fact that Harold so often went running to his friends at the NAS. She felt he should discuss things with her more frequently. They did sometimes make decisions together, but on all the major matters Harold and the NAS had their way. Their herd was predominately Friesian, and Mary never did build up her herd of pedigree Jerseys.

***

Running the farm left little time for treats but the family did enjoy going to the market at Gloucester every Saturday. Mary, with Linda tugging on one arm and Margaret in the pushchair, liked to browse round the shops, whilst Harold and his father went off to look at the stock. The town was full of noise and bustle, quite exciting after the isolation of the farm.

The family did not own a television but they had a radio, which was always switched on in the mornings, tuned to the BBC World News. Mary half-heartedly listened to what was happening in the rest of the world. One grey, rainy morning, Saturday the 16th of August 1952, she was appalled to hear that the little North Devon village of Lynmouth had been devastated by a flood. Mary remembered their holiday and the night they had spent camped on Countisbury Hill. It had rained torrentially then, but this must have been much worse!

"There's an awful thing on the news," she said to Harold when he came in for breakfast: "A lot of people have been killed at Lynmouth!"

Over the following months the whole nation responded to help rebuild the beautiful little village, which lay between the Twin Rivers of the East and West Lyn. Mary still loved Exmoor and nurtured a secret, private dream that she might live there one day.

In the autumn Linda started at a little nursery school, and Mary drove her there every day. It was much easier with just one child to look after, and Mary could return for a short while to the milking and farm work, which she loved.

But not for long! In the autumn of 1952 Mary realised with a shock that she was pregnant once again. The baby would be due the following spring.

Margaret was now an energetic and noisy toddler. She had to be left to her own devices a lot of the time, wobbling down the rows of crops just as her sister had done.

One day Mary looked up from working in the vegetable garden and there was no sign of her. She ran round the farm buildings and searched inside the house, but Margaret was nowhere to be found.

She ran out to Harold on the tractor.

"Margaret's missing!" she screamed.

He joined the search. They even looked in the meadow down by the river.

"Oh Harold!" Mary said as, close to tears, she stood on the bank. "Could she have made it down here?"

"No," said Harold. "It would surely be impossible for Margaret to get this far on her own!"

Mary began to panic.

"Come on then Harold. We must get back up nearer the house! Search thoroughly!"

Mary's breath was coming in great gasps as she climbed the slope back to the farmhouse.

Harold sped down the drive on the tractor and doubled along the lane in both directions, shouting for his daughter.

They both met at the house.

"She could have gone in," Mary said. "The kitchen door was open."

They checked every room and opened all the cupboards but there was no sign of Margaret.

"She must be in the farm buildings somewhere," Harold yelled: "I hope she's not hurt herself!"

They ran into the yard and Mary plunged headlong into the barn, rubbing the tears away so she could see clearly. Suddenly she saw the big bin where they stored the cattle cake.

"Oh no!" she whispered aloud: "Not in there!" Mary knew the bin was airtight.

She whipped off the lid, and there was Margaret inside, quite unperturbed and contentedly nibbling at the sweet, crumbly cattle cake. She looked up at her mother with a broad grin, green crumbs all round her mouth.

"Oh thank God!" Mary gasped, sweeping her into her arms. The lid had a catch, which clicked tight when it was shut. It must have dropped into position, locking the little girl inside. Another minute or so and Margaret would surely have run out of air!

"Harold! Harold! I've found her!"

Like her mother, Margaret had a liking for sweet things, and she had clambered into the bin in search of the cake, which was rich in molasses. Apparently she had no fear of the dark!

As the months progressed Mary began to feel increasingly weary. Two pregnancies so close together, breast feeding both babies, plus the continual hard work of the farm, had worn her down, and this time Mary did not bloom with health.

They had launched into poultry keeping again, and Mary had a hundred and fifty hens to look after. In addition two sows now occupied the sties at the end of the cowshed, and both had litters of piglets constantly clamouring for food. Mary boiled up swill from household scraps, added barley and maize, and staggered across the yard to slop the swill into the troughs. She was afraid she might be knocked over and soon she could no longer do this heavy work. Harold or Fred had to add it to their list. There were never enough hours in the day!

Mary, feeling ill and run down, had to struggle on, helping with the work as much as possible.

Fred Cooper was their mainstay and Harold and Mary were grateful to him. He had a great desire to have some livestock of his own but there was little room on the farm.

"It would have to be something small!" Mary laughed.

One day some people in the village had a spare swarm of bees.

"Would these count as livestock?" Mary asked.

Fred replied that he would be delighted. The owners sent over the hive and Harold took Fred to the village to bring the swarm, buzzing alarmingly in a barrel, home to Tan House. When the bees were released they swarmed out and vanished into the hive. Harold, Mary and Fred stood watching in awe.

"Well," said Harold. "As livestock goes they may be small... but they certainly make up for it in numbers!"

Mary insisted the hive was sited a good way from the house as she did not want the children to be stung. Fred was told the

329

bees were his responsibility, but Mary did once try to collect the honey and her hands were badly stung. The stings hurt so much that she was unable to help with the milking for several days.

"I'll not have anything more to do with them!" she said sharply; but she did enjoy seeing the jars of rich honey on her pantry shelves, alongside the jams and marmalade, which she had made.

Through the winter of 1952/3 she struggled against the cold, bent double in the field cutting the kale. It was now Margaret's turn to wear the brown corduroy coat made from the Land Army britches as she ran up and down between the rows. Mary envied her such energy, knowing that her own had fled.

As the months slipped by, Mary's pregnancy was coming to an end. She thought with pleasure how this would be her second springtime baby.

Thank goodness, Mary thought, it's a lot easier than having a baby in the depths of winter!

She decided that she did not want to go into hospital for this birth. Her previous two confinements had been so easy that she wanted to have the baby at home. She looked at the empty drawing room with its big window and wide elm floorboards and told Harold she would use this.

Harold and her father dragged a bed into the room, together with a big old chest of drawers from the Nortons' cottage, and the nursing chair, which had served for both their previous babies.

There was a big wall cupboard in the room and Mary began to squirrel away things which she felt would help. A large tin of barley sugar sweets went onto one shelf, plus some books for reading, and a bottle of lemonade. On another shelf Mary piled baby clothes and nappies. There were not many hand-me-downs after the rough treatment from the girls but her mother and Gladys Norton had crocheted and knitted fresh sets.

Two weeks before the baby was due, Mary's cousin Maisie arrived. She had offered to stay and look after the house and its occupants whilst Mary took her two weeks bed rest after the birth. Maisie and Mary Sherman liked each other and were soon hard at work, showing the mum-to-be that things were going to run smoothly.

On a glorious spring day, just as the daffodils beneath the window were bursting into bloom, Mary felt once again the first pangs of labour. Maisie found her in the pantry, bent over the potato sack.

"Good gracious!" she said, as she helped her cousin into the kitchen. Mary took a deep breath and leant on the AGA.

"Here we go again," she joked: "About to drop another calf!

"I hope it's a male calf this time," she added with a giggle. "We need one to grow up big and strong and help around here!"

"That's as may be," said her kindly cousin, "but you're dreadfully thin, Mary. You haven't an ounce of fat on you!"

Mary was sitting patiently on the bed when the midwife arrived.

"Good heavens! Look at you!" the woman said, alarmed. "You're so pale and far too thin for a pregnant woman! I think you must be anaemic! You must get something from your doctor. I hope to goodness this birth is going to go alright!"

"I'll be fine," said Mary. "Our cows do it all the time! My husband's constantly reminding me!" Both women broke into laughter.

"Well, all the same, I hope the doctor gets here soon," quipped the midwife.

But the baby had other ideas, and a short while later Mary gave birth to her first and only son.

She lay back on her pillows feeling truly exhausted whilst the midwife bathed the baby. At last he was wrapped in a shawl and placed in the carrycot. Mary raised herself on one elbow to gaze at him.

"You can see he's a boy," she said.

"He's going to be big," said the midwife. "He has very big feet, and they always grow to fit the feet!"

Harold had heard the baby cry and he knocked gently, peering sheepishly round the door.

"You've a fine son," the midwife said, and Harold beamed with pleasure. After he had been allowed a quick glimpse, he was hustled away. Mary was bleeding quite heavily and the midwife was anxious.

"I don't want to leave you," she said: "I'm worried you might haemorrhage. Is there anything I can get you?"

"There're some barley sugars in that cupboard," Mary said weakly.

"Good!" said the midwife: "that's just the thing!"

Mary drifted in and out of sleep. There was a heaviness dragging down her eyelids and the room seemed to swirl in a strange soft mist. It was hard to muster the strength to roll aside so the kindly midwife could put fresh sheets on the bed.

A little while later, to everyone's relief the doctor arrived. He checked Mary over and examined the baby, and after he had pronounced that all was well, both he and the midwife departed. Harold crept into the room with a cup of hot chocolate. Mary was grateful.

"A son at last," she said, smiling. "And we shall use the name we planned. He's our son, John."

Mary couldn't stop looking at her big strong baby. Here at last was the boy that Harold so desired. This tender infant was their promise of the future, and all their hopes that they would have someone to take over the farm when they grew too old. She did not know in those precious moments that it would never be, and that her happy life on the farm would soon change forever.

The following morning Mary awoke to her baby's cries. It was strange to find herself in an empty bed, with no husband by her side. It was five o'clock and the house was quiet.

She slipped out of bed and lifted John from his cot. He was wet, and red in the face from crying, with that strange little new-born cry which Mary remembered so well.

As she held him against her he was searching round for breakfast. Mary sat down on the nursing chair, which had been pulled up by the window. Outside the world was springtime beautiful, dewy wet and sweet. The trumpets of the daffodils glinted with moisture and she could hear the dawn chorus from the copse.

"Well, this is your world, little son," she whispered as she hugged him warmly to her. It came to her, unexplained and unbidden, that of all her children he would be the one with farming in his blood.

She leaned over and grabbed a clean nappy and gently eased it beneath him. She feared she would soon be as wet as the lawn!

Mary was tenderly replacing the baby in his carrycot, fresh, clean and fed, as Harold crept in to ask if all was well.

"You don't have to whisper," she said.

The infant lay relaxed, a dribble of milk on his chin, his eyes rolling back in the blissful, self-indulgent sleep of the well-fed infant.

Mary never would allow what she called 'creeping' around her babies. They had to put up with the everyday noises of the farm, with scant consideration for their sleep. As a result they slept soundly, no matter what was going on around them.

"Fred and me are going out to do the milking," said Harold, and vanished.

A short while later Maisie came up, bearing the breakfast tray. As Mary ate, leaning back on her pillows, the early morning sunshine streamed in, filling the room with its joyous golden beams, and lighting on the face of her sleeping baby boy.

CHAPTER THIRTY-ONE

A BIG PARADE AND A COMPETITION!

Mary now had two children under five years old, and a baby to look after.

The world was changing all around her. King George VI had died, the coronation of the new queen, Elizabeth II was only weeks away, Edmund Hilary had conquered Everest, and the brave new world of 'Rock and Roll' was bursting onto the scene. But all this hardly touched Mary! Her burning concerns were how to look after her family and continue helping with the farm.

Added to these problems, her health had deteriorated. The anaemia, which had dogged her final pregnancy, refused to leave her, and Mary, wrapped up in her toils, did not go and see the new doctor who had taken over the surgery in Berkeley.

"Mary, you are so pale and thin!" her friends kept saying.

"Oh don't worry! I'm fine!" was always her reply.

I'll just crack on, she thought to herself. The problem will soon go away.

Her life was just too busy to fit in a trip to the doctor and any treatment which might be prescribed. Instead she was breastfeeding John, or running Linda to nursery school, or helping with the afternoon milking, John in his carrycot, and Margaret running up and down the cowshed. There was no time for rest or to think of her health! Mary had always been so fit and strong!

I'm fine, she thought. I'll soon feel better!

But she could not ignore a national occasion as great as the coronation! A big parade was planned in Berkeley, and the girls were keen to join in.

After feeding John in the evenings, Mary brought out her sewing machine and made matching white dresses for the girls, trimmed with red, white and blue ribbon. Bent over the machine she felt so tired that her head ached.

Harold sat resting in his armchair reading 'Farmer and Stockbreeder' whilst, in the background, the radio focused on the royal occasion. Richard Dimbleby spoke of the plans for the great day whilst the whole nation listened. Even the famous 'Archers' were full of it!

"It's going to be one heck of a day," drawled Harold, occasionally looking up from his paper. "You're putting in a lot of work Mary. I hope the girls are going to appreciate it!"

On the day of the parade the weather was fine and sunny and Linda made up her determined little mind that she wanted to ride her tricycle into town. This meant that Margaret would also have to ride hers.

Well, thought Mary: I don't suppose it will do any harm!

But this last minute decision meant that the tricycles would also have to be decorated. Mary searched around for leftover scraps of fabric and ribbons, which she rapidly tied around the trikes. Union Jack flags had been purchased for the occasion and the girls were very excited and keen to wave them.

Soon all was ready and the girls looked enchanting with their new dresses and red, white and blue ribbons in their hair.

"Very patriotic!" commented Harold. "I wish I could spare the time to come too."

All that remained was for poor Mary to breast feed John and hand him over to Granny Norton who was going to babysit.

At last Mary and the girls were under steam. Or rather, pedal power! It was about a mile into Berkeley and mostly downhill but it soon became obvious that progress was painfully slow.

Linda pedalled lustily, but little Margaret's legs weren't up to it. Mary, carrying the Union Jacks, and bent almost double, had to push her along whilst at the same time keeping an eye on her elder daughter, whizzing away in front.

The hill steepened and suddenly Linda began to accelerate.

"Steady!" shouted Mary. "Use your brakes!"

But the trike went faster and Mary, still bent over pushing Margaret, had to lollop into a run. Without warning, Linda's trike hit a stone and overturned, throwing its rider in her wonderful new dress onto the ground. Chaos ensued as Linda wailed heartily and Mary dusted down the dress and righted the trike.

Soon the little procession was on its way again but Linda was shaken and her legs were tiring. In the rush Mary had forgotten her watch, but she knew that it was going to be a close run thing!

At last they arrived in the High Street. A band was playing and people were milling about everywhere, but Mary noticed that they were not in an organised line and the children were running about quite unconcerned. Chilling doubts began to form in her mind.

As they joined the excited throng, Mary gasped, "Where is the parade?"

"Its over!" exclaimed a young mum. "You've missed it!"

"Oh no!" groaned Mary.

As realisation dawned Linda began to wail and Margaret, who wasn't at all sure what it was all about, decided to cry too. Soon both girls were screaming fit to bust.

"Oh Lord!" breathed Mary, half dragging, half pushing them along on their tricycles.

At last she caught sight of a funfair further up the street.

"Come on," she squeaked. "You can have a go on the roundabout!"

Thus soothed, the girls stop crying and Mary wiped their eyes and gave them the little flags to wave. Thus passed the momentous Coronation Parade at Berkeley!

***

Fred's time with them drew to a close and Harold knew it was going to be hard to replace him. Once again they had to interview students, and this time they chose a young girl, Ann Denby.

In November John caught a dreadful cold, which rapidly turned to an exhausting, chesty cough. Mary was very anxious and called in the doctor.

"Your baby has severe bronchitis," he said. But Mary was sure her baby was suffering from pneumonia. When she tried to feed him he turned away from her breast, and he cried miserably, his little face flushed with fever. Mary stayed beside him as much as she could, but she was afraid to take him out to the cold cowshed, so she could not help with the afternoon milking. Poor Harold looked terribly stressed, with only an inexperienced girl to help him.

That evening he said to Mary: "This farm is too much for us. The hard work will kill us both!"

Mary had heard similar comments from her husband before but this time he sounded as if he really meant it. To leave Tan House was unthinkable, and she pushed her husband's comments from her mind.

That night John was so ill she could not leave him. He was soaked in sweat and fighting for breath. Sometimes as he choked his breathing would stop.

"Oh my God!" she cried and she had to lift him up and shake him like an ailing clock, to restart his breathing.

She sat with him downstairs by the AGA, and as she looked at the darkness outside, terrible fears began to loom in her mind. *Would he die? She remembered her little brother, swept away by peritonitis whilst still tiny. Did her family have a male child curse? Would her delightful little John die too?*

She did not know what to do! One moment she was bathing him with a wet flannel, trying to cool him from the raging fever, and the next she was wrapping him round and holding him close, in case he should take further cold. Her poor infant choked and coughed and struggled, and all the time a cold wind rattled round the lonely farm, and an owl screeched down by the Berkeley Pill.

As the winter dawn broke, flushing the trees to the east in a pale peachy glow, the baby suddenly quietened and began to breathe more easily. She felt the heat flow out of him and his face turned a healthier pink.

Harold came down, a jumper thrown on over his pyjamas.

"How is he?" he asked anxiously.

"He's had a terrible night," Mary replied "but I think the crisis is past."

"Thank God!" gasped Harold. "I'm sorry I left you to it. I was so flaked out!"

Within a week John was almost recovered, but for a long

337

time afterwards he suffered from a weak chest.

***

The following summer Mary felt they all desperately needed a holiday. Her Land Army friend, Jean Warren, had seen an advertisement in 'The Lady' for a holiday house at Portcothan Bay in Cornwall.

She had written to Mary saying: 'I have found this lovely little house, called Gull Cottage, where you could stay. I have taken a cottage in Tryarnon and we could meet up during the day'.

Jean, who had married George Warren, the son of the well-known Gloucestershire farmer, now had three children of her own, Rosemary, Robert and her youngest Andy, who was the same age as John.

Mary felt the holiday together was a wonderful idea and soon all the arrangements were made. Once again her mother and father-in-law moved in to look after the farm, and her own parents decided to accompany the family to Cornwall, to help look after the children.

The cottage was right on the edge of the cliff with the restless Atlantic rollers crashing at its foot. Mary loved it at once.

Jean was already there, waiting on the lawn to greet them and introduce them to the landlady.

She drew Mary aside, giggling, "Isn't it just the perfect place? But just wait till you hear the story! The Landlady used to run a rest home in Cheltenham, but she sold it and bought this place. She has a little flat in the attic! But just guess what her name is! Mrs Restal-Little! Isn't it just a hoot?"

Mary began to feel better. It was so wonderful to see her friend again. Soon she was inside the cottage and the place was milling with excited children whilst John and Andy miraculously still slept in their carrycots.

"Come on," urged Jean. "Come and see the place before the little terrors wake up!"

Gull Cottage became a favourite haunt for Mary and her family, and it was a good place to spend time with Jean and her family.

***

In the early summer of 1954 Harold and Mary received a leaflet from the NFU announcing a competition organised by the Gloucestershire Root, Fruit and Grain Society, to find the best-producing small farm.

Harold and his father had always been known as 'tidy' farmers, and so everything was always kept scrupulously neat at Tan House.

"We've got our milk yield up to something quite amazing," Harold said to Mary, "and I think we stand a good chance. It would be a shot in the arm if we won, and also, if we ever wanted to sell this place, it would help the price!"

"Sell Tan House?" Mary said in a small, weak voice.

"Well," said Harold swiftly: "It's not that we have any immediate plans. But you know what I mean?"

Mary didn't, but a small chill seed was sown in her heart.

The couple went wholeheartedly into the contest and their friends joked that not a blade of grass was out of place at Tan House!

Prior to the judging, a man from the Society called to make an inspection. Harold took him round the fields and buildings and showed him the stock. Then it was Mary's turn to show him the house and gardens. At that time the couple had a quarter acre vegetable garden but the man remarked that the flowerbeds at the front of the house were empty and overgrown.

"You'll have to do something about those," he said to Mary. "Get some flowers in, for a start."

After the inspector had departed Mary told Harold of his comments.

"How on earth am I going to make them full of blooming flowers?" she asked, giggling at her pun.

As usual, Harold could not see the humour. Instead he said, "You must sort it out Mary! I can't be let down by your confounded flowerbeds!"

339

Mary was ruffled. She did her best but she was always so busy. She was often weeding the garden at the crack of dawn before anyone else at the farm was awake; as this was the only bit of time she could squeeze in.

Then Mary had a stroke of luck. She heard that a nursery in Gloucester was selling up and that plants could be bought cheaply. She left the children in the care of Granny Norton and shot off in the car. By the time she arrived there were only sweet williams and antirrhinums left.

"I want to clear the lot," the owner announced as Mary walked round: "so you have to buy the plants by the row! And dig them up yourself!"

"They are just what I need! I'll take a row of each!" Mary said. "I'll go and get my husband to help me with the digging!"

Harold took the request for help in good heart and they were soon at the nursery. When they had finished, the boot of the car was piled so high with plants that they had to spread the rest on the seats and floor. Mary drove home triumphant!

As she laid the plants out on the lawn she saw what a mammoth task it was going to be to put them all in.

"Couldn't you just help a weeny bit?" she pleaded. But Harold was adamant!

"You'll have to do it Mary," he said firmly. "I've a problem with the milking machines I have to sort out."

By evening the children were hungry and Harold had not seen his wife all day, but the plants were in!

"There you are!" she said triumphantly as Harold surveyed her achievement: "Instant garden!"

Thankfully there were still a few weeks to go till the judging and so the plants had time to settle in and grow.

One evening Harold sat Mary down at the kitchen table and spread some sheets of paper before her. She looked down at her husband's neatly-written figures.

"I reckon we stand a good chance of coming in the top three," Harold said, with an edge of excitement in his voice. "Look, here are the facts. On just thirty-two acres we are producing 13,000 gallons of milk a year. That's one hell of a figure! In fact, I'm not sure if any of the small farms around here can get anywhere near it! It's probably better than some with a good deal more land than us!"

After a pause Harold continued, "Here's the breakdown. We get two hundred and seventy gallons off each acre of grass, which, when you take everything out, means twenty-three pounds an acre profit. That's marvellous in my opinion! Mind you, I have to work my guts out to get it!"

Mary knew it was a fantastic achievement. They had run the farm for ten years and made a real success of it. They had shown that Harold's intensive, electric fenced strip-grazing methods were truly viable.

"On top of that," he continued, "we have at present, four Wessex sows churning out litters, and one hundred and fifty hens popping eggs and a lot of other stuff out of their blasted bottoms all day long!"

"I don't suppose you could come up with a figure for how many times we've moved the electric fences?" asked Mary, a glitter of fun in her eye.

"No I couldn't!" shouted Harold, and stomped out!

Mary had to follow him and put her arms round his neck and explain that she hadn't really meant it.

***

The night before the judging, Harold and Ann their student girl began the task of washing down every cow. A great deal of bad temper went on and Mary had to keep apologising to the girl. At last the job was done. "I'm not going to blasted well polish 'em!" puffed Harold.

The next morning everyone was up early, and every last thing on the farm was checked.

"Now then you lot!" said Harold as he moved the cows onto a new strip of grazing, "don't you go lying down and getting green stains on your backsides!"

Mary took Linda and Margaret off to school and was back home just as the judges arrived. She waited indoors with John.

At last it was over. The judges, refusing a cup of tea, said a polite 'Goodbye', but, of course, they were not prepared to comment!

During the next few weeks, as the memory of all the

preparations, and judging day itself faded, the competition began to feel unreal. But try as they might, Harold and Mary couldn't keep it out of their thoughts. They chose hardly to mention it but sometimes Harold would become impatient. He hated to be kept waiting for anything.

"What are those confounded judges doing?" he yelled, red-faced, and stomping about the cowshed. "I do all this work every damn day and they haven't the decency to hurry up with their decision!"

Then one morning there was a letter with the Root, Fruit and Grain Society logo on the envelope.

"Well, this is it!" he stormed, "they've had the goodness to tell us our farm is no damn good!"

He slit open the letter with a flourish and read it. For a moment there was a silence and his face turned red.

Oh dear, thought Mary: He's not going to take it kindly if we haven't been placed. Poor dear Harold! He works so hard!

"No luck then?" asked Mary softly.

"NO BLOODY LUCK?" shouted Harold. "WE'VE BLOODY WELL WON IT!"

CHAPTER THIRTY-TWO

*FAMOUS FARMERS AND A HEART-BREAKING
DECISION!*

Soon all their friends knew that, with just thirty-two acres, Harold and Mary had taken the prize for the best small farm in Gloucestershire.

It was so exciting! The news desk of 'The Farmer and Stockbreeder' rang, requesting an interview, and suddenly a reporter and photographer arrived on the doorstep. The photographs in the resulting newspaper cutting show a farm of unbelievable tidiness. The hedges are trimmed, the grass clean, and even the cows are sparkling!

There are several pictures of Harold, clad in farm overalls, cloth cap and boots, and one of land girl Ann Denny, but none of Mary.

A photograph taken of the couple after the presentation shows them standing at their front door. They are both dressed in frayed overcoats, soiled by hard work. A light pattering of rain has just fallen upon the couple, leaving tiny dots upon their worn clothing.

Harold looks weary but has managed to smile, and Mary stands, pinched and thin, deathly pale. Gone is the healthy glow of earlier pictures. The anaemia and tiredness, which dogged her in those latter two years at the farm, is plain to see.

The late evenings, when the children were tucked in bed, were the only times that the couple could find relaxation together. Harold often slumped in his armchair. He knew that the struggle to keep the farm going was draining his strength. He missed Mary, his staunch partner who in their child-free days had worked so constantly beside him. He did not regret the children, in fact he revelled in the joy of fatherhood, but he was just dog-tired.

Perhaps it's time we took on a less frantic way of life, he thought. Perhaps I should get out of farming and take a more normal job.

He knew that his contacts brought him opportunities, but then he would look at Mary and he knew how much she wanted to farm.

"Strewth, Mary!" he said one night, "I don't know how much longer we can keep this up! We either have to branch out and take a bigger farm, or change things completely."

"Change things?" Mary tried to keep the anxiety out of her voice.

"We could chuck it in!" said Harold, looking away so as not to meet her eyes. "Get out! Try an easier life!"

"You mean, sell Tan House Farm?" Mary tried to sound unconcerned.

"Well, we could. My friends at The Fatstock Corporation keep hinting that I could have a job with them."

"What sort of job?"

"Travelling around for them. Inspecting things."

"Inspecting things?"

"Yes, cattle, stock, that sort of thing."

"Oh!"

"I'm not saying we jump straight in. I suppose we could have a look around, see what farms are coming up."

"We have a good income, Harold, but we haven't been spending it. We've been investing it all in the farm. I rather hoped…"

"Yes, I know Mary, we've both gone without. We might have enough money to rent a farm. Take a tenancy on a much bigger place."

"I'd love that, Harold! Perhaps I could have a chance to build up that Jersey herd you used to promise."

It hurt that Harold just used the Jersey cream to enrich the milk from the Friesians.

"I'm not promising," said Harold hastily, as if he didn't want to dwell on the subject.

Mary looked down at the pile of socks she had been darning. All that work and scrimping and saving, and they might

344

leave farming! She arose quickly, anxious that Harold should not see how upset she was.

**

A few days later an invitation arrived from their branch of the NFU, for Harold to give a lecture on farming a small acreage.

"It appears we're famous now!" Harold said, with more good humour in his voice than Mary had heard for a long time.

The occasion was to be held in the De Lux Cinema in Gloucester. 'De Loo', as it was humorously known locally. Harold looked very distinguished in his dark suit and bow tie. Mary dressed simply in a skirt and twinset. Her wardrobe no longer held the evening clothes of her former days.

It was a rainy night and after they had parked, they splashed across the pavement into the bright lights of the cinema foyer. But no film was showing! Posters announced that Harold Norton, the prize winning farmer, was to give a talk on achieving a high milk yield from a small acreage!

Harold was obviously the honoured guest of the evening! He was whisked away by the officials and Mary found herself left in the crowded foyer. She nodded and spoke to acquaintances for a few minutes, and then they too moved off, anxious not to miss the start of Harold's talk.

Mary caught sight of an NFU official she recognised.

"Ah there you are," he said when he saw her.

"Where shall I sit?" asked Mary nervously. "Will I be on the stage with my husband?"

"Goodness no!" said the man, hastily: "We've only put out one chair; and all Harold's demonstration material. Come, follow me."

Mary, feeling downcast, followed obediently as they climbed the stairs to the balcony. It was very crowded and she had to scramble along the row, treading on everyone's toes and apologising in an anxious whisper, till she reached one squashed but empty seat.

Harold's speech had already started and everyone was listening intently.

"Oh do please hush!" said the woman in the next seat as Mary struggled to remove her wet coat.

Feeling decidedly uncomfortable and out of things, she sat in silence listening to the famous farmer!

Afterwards, as they drove home, Harold was very pleased with himself.

Mary felt upset that she had not been included in the evening.

After all, she thought: We have always been partners in the farm. True, she was tied up with the children, but she still did what she could to help with the farm work.

Just one week earlier she had done the afternoon milking single-handed whilst Harold was tied up with his NAS friends, and John had howled in his pram through the whole thing!

But Mary did not argue. She sat quietly, with her hands in her lap.

***

In July they managed to get away for a few days to 'Gull Cottage'. Mary Sherman accompanied them, and they met up with Jean and George Warren and their family once again. The holiday started off well but poor Edith broke her leg whilst playing cricket on the beach, and had to be rushed to Truro Hospital. Mary visited her mother at the hospital every day, and at the end poor Edith was brought home on a stretcher on the train.

Harold did not appear rested by his short holiday and returned to his labours in a morose mood.

The months slipped by and the farm and the children continued to occupy Mary's every waking moment. By the spring of 1955 John was two years old, but Mary had still not recovered her health. Pale and thin, she always felt tired.

As she was climbing into bed one night, Harold was leaning against his pillows reading the local paper.

"What do you think of that?" he asked, pointing to the property page.

It was an advertisement for a farm to rent, high in the Cotswolds.

"Over a hundred acres," Mary said, trying not to appear too excited. If Harold had looked at her at that moment he would have seen that suddenly the drawn, pinched look had left her face, and she was young again. But he was still staring at the paper, a deep frown denting his forehead.

"We'd have to sell this place to raise the capital," he said, "and it would still be a hellish lot of work!"

Mary could not meet his eyes. She wanted the farm so much.

"The truth is, Mary, I've had a skinful of farming. I could have an easier life working for the NAS. It would be better for you and the children too. You'd have more time for them. You wouldn't have to juggle your time about, the way you do."

Mary was glad that he had noticed.

"Farming's not what it was after the war," said Harold. "It's going into decline again. I can see all the signs. Dad says…"

He looked at Mary and his voice trailed off.

"Alright," he said gently. "We'll take a look at the farm. It might be an opportunity. You'll have to arrange for your mum to look after the children for a few hours."

Mary wondered if he was regretting mentioning it.

An appointment to view was made via the agent, and after breakfast on Sunday morning they drove off to the Cotswolds. George Norton came along too, to give his opinion, and Mary's father also decided to join them.

Mary sat in the backseat of the car, leaning against her dad, grateful that he was there. She was aware that this occasion was very different from the time, so long ago, when they had all gone to look at Tan House Farm. Then she and Harold had been young and free, and full of their dreams.

The grey stone farmhouse stood high on a bank, and there was a spring, running into a stone trough near the gate. They all piled out to look. The farm buildings certainly appeared in good shape. It was a bright day and the little party walked briskly round the fields. Mary was keen to see inside the house but a pall of disapproving silence hung over Harold.

"What do you think, Dad?" he asked, as they gathered in the little cobbled yard in front of the milking shed.

"Well, its fine enough, in its way," said George, "not bad

land and all that."

Fred was watching his daughter's face. He laid a hand on George's arm: "You're the expert," he said. "What's your honest opinion? I could come up with a few more pennies if you thought it was right for them."

"It's not the farm itself," said George, his hands deep in his pockets, and his eyes wandering round the neat buildings. "It's a right enough place. It's just the times, Fred. I'm sure the bottom's going to fall out of farming soon. Things aren't like they were after the war. We're in for another decline. It's a risky business taking on a tenancy. You're tied in legally, and if times get tough it's not easy to sell your lease and get out!"

"Could they get into trouble, George? Give me your opinion!" Fred was almost leaning over the man.

"I think they could," replied George, his mind made up.

For the first time in her life Mary really resented her father-in-law.

She heard a weak voice saying: "We can make up our own minds though."

She might have been a mouse. Nobody was listening.

As they drove back to Tan House Farm everyone was chatting as if nothing monumental had happened. Everyone except Mary, who sat in silence. For her it was the end of a dream.

The Christmas of 1955 came and went. Mary was still unwell and depressed. At midnight on New Year's Eve she stood in the barn listening to the bells ringing out over the Severn Vale. They were ushering in new hopes for all. She didn't know quite what she was doing in the barn at midnight. She and Harold had been having a quiet little celebration on their own with some sherry and leftover Christmas cake, when she had suddenly felt the desire to go outside into the cold crisp air. She scratched the rime from the door jamb with her finger.

I'm rubbing out my life here, she thought to herself: I shan't be here much longer.

A few weeks later Harold went into Gloucester to see his friends, and he was gone a long time. Mary and Ann worked hard all day. They cut the kale for the cattle and did the afternoon milking.

When Harold returned at teatime he was in a good mood.

"I had a jolly lunch at The Bell," he said, slapping strawberry jam on his bread. "A lot went on, I can tell you!"

Mary stood watching him.

He waited till Ann was gone and then turned to Mary and said. "They offered me a job, as a Fatstock Inspector. I'd like to take it Mary. It's a great opportunity."

So there it was. It really was going to happen!

"Might you be able to fit it in with your farm work?" asked Mary, clutching at straws.

"No," said Harold, determination in his voice.

He would start as soon as Tan House Farm was sold. The job would involve him travelling all over Somerset, inspecting cattle before they went for meat. Mary felt as if her life was falling away like the steady drip, drip of blood from the slaughtered beasts.

CHAPTER THIRTY-THREE

A FRESH START!

Once the decision was made to sell the farm, things moved with lightning speed. Mary was swept along! The anaemia made her so weak and tired that sometimes she too found herself thinking that selling up was the best option. Because she was so busy she never took the time to go to the doctor and, to this day she feels that she made a big mistake. A course of iron tablets might have made things altogether different!

A Welshman bought the farm, lock, stock and barrel.

"This is great," enthused Harold. "He wants all the cows, pigs and hens in with the deal. It will save us a lot of trouble."

The couple pored over the map and considered where they would like to live.

As Harold's job would take him all over Somerset, their choice of location was large.

"It must have good schools for the children," Mary said. "And I'd like countryside close by!"

In the end they chose the bustling little town of Taunton.

"Let's look for something on the outskirts," said Mary, "perhaps in a nice country village."

They asked the estate agents to send them details of available properties.

There was such a good choice that the couple felt sure they would be able to find the right one in a single day of looking! It was arranged that the girls would stay behind at school, but three-year-old John would go with them.

As they drove to Taunton Mary jiggled the agents' handouts on her lap. She really liked the look of a house at Staplegrove, a small village in the countryside right at the edge of the town.

"Let's look at it first," she said. "It's lovely. In the picture it looks like a dolls' house!"

When they drove up outside it Mary felt better still. 'Sandene Lodge' was a lovely square red brick house, which had been built just after the First World War. Three large elms stood in the hedge at the front.

"It's an omen!" said Mary remembering the elms, which had filled the hedges when they first moved into Tan House Farm. Also the name was a little similar to Sandhurst, the place where her Uncle Bert and Aunt Annie lived.

"It's a coincidence," said Mary. "I can't wait to have a look inside!"

The village was pleasant and there was a farm opposite the house.

Soon they were exploring in the house. It was smaller than the farmhouse but Mary didn't mind because all the rooms were well-proportioned with high ceilings. There was a lovely south-facing lounge with windows in two walls, and a fireplace with beautiful turquoise blue tiles.

The dining room with its York Minster stone fireplace was light and spacious too, and Harold immediately claimed it as an office. Upstairs were four nice bedrooms and a pleasant bathroom.

"We don't need to look any further," Mary said. "This house was made for us!"

Harold agreed. He stayed indoors, having a second look at the rooms whilst Mary and John went out into the garden. John was three, only a few months older than his mother had been when she had moved into 'Oakboro' so many years ago.

Mary and John sat down on a seat in the garden. It was February and a large clump of snowdrops was just coming into flower in the border at their feet.

"Well, do you like it?" Mary asked.

John was silent for a while, and then he took Mary's hand and said sadly, "Yes. But where are the pigs, Mummy?"

Mary was touched to her heart. She knew in that moment that her son was the only one of her three children who wanted to farm. They locked eyes, sharing a passion which both knew would never leave them.

John's bottom lip was trembling and he quickly bit into it.

Mary knew her son's life was not always completely happy. The girls were very close, and sometimes bullied him.

As an early blackbird sang in the tree above them Mary made a silent vow that one day, however far in the future it might be, she and John would have a farm once more.

But there was no time for sadness in their present. The move was going to mean a fresh start for them all. Poor dear Harold, who always looked exhausted by the relentless toil of the farm, would have a good new job with regular hours, the children would benefit from the excellent schools, plus the increased 'social life', and Mary would still have the countryside around her.

At that time, in 1956, Staplegrove was still a country village with a manor house and a rectory. But sadly, it was soon to be swallowed up by Taunton. Both the manor and the rectory were converted into flats, and building went on all around, but it still managed to maintain a good deal of its rural character for most of the twenty-three years that Mary was to live there.

On that February day Mary fought a battle to keep her thoughts light and optimistic.

"Come on, John," she said, rising from the seat, "let's go and see which bedroom you would like."

The little boy slid his legs to the ground, took Mary's hand and skipped beside her as they crossed the garden.

A short time later, on the traditional day for farm moves, March the 25th, the little family moved to Staplegrove.

It was a fine sunny day but Mary was feeling unwell. Packing up their home had been a huge task. The lorry stood in the farmyard full of their worldly goods.

"Do you want to take a last look around before we leave?" asked Harold.

Mary declined, feeling it would be far too painful.

"Come on then," he said. "It's time to go!"

As Mary's feet crossed the yard for the last time, her thoughts were brimming.

Maybe, she thought, we are not leaving. All of us, in one way or another, will remain here forever. No one can take from us the years that we have had!

She remembered so many times. Haymaking under

cloudless skies, making silage together in their early days, hand hoeing the crops on terrible rainswept mornings; and all the time, like a heartbeat keeping time to their lives, the twice daily milking of the cows!

She could see herself and Harold in their young days, making love under the May blossom, stamping the mud from their feet as best they might after coming in from the fields on bitter winter afternoons, struggling with the 'Valour' stove, making, mending and making do! Then the triumph of their success, the little battles faced and won which make up all of human life.

And she was not leaving alone. She was taking with her three wonderful children, little ones to care for and watch joyfully as they grew. Rich treasure indeed! And she had Harold; dear, dependable hard-working Harold who had given her these wonderful years and had worked alongside her, sharing her dreams, and for whom she now gladly made this sacrifice.

She had been a farmer for eleven years. She and Harold had beaten all the odds and made a very successful living out of a small acreage. They had had a good life and built a great family. Now they were making a fresh start in a lovely new home!

She bundled the children into the car and as they drove away her eyes were dry and she never looked back!